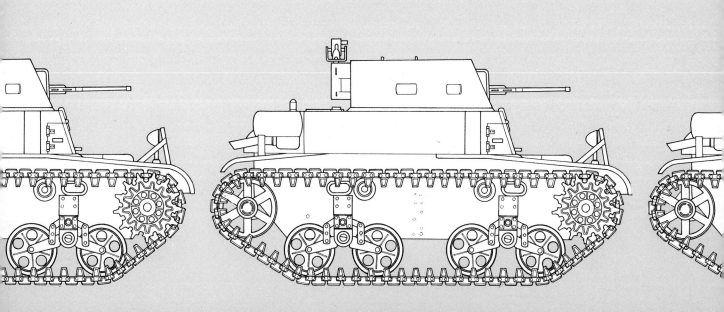

The Illustrated Encyclopedia of 20th Century

WEAPONS
AND
WARFARE

The Illustrated Encyclopedia of 20th Century

WEAPONS AND WARFARE

COLUMBIA HOUSE/New York

Editor: Bernard Fitzsimons
Consultant Editors: Bill Gunston (Aviation)
              Ian V. Hogg (Land Weapons)
              Antony Preston (Naval)
Deputy Editor: Suzanne Walker
Copy Editor: Michael Maddison
Assistant Editors: Will Fowler, Richard Green,
              Corinne Benicka, John
              Liebmann, Michael de Luca
Editorial Assistant: Julie Leitch
Art Editor: David Harper
Assistant Art Editor: John Bickerton
Design Assistants: Jeff Gurney, John Voce
Production: Sheila Biddlecombe
Picture Research: Jonathan Moore
Contributors: Charles Gilson, Bill Gunston,
              Mark Hewish, Ian V. Hogg, Hugh
              Lyon, Pamela Matthews, Kenneth
              Munson, Antony Preston, John A.
              Roberts, Anthony J. Watts,
              John S. Weeks
Illustrator: John Batchelor

Cover Design: Harry W. Fass
Production Manager: Stephen Charkow

"War educates the senses, calls into action the will, perfects the physical constitution, brings men into such swift and close collision in critical moments that man measures man."

—Ralph Waldo Emerson

INTRODUCTION

Through a number of entries in Volume 6 of *The Illustrated Encyclopedia of 20th Century Weapons and Warfare*, can be traced the evolution of the modern tank. Of the three main qualities of a tank—firepower, mobility and protection—Walter **Christie**, the American pioneer, went for speed and maneuverability above all. His ideas were, appropriately, taken up by the US Cavalry (among others), who termed their vehicles **Combat Cars** to circumvent the ruling of Congress that only the Infantry could have tanks. Christie's ideas materialized in Britain as the **Cruiser** series, including the **Comet, Convenanter, Cromwell** and **Crusader**, which sacrificed armor protection for mobility. The counterpart of the Cruiser in Britain was the Infantry Tank, of which the best-known and most numerous was the **Churchill**, intended to support Infantry operations and which consequently stressed protection at the expense of speed. Large numbers of both types, as well as various hybrids, were produced, but since the Second World War, the emphasis has been on vehicles which combine the essential qualities in more balanced proportions. The first British example, the **Centurion**, was originally dubbed the Capital Tank, though both the Centurion and its successor, the **Chieftain**, have become known as Main Battle Tanks.

Tank development in France between the wars was somewhat neglected, the French having pinned their hopes of future security on the Maginot Line, a massive chain of fortifications along the border with Germany, and the **Char** series reflects this lack of application. The Char 2C—the ironically named Char de Rupture, or breakthrough tank—was a design which had survived since 1918, and which looked as though it would have fitted into the Maginot Line quite comfortably; the six still in service in 1939 were destroyed by German bombers before they were called on to carry out any breakthroughs.

In recent years, the tank has had to face a new threat in the form of guided missiles with hollow-charge warheads, such as the wire-guided **Cobra 2000** and the cannon-launched **Copperhead**. At sea, the modern ship-to-ship missile, able to deliver explosive power roughly equivalent to that of an 8-in. shell at anything up to radar range and with the probability of a first-round hit, has given rise to the maxim that the smaller a modern warship is, the heavier the punch per ton it can deliver.

The vessels which demonstrate this principle most clearly are the modern—and increasingly popular—fast patrol boats such as the **Combattante** type, which give a good indication of the wide variety of surprisingly powerful armament which can be accommodated in relatively small vessels. The even smaller **Constitucion** Class, built by the British firm of Vosper Thornycroft for the Venezualan Navy, again offers a choice of gun or missile armament and, at roughly one-fifth the cost of a modern guided-missile destroyer, represents a sound investment for a small navy concerned primarily with coastal defense.

In some ways the position of the fast patrol boat in the navy is analogous to that of the torpedo boats of the 1880s which, armed with the contemporary equivalent of the ship-to-ship missile, posed enough of a threat to frighten battle fleets of ironclads into impotence. They were countered by the torpedo-boat destroyer which itself evolved into the true destroyer.

A crucial step in this evolution was the development of the steam turbine, and the British destroyers **Cobra** and **Viper** were the first warships in the world to be fitted with this type of machinery. It was crucial because the essence of a destroyer design is speed: even after 80 years of development, the fundamentals of destroyer design remain a long slender hull packed with machinery and weapons and devoid of any armor—the achievement of which pushed shipbuilding technology to its limits.

A number of entries in Volume 6 deals with this type of vessel, among them the Argentine **Commodoro Py**, Italian **Condore** and French **Cyclone** Classes of torpedo boats, the British **Cossack** Class, the first major destroyer class to combine the steam turbine with completely oil-fired boilers, the First World War **Clemson** Class flush-deckers and the more recent **Charles F Adams** Class, the first ships to be designed from the hull up as guided-missile destroyers. Even in the latter, which is a much larger type of ship, the light, unarmored hull and high-speed machinery remain firmly in the destroyer tradition.

Centurion

British tank. Centurion was born of a 1943 specification calling for durability, reliability, a weight of 40 tons, a width not exceeding 325 cm (128 in) so as to be able to cross Bailey bridges, powerful armament, sufficient armour to withstand the German 88-mm (3.46-in) gun, and sufficient room inside for the crew to operate in moderate comfort. The weight restriction was later relaxed since it appeared that the desired protection could not be attained within 40 tons.

In February 1941 the final specification of the 'A41' tank was approved, calling for a 17-pdr gun as the main armament, supplemented by a coaxial 20-mm (0.79-in) Polsten gun, one or two coaxial Besa machine-guns and an additional Besa in the rear of the turret. Power was to be provided by the Rolls-Royce Meteor engine. By May 1944 a mock-up had been made and 20 prototypes ordered, and in May 1945 six of the first production prototypes were rushed to Germany but arrived too late to be tested in action.

Production was continued after the war, and several important modifications appeared. The Mk 2 Centurion had more hull armour, a cast turret instead of the original fabricated design, a single coaxial Besa instead of the 20-mm Polsten gun, the rear Besa replaced by an escape hatch, and the main armament stabilized in both elevation and azimuth. This model appeared in the summer of 1946 and after the first 100 had been built the main armament was replaced by the 84-mm (3.3-in) 20-pdr gun, which turned the designation into Mk 3.

Centurion first saw action in the Korean War in 1951 and soon proved itself as probably the best tank in that theatre, notable for

Above: **A Centurion AVRE (Armoured Vehicle Royal Engineers), one of the specialist roles in which the Centurion chassis is employed. It has a demolition gun, bulldozer blade and platform for a fascine bundle.** *Below:* **A Centurion bridgelayer positions its 15.8-m (51 ft 10 in) bridge**

its uncanny ability to climb impossible hills so as to dominate large stretches of enemy country by its superior firepower.

In 1952 the Mk 5 model appeared. Changes included the substitution of the American Browning machine-gun for the Besa in the interests of NATO standardization, elimination of the escape hatch, reshaping of the turret and the addition of a cupola-mounted machine-gun.

While this model was being built, a much greater redesign was being done, resulting in the Mk 7. This had a new hull with thicker armour, increased fuel capacity, better ammunition stowage and improved driver's controls. The turret of the Mk 5 was still used on this model, but a new turret with better gun control equipment and a contra-rotating commander's cupola was then developed and the combination of this with the improved hull became the Mk 8 in 1955.

In 1957 a further improvement came with the adoption of a new 105-mm (4.1-in) high velocity gun in place of the 20-pdr as main armament, and this model became the Mk 9. Most of the Centurions in British service were withdrawn and fitted with the new gun in subsequent years. This model was also sold widely abroad. Subsequent changes included the addition of infrared driving and sighting equipment, a 0.5-in (12.7-mm) ranging mg, and greater ammunition capacity.

In addition to its use as a main battle tank, the Centurion chassis has formed the basis of a number of specialized vehicles including an Armoured Recovery Vehicle (ARV) with heavy duty winch, an AVRE with 165-mm (6.5-in) gun and bulldozer blade, a bridge-layer carrying 15.85-m (52-ft) bridge and a Beach ARV intended to recover tanks 'drowned' while swimming ashore. A number of experimental designs, including self-propelled 25-pdr and 5.5-in (140-mm) guns, a flame-thrower and a Swingfire missile tank have been tried and abandoned.

Countries using Centurions have included all Commonwealth countries, Denmark, Egypt, India, Iraq, Israel, Jordan, Lebanon,

HMS *Curacoa*, a British light cruiser of the *Ceres* Class which saw service in both World Wars

Their basic design was a repeat of the *Caledon* Class but they adopted a new armament disposition which required the rearrangement of the superstructure and forward compartments. The second 6-in (162-mm) gun was placed before, instead of abaft the bridge, and fitted one deck higher, on a new shelter deck, so as to be superfiring over the foremost 6-in gun. This necessitated moving the boiler rooms 5.5 m (18 ft) and the bridge 14 m (46 ft) further aft. The latter structure was also increased in height by 2.1 m (7 ft) which, together with the higher position of the second 6-in and other mods, added substantially to the topweight so, in order to maintain the level of stability, the beam was increased by 229 mm (9 in). The length was also increased and displacement went up by 100 tons.

The general effect of these changes was to improve seaworthiness and firepower although, like the earlier vessels, they were still 'wet' forward and rolled badly, but with a

higher bridge and at least one gun with a reasonably high command the effect on fighting efficiency was reduced. Most of the standard modifications made in the earlier 'C' Class cruisers were adopted in this class prior to completion. Two 2-pdr guns were added shortly after completion except in *Cardiff* and *Ceres* which did not receive them until 1923-24. The conning tower was removed from all during 1918 to compensate for the addition of a revolving aircraft flying-off platform amidships but only *Coventry* was so fitted and hers was removed in 1921/22.

On completion the *Cardiff* and *Ceres* joined the 6th Light Cruiser Squadron of the Grand Fleet while the remainder joined the Harwich Force, the *Curacoa* becoming flagship of Commodore Tyrwhitt. Because the disposition of the 6-in guns was similar to that of many British battleships they received the nickname 'Tyrwhitt's Dreadnoughts'. The *Cardiff* took part in the Heligoland Bight action of November 1917 and led the High

Libya, Netherlands, Kuwait, Sweden and Switzerland. It has proved to be one of the best of postwar designs, largely since the original design allowed for modification and up-gunning without major redesign.

See also AVRE.

(Mk 13) *Weight, combat loaded:* 52 tons *Length:* 7.8 m (25 ft 7 in) *Width:* 3.3 m (10 ft 10 in) *Height:* 3.0 m (9 ft 10 in) *Road Speed:* 34 km/h (21 mph) *Range:* 190 km (118 miles) *Armament:* 105-mm (4.1-in) gun *Ammunition carried:* 64 rounds *Power unit:* 650-hp Rolls-Royce Meteor V-12 *Armour:* 152 mm (6 in) *Crew:* 4

Ceres

British light cruiser class. The five ships of the *Ceres* Class were ordered in March/April 1916 under the Emergency War Programme. All were laid down in 1916 and launched and completed in 1917 except *Coventry* which completed in 1918.

Centurion Mk V. The 'Cent' has served with armies throughout the world and seen action in the Middle East, Vietnam, India and Korea. A popular tank, it mounts a powerful 105-mm (4.1-in) gun which has proved effective against Egyptian-crewed Russian tanks and Pakistan-crewed American tanks. The Mk V substituted a Browning machine-gun for the original Besa, and added a second machine-gun mount on the cupola

Seas Fleet to Scapa Flow when it was surrendered in 1918. All went to the Baltic in 1919 where *Curacoa* was damaged by a mine on May 16. The majority of the ships' peacetime service was on foreign stations.

During 1936/37 the *Curlew* was converted into an antiaircraft cruiser, the old armament being removed and ten single 4-in (102-mm) Mk V AA guns, 16 2-pdr pom-poms (2×8) and eight 0.5-in (12.7-mm) mg (2×4) substituted. The bridgework was remodelled and a large air defence position and AA director added on top of the tripod foremast; a second AA director was fitted aft. The same conversion was carried out in the *Coventry* during 1938/39.

The *Curacoa* was taken in hand during 1939/40 and modified to a different plan. An AA director was added fore and aft as in the earlier ships but the 6-in (152-mm) guns were replaced directly by twin 4-in (102-mm) mountings (4×2) except in B position where a 4-barrelled pom-pom was fitted. The two single pom-poms were retained and eight 0.5-in (12.7-mm) mg (2×4) added. It was intended to convert the remainder of the class but the outbreak of war brought an end to the programme. Wartime additions were limited to the fitting of radar and additional light AA guns.

All three of the AA ships were lost in the early years of the war. The *Curlew* was sunk by aircraft in Ofot Fjord on May 26, 1940 during the Norwegian campaign, the *Curacoa* was cut in half by the liner *Queen Mary* on October 2, 1942 while escorting that ship across the Atlantic and the *Coventry* was

sunk by aircraft in the Mediterranean on September 14, 1942. The *Cardiff* served as a gunnery training ship during 1940-45. The *Ceres* served in several theatres until 1944 when she became an accommodation ship at Portsmouth. Both ships were sold for scrap in 1946.

Cardiff (built by Fairfield)
Ceres (built by J. Brown)
Coventry (built by Swan Hunter)
Curacoa (built by Pembroke dockyard)
Curlew (built by Vickers)

Displacement: 4290 tons (standard), 5300 tons (full load) *Length:* 137.24 m (450 ft 3 in) *Beam:* 13.26 m (43 ft 6 in) *Draught:* 4.42 m (14 ft 6 in) mean *Machinery:* 2-shaft geared steam turbines, 40 000 shp=29 knots *Protection:* 76 mm (3 in) sides, 25 mm (1 in) deck *Armament:* 5 6-in (152-mm) (5×1); 2 3-in (76-mm) AA (2×1); 2 2-pdr AA (2×1); 8 21-in (53-cm) torpedo tubes (4×2) *Crew:* 460

Cesarevitch

Russian battleship built in 1899-1904. As a result of the Franco-Russian Treaty of 1891 the French navy agreed to supply Russian shipyards with technical assistance to build up their fleet, with a view to collaborating in any future conflict with Great Britain. Unfortunately French theories of ship-design contained some fallacies, and these were embodied in the new Russian ships.

The *Cesarevitch* was a prototype for the *Borodino* Class and was to be built in France.

The French constructors considered that ordinary vertical bulkheads would be too weak to withstand torpedo explosions, and so they extended the lower armoured deck downwards to form an inner skin. The weight of this system could in practice only be offset by keeping the belt armour as shallow in depth as possible. But French designers also favoured high freeboard and big superstructures with secondary guns in turrets, so that light anti-torpedo boat guns had to be sited low down in the hull. With the ship in deep load condition this meant that these small gun-ports were all close to the waterline, and any flooding would cause a rapid heel.

The *Cesarevitch* was delivered by her French builders in August 1903 and was soon sent to join the Far Eastern Fleet's 1st Pacific Squadron at Port Arthur. On the night of February 8/9, 1904, before war was declared, she was torpedoed by a Japanese destroyer. The torpedo hit aft under the quarter, and the shell plating and frames were ruptured over an area 9 m × 3 m (30 ft × 10 ft). She was repaired in four months by means of a cofferdam built around her stern, as Port Arthur had no dry docks big enough to take battleships. Even so she was not fully effective; her gun mountings were defective, and as the spares had not been delivered she had not fired her 12-in (305-mm) guns before war broke out. To make matters worse her machinery gave constant trouble.

The ship wore the flag of Admiral Vitgeft at the battle of Shantung on August 10, 1904, during which she was hit by 13 12-in (305-mm) shells. One burst at the base of the foremast, and the splinters wounded Rear-Admiral Matusevitch and killed Vitgeft (only one leg could be found). She careered out of control and lost contact with the rest of the Fleet, and so she eventually set a course for Vladivostok independently. She failed to make it and had to offer herself for internment by the Germans at their colony of Kiao-chao (Tsingtao). She eventually returned to the Baltic in 1906 and joined the Training Squadron. She cruised in the Mediterranean several times and performed rescue work after the Messina earthquake in 1908.

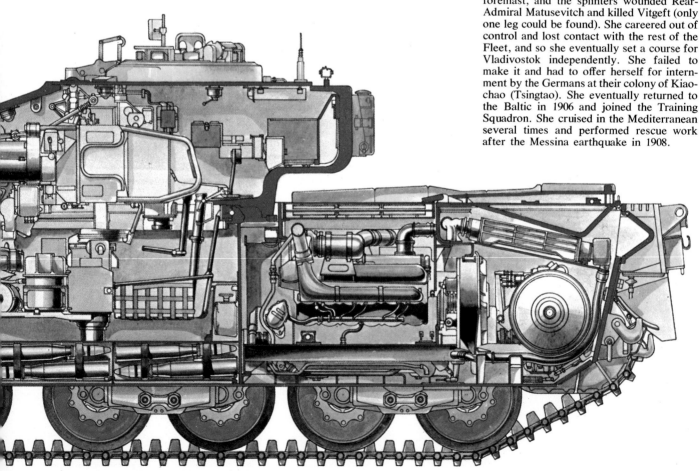

Cessna

The Imperial Russian battleship *Cesarevitch* at Port Arthur before the battle of the Yalu in 1904

Name	laid down	launched	completed	builder
Cesarevitch	5/1899	23/2/1901	8/1903	La Seyne, Toulon

In August 1914 she joined the Battleship Brigade of the Baltic Fleet but saw little action until 1917. After the fall of the Czar the Kerensky government renamed her *Grazhdanin* (citizen), and she joined her half-sister *Slava* in the heroic defence of Moon Sound. During the battle which ensued she was hit by 12-in shells from the German Dreadnoughts *Kronprinz* and *König*, and was forced to withdraw.

Her subsequent career is slightly mysterious as there is a report that she was torpedoed by German seaplanes, but she survived to become part of the new Red Fleet. However she was quite worn out and of no military value, and so she was scrapped after the Civil War. Exact details are lacking as some sources claim that she was scrapped in Germany in 1922, others that she was scrapped at Leningrad in 1923-24. All that is certain is that no longer existed by 1924.

Displacement: 13 380 tons (normal) *Length:* 118.5 m (388 ft 9 in) oa *Beam:* 23.2 m (76 ft 1 in) *Draught:* 7.9 m (26 ft) light *Machinery:* 2-shaft vertical triple-expansion, 15 300 ihp=18 knots *Armament:* (As built) 4 12-in (305-mm)/40-cal (2×2); 12 6-in (152-mm)/45-cal (12×1); 26 75-mm (3-in) (20×1); 20 47-mm (1.85-in) (4×1); 8 37-mm (1.45-in) (8×1); 6 17.7-in (45-cm) torpedo tubes (2 underwater, 4 above water); (After Russo-Japanese war) 4 12-in; 12 6-in; 14 75-mm; 4 47-mm; 2 37-mm; 2 17.7-in torpedo tubes (beam, underwater) *Crew:* 774 (825 by 1918)

Cessna

US military lightplanes (various functions). Many of the world's air forces, notably in Africa, Asia and South America, use assorted Cessna single- and twin-engined light aircraft for various military duties. In most cases these are 'off the shelf' civil machines, with avionics and/or military equipment fitted to suit requirements.

At the lower end of the scale, single-engined types include the two/three-seat Cessna 150 or A150 (100-hp Continental O-200 flat-four), used mostly for training by the air forces of such countries as Ecuador, the Ivory Coast, Sri Lanka and Zaïre. Four-seaters include the Models 180 (230-hp Continental O-470 flat-six), used by the Australian army, and its derivative, the swept-tailed tricycle-gear 182 Skylane, used by the Canadian army, both in the utility transport role.

For utility and liaison nearly 20 nations have (or have had) the Cessna 185 Skywagon or its military equivalent the U-17A or B.

This type has six seats, a fixed tailwheel gear, non-swept fin, and a 260-hp IO-470 fuel-injection engine. The similarly powered 206 and turbocharged 207 Skywagons, with tricycle gear and a swept fin, were supplied to Bolivia, Indonesia, Israel and Turkey.

Among the light twins, one of the best known types is the five-seat Cessna 310, ordered originally as the U-3A liaison and cargo transport for distribution under the US Military Assistance Program. This early straight-finned version, with two 240-hp O-470 engines, was followed by the 'all-weather' 310E (U-3B) with 260-hp IO-470s, a swept fin and, on later models, canted tip-tanks. Cessna 310/U-3 models have been supplied to Bolivia, France, Haiti, Indonesia, Iran, Saudi Arabia, Tanzania and Zaïre. The Model 320 Skyknight is essentially a turbo-charged development of the 310.

The twin-boom 'push-pull' Super Skymaster (Cessna Model 337) was produced initially for the USAF as the O-2A (AOP, liaison and forward air control) and O-2B ('sky-shouting' psychological warfare) and was used in these roles in Vietnam. With two 210-hp Continental IO-360 engines, it seats up to six persons and can be fitted with four underwing pylons for gun or rocket pods, flares or supply containers.

Larger Cessna twins, serving in small numbers, are the Model 402 (Royal Malaysian Air Force), and the Models 401 and 411 (Bolivia, France, Indonesia, Saudi Arabia and Singapore). The Model 411 is powered by two 340-hp Continental GTSIO-520 flat-sixes and seats up to eight.

See also Dragonfly.

(Cessna 185D) *Span:* 10.97 m (36 ft 0 in) *Length:* 7.98 m (26 ft 2 in) *Gross weight:* 1451 kg (3200 lb) *Maximum speed:* 283 km/h (176. mph)

(Cessna 310E/U-3B) *Span:* 11.25 m (36 ft 11 in) *Length:* 8.79 m (28 ft 10 in) *Gross weight:* 2313 kg (5100 lb) *Max speed:* 383 km/h (238 mph)

(Cessna O-2A) *Span:* 11.63 m (38 ft 2 in) *Length:* 9.07 m (29 ft 9 in) *Gross weight:* 2100 kg (4630 lb) *Maximum speed:* 320 km/h (199 mph)

Cessna U-3B administration, cargo and liaison aircraft, in service with the USAF since 1957

Top: **The Cessna O-1 Bird Dog light observation and FAC aircraft which was known by the Viet Cong as 'the little old lady'.** *Above:* **The Cessna O-2, which also saw extensive use in Vietnam**

CETME

Spanish automatic rifle. The CETME Model C is the Spanish army issue rifle, manufactured by the Centro de Estudios Tecnicos de Materiels Especiales of Madrid.

In 1944-45 a number of German firms were working on improvements to the MP44 assault rifle, under the project name Gerät 06 or MP45. One of the more successful designs was that of the Mauser company, who developed a roller-locked delayed blowback breech mechanism of considerable simplicity. The work was not completed when the war ended, and the French took up the work at Mulhouse, taking with them a Mauser engineer named Vorgrimmler.

After a few years, Vorgrimmler moved to Spain and took up employment with CETME in Madrid and interested them in the roller-locked breech design, from which CETME developed an automatic rifle. Their first models were in 7.92-mm (0.312-in) calibre, using an unusually long spire-pointed bullet. In 1956 the German Army ordered 400 rifles in 7.62-mm (0.30-in) NATO calibre. After some experience with them, they requested some modification and as a result the Heckler & Koch company were licensed to produce their own variant, which eventually became the German army's G3 rifle.

In 1958 the Spanish army adopted the CETME Model C in 7.62-mm calibre, using a less powerful cartridge than that used by NATO. It is still in production for the Spanish army but has not been exported.

The rifle is operated by blowback of the cartridge case unlocking a two-piece bolt; two rollers, working against inclined faces in the bolt and receiver, delay the opening until the breech pressure has dropped to a safe level. Single shots are fired from a closed breech, but when set for automatic fire the breech remains open after the last shot so as to permit some cooling to take place.

Calibre: 7.62-mm (0.30-in) *Length:* 1016 mm (40.0 in) *Weight:* 4.49 kg (9 lb 14 oz) *Barrel length:* 445 mm (17.5 in), 4 grooves, right-hand twist *Magazine:* 20-round detachable box *Rate of fire:* 600 rds/min *Muzzle velocity:* 762 m/sec (2500 ft/sec)

The Spanish CETME (Centro de Estudios Materiels Especiales) assault rifle. This is an early model with the light machine-gun magazine and heavy barrel

Ceuta

Name	laid down	launched	completed
Melilla	10/1914	7/1916	2/1917
Ceuta	8/1916	8/1919	1/1920
Marasesti	7/1914	1/1918	5/1918
Marasti	1/1914	3/1917	7/1917

Ceuta

Spanish destroyer class. Romania ordered four fast scouts in 1913 from Italian shipyards. They were all built at Pattison, Naples, and were to have been named *Vifor*, *Viscol*, *Vartez* and *Vijelie*. They were still incomplete when Italy entered the First World War on May 24, 1915, and were requisitioned and completed by the Italian Government.

They were the fastest ships in the Italian navy when they were completed. *Vifor* was renamed *Aquila*, *Viscol* became *Falco*, *Vartez* became *Nibbio* and *Vijelie* became *Sparviero*. *Aquila*, *Nibbio* and *Sparviero* were completed with an armament of three 6-in (152-mm)/40-cal, four 3-in (76-mm)/40-cal, two machine-guns and four 17.7-in (45-cm) torpedo tubes and 44 mines. They were rearmed after the war with five 4.7-in (120-mm)/45-cal (later reduced to four), four 3-in (76-mm)/40-cal, two machine-guns and four 17.7-in (45-cm) torpedo tubes. *Falco* was completed with five (later reduced to four) 4.7-in (120-mm)/45-cal, two 3-in (76-mm)/40-cal, two machine-guns, four 17.7-in (45-cm) torpedo tubes and 38 mines (the mine rails were later removed).

Nibbio and *Sparviero* were repurchased by Romania on July 1, 1920 and renamed *Marasesti* and *Marasti* respectively. They were finally discarded in 1964-65. *Aquila* and *Falco*, reclassified as destroyers on September 5, 1938, were transferred to Nationalist Spain on January 5, 1939. They were renamed *Melilla* and *Ceuta* respectively. Two smaller destroyers, *Guglielmo Pepe* (renamed *Huesca*) and *Alessandro Poerio* (renamed *Ternel*), were also transferred. *Melilla* and *Ceuta* were eventually discarded,

Ceuta in 1949 and *Melilla* the following year.

After this transfer to Nationalist Spain, *Ceuta* and *Melilla* were temporarily disguised with a fourth funnel aft to resemble the Spanish *Alsedo* Class destroyers. The 4.7-in (120-mm) guns were in twin mounts fore and aft, and the torpedo tubes in pairs on each broadside amidships.

Based mainly in the Baleares islands, they fought several actions with Spanish Republican forces. After the end of the civil war they were mainly used for training.

Displacement: 1400 tons (standard) *Length:* 95.25 m (312 ft 6 in) oa *Beam:* 9.37 m (30 ft 9 in) *Draught:* 3.23 m (10 ft 7 in) *Machinery:* 2-shaft turbines, 38 000 shp=34 knots *Armament:* 4 4.7-in (120-mm); 2 3-in (76-mm); 4 17.7-in (45-cm) torpedo tubes *Crew:* 160

CF-5, Canadair Canadian production version of US F-5 'Freedom-Fighter' jet fighter aircraft See **F-5, Northrop**

CF-100, Avro Canada (Canadair)

Canadian two-seat all-weather interceptor. Canada's first entirely indigenously designed aircraft, the CF-100, often referred to as the Canuck, was remarkable in many ways. Initial design began in 1946 in response to a Royal Canadian Air Force requirement for a long-range, fast-climbing jet interceptor and the first prototype flew on January 19, 1950, a comparatively short gestation period considering the newness of the design team.

The first two of these straight-wing aircraft were powered by two Rolls-Royce Avon turbojets mounted on top of the wing roots and alongside the conventional all-metal fuselage, but the intention was always eventually to use a pair of Canadian Orenda engines. These were installed in the ten pre-production Mk 2 aircraft, producing 2722 kg (6000 lb) of thrust each.

The first full production-standard CF-100, the Mk 3, flew for the first time in October 1952, powered by 2948-kg (6500-lb) thrust Orenda 9s, and entered service the next year armed with eight 0.5-in (12.7-mm) Colt-Browning machine-guns in a retractable ventral tray. This armament was supplemented in the Mk 4A by wing-tip pods of 2.75-in (70-mm) folding-fin air-to-air rockets after the fashion adopted by the United States Air Force in the Northrop F-89 Scorpion. The Mk 4A also introduced an improved radar in the form of the Hughes APG-40 and a collision-course interception computer.

The Chilean protected destroyer *Chacabuco*, launched in 1898 at the Armstrong yard at Elswick, and shown here shortly after her launch. She remained in service with the Chilean navy until 1952

Increased power (Orenda 11s of 3230-kg [7275-lb] thrust) and all-rocket armament came with the Mk 4B Canuck which, with the 4A, became the most produced version of this pioneering all-weather fighter, a total of 510 being produced. Development, however, was not continued and the Mk 5 flew for the first time in 1955. For better performance at high altitude, 1.06 m (3 ft 6 in) untapered sections were added to each wing tip and the tailplane area was also slightly increased—this in fact raised the combat ceiling by 1219 m (4000 ft). Larger wing-tip rocket pods were also fitted to the Mk 5, which became the only model to be exported, 53 ex-Canadian air force models being sold to the Belgian air force, deliveries commencing in December 1957. United States security regulations prohibited further exports, as some US equipment was fitted.

With its then quite advanced fire-control system, the CF-100 was an obvious candidate for missile armament and the proposed Mk 6 was to have mounted Sparrow II missiles and been powered by afterburning Orenda 11R engines. This, however, was the time of the ill-fated Canadair CF-105 Avro Arrow development, and the Mk 6 was cancelled in the belief that the Arrow project would render it redundant. The CF-105 programme itself was subsequently cancelled.

Span: 18.54 m (60 ft 10 in) over rocket pods *Length:* 16.5 m (54 ft 1½ in) *Maximum loaded weight:* 16780 kg (37000 lb) *Maximum speed:* 1045 km/h (650 mph) *Maximum range:* 3200 km (2000 miles)

CF-101 Canadian Armed Forces designation for US McDonnell F-101 Voodoo jet-powered all-weather interceptor and reconnaissance aircraft See **Voodoo**

CF-104, Canadair Canadian production version of US North American F-104 Starfighter multirole fighter aircraft See **Starfighter**

CG-4 USAAF designation for Waco Hadrian troop-carrying glider See **Hadrian**

CH-3 US Navy designation for Sikorsky S-61 helicopter See **Sea King**

CH-46 US Marine Corps designation for Boeing-Vertol helicopter See **Sea Knight**

CH-47 US Army designation for Boeing Vertol Model 114 helicopter See **Chinook**

CH-53 US Navy designation for Sikorsky S-65 helicopter (and developments) See **Sea Stallion**

CH-54 US designation for Sikorsky S-64 helicopter See **Tahre**

CH-113 Canadian Armed Forces designation for Boeing Vertol CH-46 See **Sea Knight**

Chacabuco

Chilean protected cruiser built 1896-1902. She was built as a sister to the Japanese *Takasago* but as a private speculative venture. Fortunately for her builders, Armstrongs, the reputation of their 'Elswick cruisers' stood so high that she was snapped up by Chile in the year of completion. She was built as Job No 665 and took the name of *Chacabuco* on purchase.

In 1941 the ship was rearmed with 6-in (152-mm) guns in place of the old 8-in (203-mm) and 4.7-in (120-mm) guns, and had ten 20-mm (0.79-in) Oerlikon AA guns added. In addition she had funnel caps fitted. She remained in service with the Chilean navy until 1952, making her the last of the Elswick cruisers in service.

Displacement: 4500 tons (normal) *Length:* 109.73 m (360 ft) pp *Beam:* 14.17 m (46 ft 6 in) *Draught:* 5.18 m (17 ft) *Machinery:* 2-shaft triple-expansion, 15750 ihp=24 knots *Protection:* 114 mm (4½ in) deck; 114 mm (4½ in) gunshields *Armament:* 2 8-in (203-mm)/45-cal QF (2×1); 10 4.7-in (120-mm)/40-cal QF (10×1); 12 76-mm (3-in) (12-pdr) QF (12×1); 6 47-mm (1.85-in) (3-pdr) QF (6×1); 2 14-in (35.6-cm) torpedo tubes (above water, bow and stern) *Crew:* 400

Name	laid down	launched	completed	builder
Chacabuco	11/8/1896	4/7/1898	1902	Armstrong & Mitchell, Tyne

Chaff

Passive electronic-warfare technique. In 1937, when radar was in its infancy, researchers in Britain and Germany recognized that it might be possible to blot out the radar 'blip' caused by an aircraft or other target by filling the surrounding atmosphere with millions of small dipole aerials, each of which would give rise to a small blip so that the whole cloud would obliterate any informative picture on the enemy radar display.

The first research used fine wires, but a much better answer was thin metal foil. Aluminium was best, used either alone or gummed to paper backing, with minimum

Beken of Cowes

Chaffee

sinking speed through the atmosphere and cut to suit the wavelength of known enemy radars. Britain called the highly secret material Window, while the German name was Düppel, after the country estate where trials began. Each was terrified of using it, knowing how potent it would be to the enemy. But in May 1943 the Japanese suddenly used it over the Solomon Islands. They used tissue backing and called it Giman-Shi (Deceiving Paper); the Americans named the extremely effective aid chaff, and this name stuck.

During the Second World War chaff was factory-made by the ton, each ton containing about 80 billion foil strips packaged into tight bricks. (There is a tale of RAF bomber crews, not having been instructed, deliberately dropping the bundles with the wrapping unbroken "so that it might do some good").

Today chaff is by far the most important technique in passive radar defence (passive=not emitting electronic signals). Modern chaff technology is extensive and clever. The simplest chaff payloads are factory-made cartridges fired by ejector squibs or various expulsion systems from a multi-barrel dispenser which may be installed in the aircraft or other weapon platform, carried in an external fairing or in a payload pod in place of an item of ordnance. Chaff cartridges often intermix with active jammers and IR (infrared) flares, the three together being known as expendable countermeasures.

The performance of a chaff payload is given by its RCS (radar cross-section) and bloom time (the time needed from ejection to burst and scatter its foil slivers to maximum, or 90% maximum, extent). In tactical systems RBC (rapid-bloom chaff) is almost universal, each payload having foil or metallized glass dipoles sized to meet the expected threat and blooming within 2 seconds (often less) to give an RCS as large as a tactical aircraft. Repeated burst of RBC will continually break the lock of hostile tracking or missile radar.

Certain chaff installations are more comprehensive and versatile. Large bombers, EW (electronic warfare) aircraft and the latest attack platforms carry cutter dispensers loaded not with precut chaff but with drums loaded with perhaps 1000 km (620 miles) of foil roving or metallized glass. Elint (electronic intelligence) carried in the same or different aircraft measures the characteristics of the enemy radars actually being used at the place and time of the attack. The threat is automatically countered by feeding the multiple rovings past cutter blades that shear off the chaff to the correct length before it is blown out through a dispersing nozzle.

Chaffee

The US Light Tank M24, christened in honour of General Adna R Chaffee, 'Father of US Armored Forces'. Design of the M24 was begun in mid-1943 in order to replace the M5A1 light tank, which suffered from insufficient armament, lack of room in the turret and overheating of the engine. The work was done by the US Ordnance Department and the Cadillac Motor Division of General Motors, and the first production vehicle appeared in April 1944.

A small number entered service in time to be used in Europe, seeing action at the crossing of the Rhine and in the latter stages of the campaign against Germany. Total production was some 4415 vehicles and they remained in service for several years, being employed in the opening stages of the Korean War. They were also widely exported and numbers are still in service.

The M24 was of conventional design, using two Cadillac V-8 engines with Hydramatic transmission. The turret mounted a 75-mm (2.95-in) Gun M6 which had been derived from a special aircraft cannon design. Suspension was by torsion bars. The basic chassis was also used as a basis for the M19 twin 40-mm (1.57-in) SP gun, the M41 SP 155-mm (6.1-in) howitzer and the M37 SP 105-mm (4.1-in) howitzer, all of which entered service towards the end of the Second World War.

Length, hull: 4.99 m (16 ft 4½ in) *Length overall:* 5.486 m (18.0 ft) *Height:* 2.47 m (8 ft 1½ in) *Weight, combat loaded:* 18370 kg (40500 lb) *Armour base:* 25 mm (1 in) hull; 38 mm (1½ in) turret *Armament:* 75-mm (3-in) Gun M6 in turret; 0.30-in (7.62-mm) mg coaxially mounted; 0.30-in (7.62-mm) mg in hull front; 0.50-in (12.7-mm) mg on top of turret *Ammunition carried:* 48 rounds 75-mm; 420 rounds .50-in mg; 4125 rounds .30-in mg *Power unit:* 2×Cadillac 110-hp V-8 gasoline engines *Maximum speed:* 48 km/h (30 mph) *Range:* 160 km (100 miles) *Crew:* 5

The M24 Chaffee, besides seeing action with the US Army in Germany and Korea, was exported to the French who used a troop at Dien Bien Phu

Hughes Helicopters

The Hughes XM230 30-mm Chain Gun mounted in an underfuselage turret on a Hughes YAH-64 attack helicopter. It has a rate of fire of up to 700 rds/min and carries a standard ammunition load of 1086 rounds. The turret is designed to collapse into the fuselage on a crash landing

Chain Gun, Hughes XM230

US helicopter gun. A requirement of the Advanced Attack Helicopter programme to provide the US Army with a battlefield support helicopter capable of neutralizing enemy tanks and vehicles, was an integral 30-mm (1.18-in) cannon to be used in conjunction with Tow or Hellfire antitank missiles and unguided rockets. Of the two finalists in the competition, Bell opted for the General Electric XM188 three-barrelled cannon, while Hughes decided to develop their own 30-mm (1.18-in) weapon—the XM230 Chain Gun—specifically for their YAH-64.

Design of the Chain Gun began in January 1973, and only four months later the first test rounds were fired from the Model A prototype. As its name suggests, the gun mechanism is driven by an electrically powered bicycle-type chain, but instead of a multibarrel configuration as used on many contemporary aircraft guns, the Hughes weapon is designed for only medium rates of fire and—like the British Aden gun—has a single barrel fed by a revolving chamber. The use of an external power source allows an open rotating bolt to be used, and gives more precise control of ammunition and internal operation. An added advantage is that operation is greatly simplified, reducing the number of parts and approximately halving the cost of comparable weapons.

By September 1973 a 2500-round firing test programme had been completed, the last 1000 rounds having been fired without any malfunction, rates of fire of up to 500 rds/min having been achieved and a high proportion of aluminium-cased rounds having been fired. Model B and C versions of the gun were then developed, the last substituting conveyor-fed linkless ammunition for the linked variety

originally used and raising the possible rate of fire to 700 rds/min. (All versions have rates of fire adjustable from single shots upwards, the rate being controlled by the speed of the chain drive.)

In December 1976, by which time over 350 000 rounds had been fired, including 2500 rounds from an airborne YAH-64, a $317.7 million contract was granted to Hughes for further development of the YAH-64 and its associated systems—including the Chain Gun—and the gun itself had at least some bearing on the choice of the Hughes machine over the Bell YAH-63. At the same time it was announced that the aluminium-cased WECOM 30 ammunition had been dropped in favour of the DEFA round used by the Aden cannon.

On the AH-64 the Chain Gun will be operated via an extremely sophisticated fire-control system, incorporating a gyro-stabilized telescopic sight mounted below the fuselage, with laser range-finding/target designation equipment and infrared for night operations. The gun is positioned below and aft of the sighting system to avoid muzzle flash interference with the night vision system, and will be fired by the pilot in the rear cockpit to give suppressive fire while the missile systems are operated by the observer in the forward cockpit.

The success of the 30-mm (1.18-in) Chain Gun inspired Hughes to develop other calibres of the weapon, and in February 1977

the company was awarded a $5.6 million contract for development of a 25-mm (1-in) version for use on the US Army MICV (Mechanized Infantry Combat Vehicle). The two-year contract called for 15 examples of the gun which will be used in comparative tests with a competing automatic weapon. The MICV Chain Gun will be powered by the vehicle's own electrical system, backed up by a self-contained battery pack. A 7.62-mm (0.30-in) version has also been developed.

Calibre: 30-mm (1.18-in) *Operation:* Externally-powered chain drive *Rate of fire:* Up to 700 rds/min

Challenger

British 2nd Class cruisers built 1900-05. Two cruisers of an improved *Hermes* type were ordered from the Royal dockyards under the 1900-1901 Estimates. They differed from the previous class in being slightly larger, and in having slightly more powerful machinery.

Encounter was transferred to the new Royal Australian Navy in July 1912, and served on patrol duty in the Pacific in 1914/15. She served on the China coast in 1915/16 and then returned to the Pacific until the Armistice. She became a submarine depot ship and was renamed HMAS *Penguin* in May 1923. She was dismantled in October 1929 but lasted until September 1932, when the bare hull was scuttled off Sydney Heads.

Name	laid down	launched	completed	builder
Challenger	12/1900	5/1902	1905	HM Dockyard, Chatham
Encounter	1/1901	6/1902	1905	HM Dockyard, Devonport

Challenger

The *Challenger* joined the 9th Cruiser Squadron in August 1914 and served in West Africa until 1915. From there she went to East Africa, where she spent the rest of the war on patrol and escort duty. She returned to Britain after the Armistice and was sold for scrapping in May 1920.

Displacement: 5880 tons (normal) *Length:* 113.69 m (373 ft) oa *Beam:* 17.07 m (56 ft) *Draught:* 6.55 m (21 ft 6 in) max *Machinery:* 2-shaft triple-expansion, 12 500 ihp=21 knots *Protection:* 76 mm (3 in) deck *Armament:* 11 6-in (152-mm)/45-cal Mk VII (11×1); 8 3-in (76-mm) (12-pdr) QF (8×1); 6 47-mm (1.85-in) (6×1); 2 18-in (46-cm) torpedo tubes (submerged, beam) *Crew:* 475

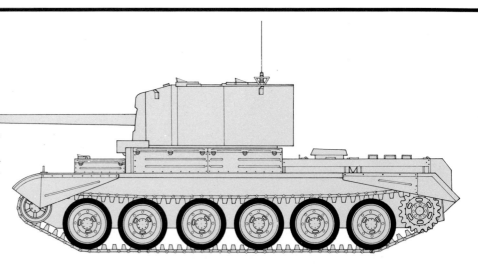

The Challenger was used in Europe in 1944-45 as a tank destroyer with Cromwell tank troops

Challenger

British heavy-gun tank developed in 1942. At that time the common complaint of British tanks was the lack of a powerful gun, and the Challenger (A30) was a modification of the Cromwell tank to allow mounting a 3-in (76-mm) 17-pdr high velocity gun. The Cromwell chassis had to be lengthened by the addition of another road wheel to each side and a large and high turret was designed in order to accommodate the breech and recoil system of the gun. The design was successful insofar as it worked, but it was ungainly and had poor performance due to the additional weight. Nevertheless, production was approved in February 1943 and an eventual total of 200 were built.

Due to the high silhouette the Challenger was somewhat vulnerable when used as a battle tank, and its role was generally that of a 'tank destroyer' to protect the ordinary cruiser tanks, a typical tank troop consisting of one Challenger and three Cromwells. It enjoyed some success in Europe in 1944-45 but did not remain long in service after the end of the war.

Weight: 31.5 tons *Length:* 8 m (26 ft 4 in) *Width:* 2.91 m (9 ft 6½ in) *Height:* 2.67 m′ (8 ft 9 in) *Speed:* 51 km/h (32 mph) *Armour thickness:* 102-20 mm (4-0.79 in) *Armament:* 1 17-pdr; 1 0.30-in (7.62-mm) Browning mg *Range:* 169 km (105 miles) *Crew:* 5

Chao Ho

Chinese 2nd Class cruiser class built 1910-12. Two small cruisers, *Chao Ho* and *Ying Swei*, were ordered in 1910 from British shipyards, intended mainly for training. They were designed by the Elswick yard, although the second contract went to Vickers, and as such they are the last of the famous 'Elswick cruisers' which dominated the warship-export market for so many years.

The design followed British practice, although smaller and more lightly armed than the contemporary *Bristol* Class. Neither ship appears to have been altered much during their long lives, apart from having their funnels capped in the 1920s. They were sunk in a one-sided gunnery duel with Japanese warships at Canton on September 28, 1937; the *Chao Ho* was beached and abandoned.

Displacement: 2725 tons (normal) *Length:* 105.46 m (346 ft) oa *Beam:* 12.8 m (42 ft) *Draught:* 4.49 m (14 ft 7 in) *Machinery:* 4-shaft

Name	laid down	launched	completed	builder
Chao Ho	11/1910	10/1911	2/1912	Armstrong, Elswick
Ying Swei	1910	7/1911	1912	Vickers, Barrow

Parsons steam turbines, 8000 ihp=22 knots *Protection:* 25 mm (1 in) deck; 76 mm (2.95 in) conning tower *Armament:* 2 6-in (152-mm)/50-cal QF (2×1); 4 4-in (102-mm)/50-cal QF (4×1); 2 3-in (76-mm)/50-cal QF (2×1); 6 47-mm (1.85-in) QF (6×1); 2 37-mm (1.46-in) 1½-pdr pom-poms; 2 18-in (46-cm) torpedo tubes (above water, beam) *Crew:* 270

Chapaev

Soviet cruiser class built 1938-1950, also known as the *Frunze* Class. After the construction of the *Kirov* Class heavy cruisers, the Soviet navy decided to revert to 6-in (152-mm) guns, but in greater numbers to provide increased rate of fire and weight of broad-

A Ford Aerospace MIM-72 Chaparral ground-to-air missile streaks away from a modified M548 cargo carrier. The Chaparral is normally mounted on an M548 cargo carrier on a four-round turret

Name	laid down	launched	completed	builder
Chapaev	1938	1940	1949	Ordzhonikidze yard, Leningrad
Zhelezniakov	1938	1940	1949	Marti yard, Leningrad
Chkalov	1939	1948	1950	Ordzhonikidze yard, Leningrad
Kuibishev	1939	1/1941	1950	Marti north yard, Nikolaiev
Frunze	1939	12/1940	1950	Marti south yard, Nikolaiev
Ordzhonikidze	1940	—	—	Marti south yard, Nikolaiev

side. Another important change was to give the guns 50° elevation for antiaircraft capability.

As with the *Kirov* design, foreign aid was essential, for the Soviets had built so few large ships since 1916. The Italians provided the basic hull-design, while the Germans provided fire-control. Originally a catapult and triple torpedo tubes were to have been provided, the catapult between the funnels and two sets of torpedo tubes in wing positions. Six were ordered, three in Leningrad for the Baltic Fleet and three in Nikolaiev for the Black Sea Fleet. All work was suspended in mid-1941, started again in 1945, and they emerged looking very like prewar Italian heavy cruisers.

The layout resembled the British *Southampton*, with two pairs of triple 6-in (152-mm) turrets (two forward and two aft) and four twin AA mountings grouped around the second funnel. However, the superstructure

Ford Aeronutronic

was distinctly Italian, as was the style of the two funnels—capped and positioned widely apart.

As the first of the new generation of Soviet ships to appear after 1945, the *Chapaev* Class aroused considerable comment. To this day most reference books credit them with a combined steam-and-diesel propulsion system, but this is not correct. Since completion they have had progressive changes to their radar, but otherwise remain as they were completed.

The *Ordzhonikidze* was captured on the slip when German forces overran the Nikolaiev shipyard on August 18, 1941, and was so badly damaged that she had to be scrapped on the slip. The *Kuibishev* was towed to Poti in June 1941 and laid up there incomplete. Construction did not begin again until 1945. The *Frunze* was also towed to Poti, but in 1942 her stern was removed to repair the cruiser *Molotov*. She was also completed after the war. The three Baltic hulls were suspended from 1941-1945, but as they were still on the slips they were exposed to the risk of bombs and shells during the siege of Leningrad.

The *Chapaev* commissioned in 1949, followed by the *Zhelezniakov*, and both ships were transferred to the Arctic in 1950. The other four were completed in 1950, and served until the 1960s. By the late 1970s only two of the class were left, the *Chkalov* (renamed *Komsomolets* in 1960) and the *Zhelezniakov*, both on training duties; the others were scrapped in the 1960s.

Displacement: 11 300 tons (normal) 15 000 tons (full load) *Length:* 202.8 m (665 ft) oa *Beam:* 18.9 m (62 ft) *Draught:* 7.3 m (24 ft) *Machinery:* 4-shaft geared steam turbines, 130 000 shp=32 knots *Protection:* 76 mm (3 in) belt; 51 mm (2 in) deck; 102 mm (4 in) turrets *Armament:* 12 150-mm (5.9-in)/50 cal (4×3); 8 100-mm (3.9-in)/50-cal (4×2) DP; 24 37-mm (1.46-in)/63-cal (12×2) AA; provision for laying 200 mines *Crew:* 840-900

Chaparral, Ford Aerospace MIM-72

US surface-to-air missile. The Chaparral round is a development of the United States Navy's air-to-air Sidewinder 1C modified for launching from the surface. The original MIM-72A version has been succeeded by the uprated MIM-72C, which is fitted with the Ford Aerospace AN/DAW-1 infrared guidance set; this allows the weapon to intercept targets at all angles, including head-on. The improved model also carries a new warhead,

the Picatinny Arsenal M250 blast-fragmentation charge filled with tungsten-alloy cubes, which is detonated by a Harry Diamond Laboratories M817 proximity fuze. Further improvements proposed for the weapon include a seeker which is immune to infrared countermeasures, a smokeless rocket motor, electronic IFF (identification, friend or foe) equipment and an antiglint canopy for the fire unit.

The missile is launched from a four-round turret mounted on an M730 tracked vehicle, a development of the M548 cargo carrier. Reload rounds are stored on the vehicle. Target range and azimuth are provided by a separate Forward Area Alerting Radar (FAAR), which directs the operator in the turret of the M730. He slews the assembly in the direction indicated by the radar and searches in elevation with his optical sight. Once the infrared seeker in the missile has locked on the round can be launched and will automatically home on to the target's hot engine, exhaust gases or parts of the structure which have been heated by friction.

Chaparral equips the US Army's low-altitude air-defence battalions, one of which is included in each of the 16 active divisions. These battalions operate two batteries of Chaparral and the same number of 20-mm (0.79-in) M61 Vulcan Gatling guns. The weapon is also in service with the Israeli Defence Forces, which scored the system's first kill in combat by shooting down a Syrian MiG-17 over the Golan Heights late in the Six-Day War. Other operators include Taiwan, Tunisia and Morocco. A naval version, Sea Chaparral, has been developed and was fitted to the destroyers USS *Laurence* (DDG.4) and *Hole* (DDG.13) in 1972/73, but is not in widespread service.

Chaparral is due to be replaced in the US Army by the Franco-German Roland II, which is being built under licence by Hughes and Boeing. The older system may be given a new lease of life, however, by the addition of Marconi DN181 Blindfire radars. These would allow the weapon to be used in all weathers and at night.

Length: 2.91 m (9ft 6½ in) *Span:* 64 cm (25 in) *Diameter:* 12.7 cm (5 in) *Max range:* 3 km+ (1.86 miles) *Warhead:* 5 kg (11 lb)

Char

French tanks. *Char* is the French word for tank, and thus all French tanks should, strictly speaking, carry the word in their nomenclature. Thus the Hotchkiss H-39 was officially the 'Char Légère H-39'. However, the tanks designed by Hotchkiss, Renault and Somua were always referred to by the names of the manufacturer; the use of 'Char' as an identifying title is therefore restricted to only a small number of designs.

Char 2C This was a First World War design of heavy 'breakthrough' tank intended to operate in the 1919 offensive. It was a 68-tonner with 12-man crew, mounting a 75-mm (2.95-in) gun in a high front turret. Ten were built before the war ended, though they were not completed until 1921 when they were each fitted with two 180-hp Mercedes engines taken from Germany as war reparations. Six of them were still in service in 1939 and were destroyed while on railway flat wagons at

Char

A French Char B1bis, factory fresh even to the chalked scrawl of a mechanic on the turret side. The B1bis had a hull-mounted 75-mm (0.295-in) gun with no traverse which was laid and fired by the driver and a 47-mm (1.85-in) low-velocity antitank gun in the turret. Though this was a good combination of fire power and the B1 and B1bis had thick armour with a 6-cylinder engine that gave a top speed of 29 km/h (18 mph) and radius of action of 210 km (130 miles) it did not perform well in action. The commander had to fire the 47-mm (1.85-in) gun and control the tank in action, some were not equipped with radios and the resultant poor tactical handling led to losses in action . The Germans used captured Char B1s as the chasses for a range of SP guns

Char

A Char B1 *bis* rolls through Paris on Bastille Day, 1938. The track and suspension system of the B1 *bis* was later adopted for the Churchill tank. Besides the turret armament of one 47-mm (1.85-in) low velocity antitank gun the B1 *bis* also mounted a 75-mm (2.95-in) gun in the hull

Right: The massive Char 2C, a 70-ton breakthrough tank designed at the end of the First World War. It had a crew of 13 men, including an officer, and mounted a 155-mm (6.10-in) howitzer and four machine-guns with four in reserve

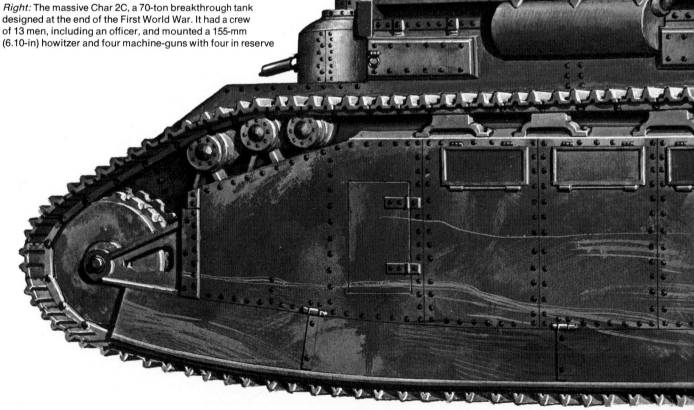

the time of the German invasion in 1940.
Char B This was a heavy tank design begun in 1929 which went into production in 1935 as the B1. Weighing 30 tons, with a crew of 4, it was armed with a 47-mm (1.85-in) gun in the forward-mounted turret and a 75-mm (2.95-in) gun in the front of the hull. While the turret could rotate, the hull gun had to be pointed by turning the tank. Driven by a 180-hp Renault engine and with 40 mm (1.57 in) of armour, it could reach 27.5 km/h (17 mph).

From 1937 the design was improved into the B1*bis*; the armament remained the same but the armour was increased to 60 mm (2.36 in) and the engine to a 300-hp aircraft motor.

Although ponderous and impressive, the Char B tanks suffered from bad design in that the crew were poorly located and the turret contained only one man, who had to command the tank and operate the gun at the same time. Their performance in 1940 suffered from this, although their armour thickness was instrumental in persuading the German army to go for heavier antitank guns.
Char D An infantry tank developed by Renault in the late 1920s which entered service in 1931 as the D1. A 13-tonner with

The crew of a Char 2C: eight were available in 1940 but were destroyed by German bombing

three-man crew, it was armed with a 47-mm (1.85-in) gun in the turret, the first turret to be of cast armour. Powered by a 65-hp engine to reach 17.7 km/h (11 mph), it had poor performance and was mechanically unreliable. Most were sent to North Africa where they remained in use until 1940.

In 1934 the D2 model appeared, with slightly thicker armour and a 150-hp engine, but it was unable to live down the poor reputation of the D1 and only 50 were built,

the army preferring the Somua S-35, which was a far better tank in every respect.

(Char 2C) *Weight:* 63 tons *Length:* 10.24 m (33 ft 7 in) *Width:* 2.92 m (9 ft 7 in) *Height:* 4.04 m (13 ft 3 in) *Speed:* 12.8 km/h (8 mph) *Armour thickness:* 45 mm (1.77 in) max *Armament:* 1 75-mm (2.95-in); 1 mg *Crew:* 13

(Char B1*bis*) *Weight:* 31 tons *Length:* 6.37 m (20 ft 11 in) *Width:* 2.48 m (8 ft 2 in) *Height:* 2.79 m (9 ft 2 in) *Speed:* 29 km/h (18 mph) *Armour thickness:* 20-60 mm (0.79-2.4 in) *Armament:* 1 75-mm (2.95-in); 1 47-mm (1.85-in); 2 mg *Crew:* 4 *Range:* 209 km (130 miles)

(Char D1) *Weight:* 14 tons *Length:* 5.3 m (17 ft 5 in) *Width:* 2.18 m (7 ft 2 in) *Height:* 2.4 m (7 ft 10½ in) *Speed:* 19 km/h (12 mph) *Armour thickness:* 40 mm (1.57 in) *Armament:* 1 47-mm (1.85-in); 2 mg *Crew:* 3 *Range:* 96.5 km (60 miles)

J I Thornycroft

HMS *Boxer,* one of the *Charger* Class destroyers which was was still in service during the First World War. Though seaworthy with a pronounced tumblehome, they were uncomfortable and living conditions were very primitive. Note the light boards on the forward funnel

Charger

British destroyer class. The first destroyers had been six vessels constructed under the 1892-93 Programme. The *Charger* Class were the follow up group of 36 ships constructed under the 1893-94 Programme. Both groups were generally similar (except that the later vessels mounted two more 6-pdr guns) and were collectively known as the '27-knotters', this being their contract speed. At a later date the entire group were officially reclassified as the 'A' Class.

Although listed as a class, individual vessels did in fact vary considerably as the Admiralty did little more than specify the speed, armament and general outline of the design and leave the details to the builders. All were flush decked with turtle back forecastles and anything from one to six funnels, they mounted a 12-pdr gun forward, two 6-pdr guns on each side and one 6-pdr aft, the single torpedo tubes being mounted on the centre line.

The achievements of the builders varied as success depended mainly on their vessels' ability to meet the contract speed. The most successful of the class was *Boxer,* constructed by Thornycroft, which averaged over 29 knots during a 3-hour trial. By comparison the *Fervent* constructed by Hanna never did, even after several modifications to her machinery, make 27 knots and was eventually taken into service without meeting this requirement.

Although seaworthy they were extremely uncomfortable vessels in anything but a flat calm and living conditions were generally somewhat primitive. Crews were paid 'hard lying' money as compensation.

The majority of the class served in home waters and a few in the Mediterranean. The *Salmon* was sunk in collision with a merchant ship in December 1901 but was later raised and repaired. The *Decoy* was sunk in collision with the destroyer *Arun* during night manoeuvres in August 1904 but could not be recovered as she was lost in deep water off the Scilly Isles. Most of the class were sold for scrap between 1907 and 1914 but 11 remained active throughout the First World War. They served mainly in local defence flotillas being employed on escort and patrol duties in the English Channel and off the East Coast. Some were equipped with depth charges during 1916-18 and the *Fervent, Lightning, Porcupine* and *Zephyr* were fitted with a 6-pdr AA gun. Two were lost, the *Lightning,* sunk by a mine in the North Sea on August 9, 1915, and the *Boxer,* sunk in collision with the SS *St Patrick* on February 8, 1918. The rest were sold for scrap in 1920.

Ardent, Banshee, Boxer*, Bruiser, Charger, Contest, Conflict*, Dasher, Dragon, Fervent*, Hasty, Handy, Hart, Hardy, Haughty, Hunter, Janus, Lightning*, Opossum*, Porcupine*, Ranger*, Rocket, Salmon, Shark, Skate, Snapper, Spitfire, Starfish, Sturgeon, Surly*, Sunfish*, Swordfish, Teazer, Wizard*, Zephyr*, Zebra.
* Units still in service during First World War.

Displacement: 240-320 tons Length: 57.9-63.4 m (190-208 ft) pp Beam: 5.8-6 m (19-20 ft) Draught: 1.5-1.8 m (5-6 ft) Machinery: 2-shaft triple expansion steam engines, 3500 to 4500 ihp=27 knots Armament: 1 12-pdr; 5 6-pdr (5×1); 2 18-in (46-cm) torpedo tubes (2×1) Crew: 50

Chariot

British 'human torpedoes' developed from captured Italian SLC-craft ('pigs'). The name 'human torpedo' was a misnomer, as they were in fact small electrically-driven submersible craft operated by two men sitting astride the body. They bore little relation to torpedoes either in speed or propulsion.

The first requirement for this type of vessel came after the successful Italian attack on Alexandria in December 1941, and the British Admiralty ordered what was virtually a carbon-copy of the Italian craft found after the operation. Their main use was to penetrate defended harbours, and the target in mind was the German battleship *Tirpitz,* hiding in the Norwegian fiords. Unfortunately the extremely cold temperatures encountered in northern waters were too much for men in their wetsuits, and it was decided to send the Chariots to the Mediterranean.

There were two marks of Chariot, but they differed in detail only. The body contained batteries, with a small electric motor aft turning a single shaft via a belt-drive. Only one set of hydroplanes was fitted, right aft. The forward operator drove the Chariot, while the second operator was responsible for attaching the warhead. This was a large detachable nose-cone, which could either be dropped on the harbour bottom underneath the target or attached to projections such as keels and bilge-keels by means of clamps and a wire rope.

Chariots were too small to undertake a voyage unaided, and were always carried to the scene of operations in special watertight containers welded to the deck-casing of a conventional submarine of the 'T' Class. The

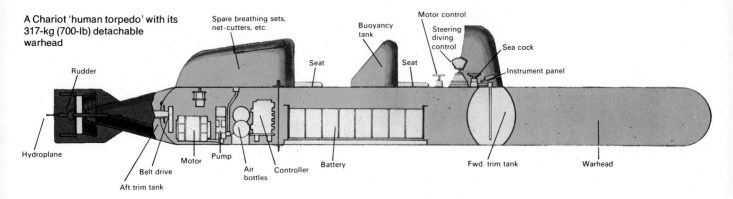

A Chariot 'human torpedo' with its 317-kg (700-lb) detachable warhead

best-known operations of Chariots were off Norway but the most dazzling exploits were achieved in the Mediterranean. In these operations Italian operators were used to penetrate Italian harbours, and several large warships in German hands were put out of action. Among the victims were the cruisers *Ulpio Traiano, Bolzano* and *Gorizia*. Understandably, the British were happy to decorate the Italian crews for these exploits, which has led to the story that Italians received British decorations for their attack on Alexandria!

Records of Chariots are incomplete and it is not known how many were built.

Displacement: 1½ tons (normal) *Length:* 7.65 m (25 ft) oa *Machinery:* 1-shaft electric motor=3½ knots *Armament:* 317-kg (700-lb) detachable explosive charge *Crew:* 2

Charioteer

British self-propelled antitank gun. It was developed in the 1950s as a replacement for the ageing Archer, for issue to Territorial Army units. It consisted of the chassis of the Cromwell tank to which a new turret carrying the 20-pdr gun was installed.

The description 'SP gun' is the official one; its application resembles the earlier American ideas of 'tank destroyers'. For all that, the Army usually referred to it as a tank and the general impression gained was of an attempt to improve the standard of the Cromwell's armament by fitting it with the Centurion's gun. In this, it was a success, and as well as being used to equip British units it was sold abroad to Austria, Finland, Jordan and the Lebanon. It went out of service in the early 1960s.

Weight: 3270 kg (28.5 tons) *Length:* 6.43 m (21 ft 1 in) *Width:* 3.05 m (10 ft 0 in) *Height:* 2.53 m (8 ft 4 in) *Speed:* 51.5 km/h (32 mph) *Armour thickness:* 14-64 mm (0.55-2.52 in) *Armament:* 1 20-pdr *Crew:* 3 *Range:* 241 km (150 miles)

Charlemagne

French battleship class built 1894-1900. These three ships—*Charlemagne, St Louis* and *Gaulois*—were typical pre-Dreadnoughts of French design, with a massive appearance but poor protection and stability. They were unusual in being a relatively homogeneous class, as the French were notorious for building 'samples'.

There were minor variations in appearance, notably in the method of handling boats; for example *St Louis* had a double-armed swinging davit, whereas *Charlemagne* had a luffing boom. All three ships were sent to the Dardanelles for the assault on the Narrows forts in March 1915. The *Gaulois* was heavily damaged on March 18 by hits from Turkish guns and had to withdraw to Malta, with her bows badly flooded. She was torpedoed by the German *UB 47* in the Mediterranean on December 27, 1916.

The *Charlemagne* suffered less damage at the Dardanelles and the *St Louis* was not hit. Both ships served at Salonika in 1916/17, but the *Charlemagne* paid off at Toulon and was completely stripped of armament in November 1917. The *St Louis* did not pay off until January 1919, when she became the overflow ship for the engineers' and stokers' training establishment at Toulon. Both battleships were condemned in June 1920. The *Charlemagne* was sold for scrapping shortly afterward but the *St Louis* was retained as an accommodation hulk until 1931, and finally scrapped in 1933.

Displacement: 11 108 tons (normal) *Length:* 118 m (387 ft 1½ in) wl *Beam:* 20.5 m (67 ft 3 in) *Draught:* 8.4 m (27 ft 6¾ in) *Machinery:* 3-shaft triple-expansion, 15 000 ihp=18 knots *Protection:* 400 mm (15¾ in) belt; 89 mm (3½ in) decks; 400 mm (15¾ in) turrets *Armament:* 4 12-in (305-mm)/40-cal Model 1893 (2×2); 10 5.5-in (140-mm)/45-cal Model 1891-3 (10×1); 8 100-mm (3.9-mm)/45-cal Model 1893 (8×1); 20 47-mm (1.85-in)/50-cal Model 1885; 2 45-cm (17.7-in) torpedo tubes (submerged, beam) *Crew:* 727

Name	laid down	launched	completed	builder
Charlemagne	7/1894	10/1895	2/1898	Brest Arsenal
St Louis	3/1895	9/1896	2/1900	Lorient Arsenal
Gaulois	1/1896	10/1896	2/1899	Brest Arsenal

The *St Louis*, a French battleship of the *Charlemagne* Class. After service during the First World War she ended life as an accommodation ship for trainee engineers and stokers at Toulon

Marius Bar

Charles F Adams

Below: The USS *Tattnall*, a guided-missile destroyer of the *Charles F Adams* Class; she is armed with Tartar and Asroc missile systems

Charles F Adams

US guided-missile destroyer class. Ordered in Fiscal Years 1957-61 and completed in 1960-64, they were the first DDGs designed from the keel up, and are basically an improved *Forrest Sherman* hull. A further three were built in US yards for the Royal Australian Navy, followed by three for the Federal German navy.

The first eight ships were allocated DD-numbers in the existing range, but were given DDG-numbers during construction, *DD.952-959* becoming *DDG.2-9*. The ships built for Australia and Germany were allocated numbers *DDG.25-30*.

The Australian ships differ in having a deckhouse amidships for the Anglo-Australian Ikara A/S missile system, and they were completed with a single-arm SAM-launcher instead of the twin type. The German ships are generally similar to USN ships but have square-topped 'macks' instead of conventional capped funnels.

The first 13 US ships had the Mk 11 twin launcher for Tartar missiles, whereas the later ships have the Mk 13 single-arm launcher. The Mk 13 weighs 60 129 kg (132 561 lb) as against 74 952 kg (165 241 lb) for the Mk 11, which allows 42 missiles to be stowed instead of 40, but the single type can fire just as fast (about 6 missiles per minute). Another difference between the groups is that the last five have a large SQS-23 bow sonar, which means that they have to have a single anchor housed in the stem to clear the dome.

The class is currently being modernized, with Standard-Medium Range (MR) missiles in place of the Tartar. It is believed that the additional topweight of new electronics may mean the removal of the Asroc launcher from between the funnels. The *Lawrence* and *Hoel* were fitted with launchers for Chaparral

A German-crewed Sikorsky S-58 circles two destroyers of the *Hamburg* Class during joint exercises between the US Navy and Kriegsmarine, with a *Charles F Adams* Class destroyer in the foreground. Besides its surface-to-air and antisubmarine missiles the *Charles F Adams* mounts two 5-in (127-mm)/54 cal guns and two triple Mk 32 12.75-in (32.38-cm) torpedo tubes. Other ships of this class have been built in US yards, three for Australia and three for West Germany

Federal German Navy

No	name	commissioned	builder
DDG.2	*Charles F Adams*	9/1960	Bath Ironworks
DDG.3	*John King*	2/1961	Bath Ironworks
DDG.4	*Lawrence*	1/1962	New York SB corporation
DDG.5	*Claude V Ricketts* (ex-*Biddle*)	1/1962	New York SB corporation
DDG.6	*Barney*	8/1962	New York SB corporation
DDG.7	*Henry B Wilson*	12/1960	Defoe SB company
DDG.8	*Lynde McCormick*	6/1961	Defoe SB company
DDG.9	*Towers*	6/1961	Todd Shipyards Inc
DDG.10	*Sampson*	6/1961	Bath Ironworks
DDG.11	*Sellers*	10/1961	Bath Ironworks
DDG.12	*Robison*	12/1961	Defoe SB company
DDG.13	*Hoel*	6/1962	Defoe SB company
DDG.14	*Buchanan*	2/1962	Todd Shipyards Inc
DDG.15	*Berkeley*	12/1962	New York SB corporation
DDG.16	*Joseph Strauss*	4/1963	New York SB corporation
DDG.17	*Conyngham*	7/1963	New York SB corporation
DDG.18	*Semmes*	12/1962	Avondale Marine Ways Inc
DDG.19	*Tattnall*	4/1963	Avondale Marine Ways Inc
DDG.20	*Goldsborough*	11/1963	Puget Sound B & DD company
DDG.21	*Cochrane*	3/1964	Puget Sound B & DD company
DDG.22	*Benjamin Stoddert*	9/1964	Puget Sound B & DD company
DDG.23	*Richard E Byrd*	3/1964	Todd Shipyards Inc
DDG.24	*Waddell*	8/1964	Todd Shipyards Inc
D.38	*Perth*	5/1965	Defoe SB company
D.39	*Hobart*	12/1965	Defoe SB company
D.41	*Brisbane*	1/1968	Defoe SB company
D.185	*Lütjens*	3/1969	Bath Ironworks
D.186	*Mölders*	8/1969	Bath Ironworks
D.187	*Rommel*	3/1970	Bath Ironworks

infrared short-range missiles in 1972-1973.

The *Biddle* was renamed *Claude V Ricketts* on July 28, 1964, in honour of the deceased vice-chief of naval operations, who had been a staunch supporter of NATO-manning of nuclear deterrent forces. The *Ricketts* then served for 18 months with a mixed NATO crew drawn from the Royal Navy, the Dutch, Italian, Greek, Turkish, Norwegian and Danish navies. The ship remained under USN control, with an American captain and part of her American crew, and the idea to prove the concept of mixed manning. Although the experiment was successful the project to build Polaris-armed surface ships for NATO was abandoned.

See also Chaparral.

Displacement: 3370 tons (standard), 4500 tons (full load) *Length:* 133.2 m (437 ft) oa *Beam:* 14.3 m (47 ft) *Draught:* 6.1 m (20 ft) *Machinery:* 2-shaft geared steam turbines, 70 000 shp=31 knots. *Armament:* 2 Tartar/Standard surface-to-air missile systems (twin- and single-arm launchers); 2 5-in (127-mm)/54-cal Mk 42 DP (2×1); 1 Asroc 8-barrelled antisubmarine missile system; 6 12.87-in (32.38-cm) Mk 32 torpedo tubes (2×3) *Crew:* 354

Charlie

Soviet cruise-missile submarine class. First seen in 1968, this group of 12 nuclear-propelled boats marked an important change in Soviet strategic thinking, for the *Charlie* 'C' Class is armed with vertical tubes for launching cruise missiles under water.

The missile is the SS-N-7 with a reported range of 48 km (30 miles), and it clearly gives a nuclear submarine a stand-off weapon with far greater range than any torpedo. It is believed to be intended for use against the US Navy's aircraft carriers, and it is significant that the *Charlies* have been seen in the Mediterranean, the home of the 6th Fleet. The SS-N-7 can be fired underwater, to rise above the surface and then acquire its target and assume a cruising mode.

As far as is known all 12 were built at the Gorky yard on the River Volga, 480 km (300 miles) east of Moscow. The rate of construction was apparently three per year. They are all part of the Northern Fleet.

Displacement: 4000 tons/5100 tons (surfaced/submerged) *Length:* 94 m (308 ft 5 in) *Beam:* 10 m (32.8 ft) *Draught:* 7.5 m (24 ft 7 in) *Machinery:* 1-shaft nuclear reactor, steam turbines, 24 000 shp=20/30 knots (surfaced/submerged) *Armament:* 8 launchers for SS-N-7 subsurface-to-surface missiles; 8 21-in (53-cm) torpedo tubes *Crew:* 100

Charlton

New Zealand machine-gun. The Charlton was one of the most remarkable weapons to appear during the course of the Second World War. It was developed and made in New Zealand in 1942 when a Japanese invasion appeared imminent and there was a general shortage of everything except rifles.

The Charlton company of Hastings, NZ, developed a conversion system which allowed the standard Lee-Enfield rifle to be modified into a gas-operated machine-gun. Cooling fins were added to the barrel and a gas port drilled into it; a gas cylinder and piston were fitted alongside the barrel. The bolt handle was sawn off and the bolt locking lug was modified to run in a cam groove on a plate which curved over the bolt. When fired, the gas passed through the port, forced the piston back and thus drove the cam plate back. As the cam groove in the plate passed across the top of the bolt, its interaction with the bolt lug rotated and opened the bolt. A return spring then closed the bolt and chambered a new round.

Since no manufacturing capacity existed in New Zealand, the design was sent to Australia and an order for 4000 was given. However, the production was stopped after a few hundred had been made since the factory was needed for making Owen submachine-guns. The Charltons were sent to New Zealand and issued for local defence, but were withdrawn in 1944. They are extremely rare today.

Calibre: 0.303-in (7.7-mm) service *Length:* 1140 mm (44 ft 10½ in) *Weight:* 7.03 kg (15.5 lb) *Barrel length:* 597 mm (23.5 in), 5 grooves, left-hand twist *Magazine:* 30-round detachable box *Rate of fire:* 500 rpm *Muzzle velocity:* 747 m/sec (2450 ft/sec)

Name	completed	builder
Chasseur	11/1909	Normand, Le Havre
Cavalier	1/1911	Normand, Le Havre
Fantassin	6/1911	F et Ch de la Mediterranée, la Seyne
Janissaire	6/1911	Penhoët, St Nazaire

Chasseur

French destroyer class, built 1908-11. After the *Branlebas* type destroyers the French navy decided to increase size to 450 tonnes for greater strength and seaworthiness. The first group ordered had reciprocating machinery, the second a mixture of turbines and reciprocating machinery, and the last (the *Chasseur* group) had turbines.

The four destroyers were built by well-established yards and the prototype was entrusted to the Normand firm. They differed considerably in detail, as French ships of the day tended to, the *Chasseur, Cavalier* and *Fantassin* having four funnels and the *Janissaire* three. She was also the only one of the class to have coal-fired boilers, making the *Chasseur* the first French destroyer to use oil fuel. Considerable difficulty was experienced with the turbines, and the French navy's opinion was that they were too 'fragile'. For this reason they did not last long after the First World War.

No fewer than six 65-mm (2.56-in) Model 1902 guns were mounted, three forward and three aft. The torpedo tubes were disposed in a bow tube and two single mountings on the centreline abaft the funnels. The torpedoes were the 45-cm (17.7-in) Model 1906.

On August 17, 1914, the *Cavalier* was in collision with her sister *Fantassin*. She was towed to Malta and repaired, but the bow tube was removed and she was relegated to the training of mechanics, stokers and divers. Her sisters continued to serve in the 3rd Squadron in the Armée Navale, and the *Chasseur* was stationed at Brindisi from 1915 to 1917. She was stricken in October 1919. The *Fantassin* was hunting a submarine on June 5, 1916, when she was rammed by the *Mameluk;* the wreck was abandoned and then sunk by gunfire from the *Fauconneau.* The *Janissaire* operated near Castellorizo in 1915/16 and was stricken in October 1920.

Displacement: 450 tons (nominal), 520 tons (full load) *Length:* 64.2-65.4 m (210 ft 8 in-214 ft 7 in) pp *Beam:* 6.54-6.60 m (21 ft 5 in-21 ft 7 in) *Machinery:* 3-shaft Parsons steam turbines, 7200 shp=28 knots *(Janissaire* 3 Foster-Wheeler boilers, others 4 Normand) *Armament:* 6 65-mm (2.56-in)/45-cal QF (6×1); 3 45-cm (17.7-in) torpedo tubes (3×1) *Crew:* 77-79

The shadow of a patrolling US Navy aircraft looms over a Soviet *Charlie* Class submarine as it passes through the Straits of Malacca in 1974

US Navy

Châteaurenault

Châteaurenault

French protected cruiser. This unique ship was designed for the purpose of commerce-raiding, with high freeboard and high speed. When painted in a late nineteenth-century colour-scheme, with black hull and light funnels, she bore a superficial resemblance to a liner. It was hoped that she might be able to approach liners without being recognized as a raider.

The ship was completed in October 1899 but she experienced severe vibration at speeds between 18 and 21 knots, and had to be returned to her builders several times. In 1914 she was in the 2nd Light Squadron, patrolling off Brest. She joined the Armée Navale in the Mediterranean in 1915 and served as a temporary flagship for the C-in-C. On February 2, 1916, she was detached to the South Atlantic to hunt for the armed raider *Mowe*. She was then refitted as a troop transport at Bizerta and served with the Eastern Army. On October 5, 1916, she picked up survivors from the AMC *Gallia* south of Sardinia, and on December 14, 1917, she was torpedoed twice by the Austrian U-Boat *UC 38* off Kephalonia. She sank slowly, allowing her crew to abandon ship.

Displacement: 8200 tons (normal) *Length:* 140 m (459 ft 4 in) pp *Beam:* 18 m (59 ft) *Draught:* 7.5 m (24 ft 7 in) *Machinery:* 3-shaft vertical triple-expansion, 24 000 ihp=23 knots *Protection:* 102-64 mm (4-2½ in) deck; 64-38 mm (2½-1½ in) casemates; 51 mm (2 in) gun shields *Armament:* 2 164.7-mm (6.5-in)/45-cal Model 1893 (2×1); 6 138.6-mm (5.46-in)/45-cal Model 1893 (6×1); 12 47-mm (1.85-in)/50-cal Model 1885 *Crew:* 587

Châtellerault

Name of French arsenal and, by extrapolation, the name applied to machine-guns developed there in the 1920s and 1930s.

During the First World War the French army suffered from the want of a good light machine-gun, and thus the development of such a weapon had high priority in postwar years. The French had received a number of Browning automatic rifles which had impressed them, and they adapted the action of the Browning to their new design.

The first priority was, in fact, to design a better cartridge than the old 8-mm (0.315-in) Lebel, and a new 7.5-mm (0.295-in) cartridge appeared in 1924 together with the first models of the new machine-gun. Unfortunately the cartridge was a bad design and gave rise to explosions and accidents with the gun. It was redesigned with a shorter cartridge case and the gun modified to become the Mle 1924/29, and as such it was a success.

The gun was gas-operated, using the normal type of piston beneath the barrel. This actuated a breech block which was tilted upward to lock into the receiver of the gun. Feed was from a top-mounted magazine, and two triggers were fitted, the front trigger giving single shots and the rear one giving automatic fire, thus doing away with the need to operate a change lever.

Due to financial problems, the supply of the Mle 24/29 was slow, but by 1938 it was standard issue in the French army as the squad automatic weapon. After the collapse of France in 1940, large numbers were taken into use by the German army in the fixed defences of the Atlantic coast.

A variant model of the Mle 24/29 was the Mle 1931, designed for use inside pillboxes of the Maginot Line and also for use in tanks. The modification consisted of removing the usual butt and replacing it with a curved shoulder-piece and fitting a peculiar side-mounted drum magazine which held 150 rounds.

Both models returned to French service after the Second World War due to the shortage of machine-guns, but they were eventually replaced by more modern designs. However it is likely that several will continue in service for some time in ex-French colonies, particularly African nations.

Name	laid down	launched	completed	builder
Châteaurenault	10/1895	5/1898	10/1902	La Seyne, Toulon

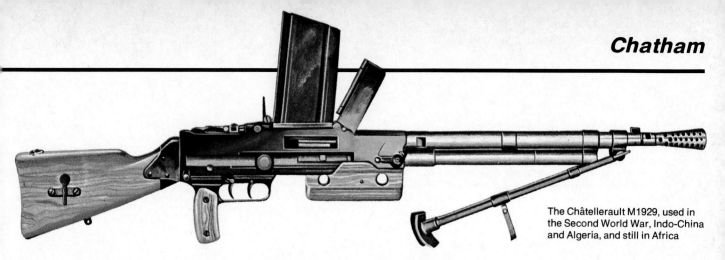

The Châtellerault M1929, used in the Second World War, Indo-China and Algeria, and still in Africa

(Mle 1924/29) *Calibre:* 7.5-mm (0.29-in) *Length:* 1082 mm (42.6 in) *Weight:* 9.18 kg (20 lb 4 oz) *Barrel length:* 500 mm (19.7 in), 4 grooves, right-hand twist *Magazine:* 25-round detachable box *Rate of fire:* 550 rpm *Muzzle velocity:* 820 m/sec (2690 ft/sec)

(Mle 1931) *Calibre:* 7.5-mm (0.29-in) *Length:* 1030 mm (40.5 in) *Weight:* 12.46 kg (27 lb 7½ oz) *Barrel length:* 600 mm (23.62 in), 4 grooves, right-hand twist *Magazine:* 150-round drum *Rate of fire:* 750 rpm *Muzzle velocity:* 840 m/sec (2756 ft/sec)

Chatham

British cruiser class. These ships were the third group of the 'Town' Class cruisers which were designed during the years immediately preceding the First World War. They were basically similar to the previous *Weymouth* Class and carried the same armament but adopted an improved system of protection which classifies them as a major step forward in British cruiser development.

Instead of the 51 mm (2 in) protective deck fitted in the earlier vessels they were fitted with vertical side armour of 51 mm (2 in) nickle steel bolted to 25 mm (1 in) thick high-tensile steel hull plating. This system was far more effective in preventing damage to the ships' vitals, and the side armour was high enough to prevent shells which passed over it from penetrating too deeply into the hull before detonating. The ships were also slightly larger, and more powerful machinery was provided to increase the speed by ½ knot.

Three were ordered by the Admiralty and a further three by the Australian government. All were laid down in 1911 and completed during 1912-13 except *Brisbane* which was laid down in Australia in 1913 and completed in 1916.

The first five of the class were serving on foreign stations in August 1914 except for *Southampton* which served in the Grand Fleet throughout the war. Most of the other ships of the class returned home and joined the Grand Fleet in 1916 but *Brisbane* remained in Australian waters and the majority of her war service was in the Pacific. The *Sydney* became famous soon after the outbreak of war when, on November 9, 1914, she intercepted and sunk the German cruiser

HMAS *Sydney,* the British *Chatham* Class cruiser which intercepted and sank the German cruiser *Emden* off Cocos Keeling Island on November 9, 1914. *Sydney,* like her sisters *Brisbane* and *Melbourne,* was ordered for the Royal Australian Navy and completed between 1912 and 1916

Chauchat

Designed by a committee in 1915, the Chauchat became the most hated gun ever issued to soldiers—it was unreliable, poorly made, and difficult to use efficiently. The poor quality of the materials used in the construction of the CSRG, as it was also known, led to a series of fraud and graft charges against the manufacturers. It was one of the few weapons captured by the Germans in 1940 that they did not re-employ

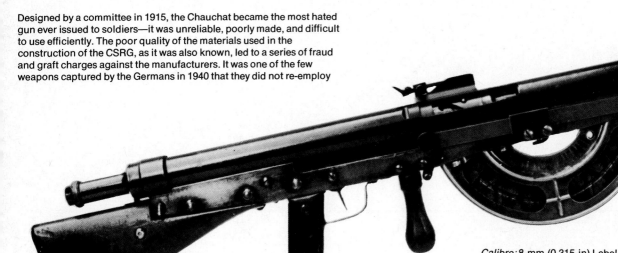

I V Hogg

Calibre: 8-mm (0.315-in) Lebel *Length:* 1150 mm (45.27 in) *Weight:* 9.07 kg (20 lb) *Barrel length:* 470 mm (18.5 in), 4 grooves, right-hand twist *Magazine:* 20-round detachable box *Rate of fire:* 240 rpm *Muzzle velocity:* 700 m/sec (2296 ft/sec)

(US .30-06 Model 1918) As above apart from: *Magazine:* 16-round detachable box *Rate of fire:* 300 rpm *Muzzle velocity:* 853 m/sec (2798 ft/sec)

Chequers

British destroyer class. The *Chequers* or *Ch* Class was the 12th Flotilla of the Emergency War Programme. Ordered in July 1942 they were of the same design as the 11th (*Caesar* Class) flotilla but incorporated new equipment under development in the later years of the war. Most important of this equipment was the Mk VI director which remotely controlled the main armament and utilized the latest type of gunnery radar which was capable of accurate 'blind fire'. This, together with additional close-range AA weapons, larger bridge, heavier masts and radar equipment, seriously increased topweight but some compensation was provided by the omission of the foremost bank of torpedo tubes.

All were laid down in 1943 but their construction was hampered by delays in the supply of equipment, particularly the new director, and none were completed before the end of the war. The last to complete was *Chivalrous* in May 1946. When they entered service they carried a close-range armament of one twin 40-mm (1.57-in) Bofors amidships, two single 2-pdr pom-poms on the platform abaft the funnel and one single 20-mm (0.79-in) in each of the bridge wings. However, the *Chevron* was completed with twin 20-mm (0.79-in) mountings in place of the 2-pdr guns and the *Chivalrous* with four single 40-mm (1.57-in) Bofors in place of the 2-pdr and 20-mm (0.79-in) guns. During the following years most of the remainder of the class were modified to the latter standard. During the 1950s X gun was removed to make way for the fitting of two 'Squid' antisubmarine mortars, and the two single 40-mm (1.57-in) guns abaft the funnel were removed. The *Chaplet* and *Chieftain* which were converted to minelayers, also had Y gun and the

Emden off Cocos Keeling Island. The *Southampton* was one of the most active and efficient cruisers of the war and distinguished herself at the Battles of Heligoland in 1914, Dogger Bank in 1915 and Jutland in 1916. During the latter she was the first to sight and report the German Battle Fleet while later she sank the destroyer *S35*, with the assistance of the *Dublin*, and the cruiser *Frauenlob* which she torpedoed during the night actions. The *Melbourne* and *Sydney* returned to Australian waters in 1919 and the *Chatham* was loaned to the New Zealand Navy during 1920-24. The three Royal Navy ships were sold for scrap in 1926 and the Australian ships between 1928 and 1936.

Chatham (built by Chatham dockyard)
Dublin (built by Beardmore)
Southampton (built by John Brown)
Brisbane (built by Cockatoo dockyard)
Melbourne (built by Cammell Laird)
Sydney (built by London and Glasgow)

Displacement: 5400 tons *Length:* 139.6 m (458 ft) *Beam:* 14.86 m (48 ft 9 in) *Draught:* 4.88 m (16 ft) *Machinery:* 2-shaft direct drive turbines, 25 000 shp=25.5 knots *Protection:* 76 mm (3 in) sides *Armament:* 8 6-in (152-mm) (8×1); 1 3-in (76-mm) AA; 2 21-in (53-cm) torpedo tubes submerged *Crew:* 475

Chauchat

French machine-gun. The Chauchat has to be given the accolade of being the worst light machine-gun ever to see military service. It was developed in 1915 at the Puteaux arsenal by three men, Chauchat, Ribeyrolle and Sutter, using a 1910 design for an automatic rifle as their starting point. The idea was to produce a lightweight automatic which could be fired from the hip during advances across no man's land and also be used as a defensive weapon in the trenches.

The mechanism was of the 'long recoil' type, one of the few times this system has

ever been used in a military weapon. In this system the whole barrel and bolt, locked together, recoil after firing for a distance greater than the length of a complete cartridge. At the end of this stroke the bolt is opened and held while the barrel is allowed to return. Then the bolt is released to run forward, chamber another round and fire again. The system has some advantages from the production aspect, since no gas cylinders and pistons have to be made, but it is highly sensitive to dust and dirt, a factor which made the weapon somewhat temperamental in the conditions of the First World War. It was chambered for the French 8-mm (0.315-in) Lebel cartridge, a rimmed round of sharply-tapering form, which necessitated the peculiar semi-circular magazine.

For all its mechanical peculiarity, the Chauchat might have succeeded had it been well made, but due to the pressures of the war it was built in pieces by a vast number of sub-contractors who then sent the parts to a central factory for assembly. The tolerances had to be loose to permit this, and the quality of the parts was poor. As a result, the Chauchat acquired an unenviable reputation for unreliability.

Since the US Army had even fewer machine-guns than the French, it was forced to buy what it could find in 1917, and the French persuaded them to take the Chauchat. 16 000 were bought in 8-mm (0.315-in) calibre and then a new model, the Mle 1918, was produced in the US standard 0.30-in (7.62-mm) chambering. Due to the better shape of the American cartridge, these models used a box magazine beneath the action. Almost 20 000 were bought, but they were of no better quality and most of them were thrown away after their first breakdown.

In spite of this, the French managed to sell numbers of these guns in postwar years, to Belgium and to Greece, where they were known as the 'Gladiator'. Their final appearance was in the Spanish Civil War, when some smart operator unloaded a number onto the International Brigades. By that time they were on their last legs and rarely fired more than two shots before jamming.

Chervonaya Ukraina Class

Name	laid down	launched	completed	builder
Chervonaya Ukraina	10/1913	11/1915	2/1927	Nikolaiev yard

Chester Class

Name and no	commissioned	builder
Chester (CL.1)	1907	Bath Ironworks
Birmingham (CL.2)	4/1908	Fore River company
Salem (CL.3)	1908	Fore River company

torpedo tubes removed.

Two of the class were sold to Pakistan; the *Chivalrous* (renamed *Taimur*) in 1954 and the *Charity* (renamed *Shah Jehen*) in 1958. All eight ships were sold for scrap between 1961 and 1971.

Chaplet, Charity (built by Thornycroft)
Chequers, Chieftain (built by Scott's)
Cheviot, Chevron (built by Stephen)
Childers, Chivalrous (built by Denny)

Displacement: 1900 tons (standard), 2535 tons (full load) *Length:* 110.57 m (362 ft 9 in) *Beam:* 10.90 m (35 ft 9 in) *Draught:* 3.20 m (10 ft 6 in) *Machinery:* 2-shaft geared steam turbines, 40000 shp=34 knots *Armament:* 4 4.5-in (114.3-mm) (4×1); 2 40-mm (1.57-in) (1×2); 2 2-pdr (2×1); 2 20-mm (0.79-in) (2×1) *Crew:* 186

Chervonaya Ukraina

Russian cruiser, completed in 1927. She was begun as the *Admiral Nalhimov*, a unit of the *Admiral Butakov* Class but construction was suspended between 1917 and 1922. On December 31, 1922, she was renamed *Chervonaya Ukraina* (Red Ukraine) and commissioned in 1927.

Having been under construction for 15 years, her design was badly outdated by the time she was completed. The designed speed of 32 knots was never attained, and by 1941 she could make no more than 25 knots. A seaplane was stowed between the funnels, with a crane on the port side, but this was removed before 1941. During the Great Patriotic War (1941-45) at least half of her 75-mm (2.95-in) antiaircraft guns were replaced by 12 37-mm (1.46-in) AA guns.

The ship remained in the Black Sea throughout her life. On November 12, 1941, while in Sevastopol harbour she was hit by German aircraft bombs and foundered in shallow water next day. Some guns were removed and used ashore, and on April 2, 1942, the wreck was again attacked by bombers, and this time she was completely destroyed.

See also *Admiral Butakov*.

Displacement: 6934 tons *Length:* 158.4 m (519 ft 8 in) pp *Beam:* 15.3 m (50 ft 2 in) *Draught:* 6.5 m (21 ft 4 in) *Machinery:* 2-shaft steam turbines, 50000 shp=29¼ knots max *Protection:* 25 mm (1 in) deck, 45 mm (1¾ in) casemates and gunshields, 76 mm (3 in) conning tower *Armament:* 15 130-mm (5.1-in) (15×1); 4 75-mm (2.95-in) AA (4×1); 12 machine-guns (12×1); 12 21-in (53-cm) torpedo tubes (4×3); provision for 100 mines *Crew:* 684-750

Chester

US scout cruiser class of 1904-08. Three experimental scout cruisers were approved by Congress in 1904. The US Navy was anxious to compare various types of machinery, and so the *Chester* was given Parsons turbines, the *Salem* Curtis turbines and the *Birmingham* triple-expansion engines. The design stressed good seakeeping, with high freeboard and a good coal supply at the expense of high speed. The armament was quite light, single 5-in (127-mm) guns forward and aft and six 3-in (76-mm) in the waist.

The machinery produced interesting variations on trials. At 10 knots the *Chester, Salem* and *Birmingham* used 16 783 kg (37 000 lb), 17 509 kg (38 600 lb) and 12 111 kg (26 700 lb) of feedwater respectively; at 24 knots (full speed) the figures were 113 398 kg (250 000 lb), 120 656 kg (266 000 lb) and 127 006 kg (280 000 lb). This showed that reciprocating machinery was superior for cruising, but turbines were more economical at high speed. Not only economical, for while *Chester* reached 26½ knots and *Salem* 26 knots, the *Birmingham* could only make 24.3 knots.

Salem was reengined in 1917 with General Electric geared turbines developing 20 000 shp. All three were rearmed during the First World War with four 5-in (127-mm), two 3-in (76-mm) and one 3-in (76-mm) AA gun, and the submerged 21-in (53-cm) torpedo tubes were replaced by deck-mounted tubes. The *Birmingham* made history on November 14, 1910, when Eugene Ely made the first powered flight from her deck.

All three saw service in 1917-18 as flagships of the destroyer squadrons, and were decommissioned in 1923. The *Chester* was renamed *York* in July 1928 to release her name for a new heavy cruiser, and all three were scrapped in 1930.

Displacement: 3750 tons (normal) *Length:* 129 m (423 ft 3 in) *Beam:* 14.32 m (47 ft) *Draught:* 5.10 m (16 ft 9 in) *Machinery:* (Chester) 4-shaft steam turbines, 16 000 ihp=24 knots (designed); (Birmingham) 2-shaft triple-expansion, 16 000 ihp=24 knots; (Salem) 2-shaft steam turbines, 16 000 shp=24 knots *Protection:* 51 mm (2 in) waterline belt over machinery only *Armament:* 2 5-in (127-mm); 6 3-in (76-mm); 2 21-in (53-cm) torpedo tubes (submerged, beam) *Crew:* 360

Chetverikov Soviet aircraft   See **ARK-3**

Chevalier

French torpedo boat, built 1891-94. In January 1891 the French Ministry of Marine decided to order three experimental types of 27-knot torpedo boats. They were intended to be 'high seas' types, capable of staying at sea in rough weather, and they were a stage in the evolution of the destroyer.

On trials the *Chevalier* reached 27.6 knots, the *Mousquetaire* made 24.77 and the *Corsaire* only 23.82 knots. The *Chevalier* saw considerable service between 1893 and 1914, and collided with the destroyer *Audacieux* in

Chevalier Class

Name	laid down	launched	completed	builder
Chevalier	7/1891	6/1893	9/1893	Normand
Mousquetaire	8/1891	8/1892	9/1893	F & C de la Méditeranée
Corsaire	12/1891	10/1892	8/1893	Ch de la Loire

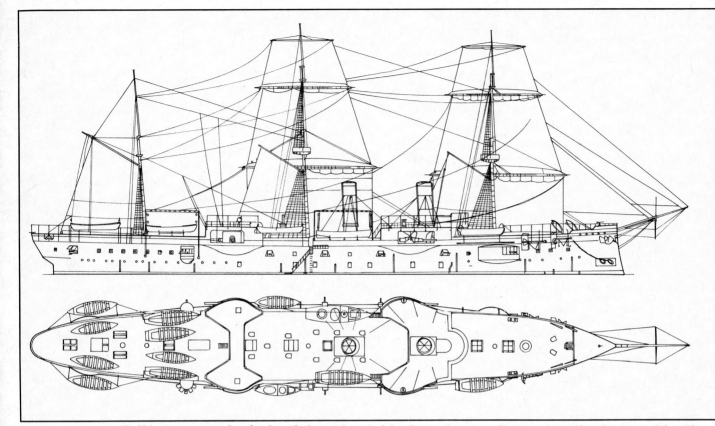

Profile and plan of USS *Chicago,* a protected cruiser launched near the end of the nineteenth century. She spent most of her time as a training ship

July 1896. From 1914 to 1918 she was in the *Division des Patrouilles de Provence* in the Mediterranean. Disarmed in June 1919, she was stricken four months later and sold at Toulon in May 1920. The *Mousquetaire* was attached to the naval academy at Brest from 1908 to 1910, and was stricken and sold in 1911. The *Corsaire* was reduced to similar status in 1898 and was used for training stokers before being stricken in 1912.

Displacement: (Chevalier) 123 tonnes (trials); *(Mousquetaire)* 124.7 tonnes; *(Corsaire)* 150.77 tonnes (trials), 171 tonnes (in service) *Length: (Chevalier)* 44 m (144 ft 4 in) pp; *(Mousquetaire)* 47 m (154 ft 2$\frac{1}{4}$ in) pp; *(Corsaire)* 47 m (154 ft 2$\frac{1}{4}$ in) pp *Beam: (Chevalier)* 4.5 m (14 ft 9 in); *(Mousquetaire)* 4.7 m (15 ft 5 in); *(Corsaire)* 4.46 m (14 ft 7$\frac{1}{2}$ in) *Draught: (Chevalier)* 1.45 m (4 ft 9 in) mean; *(Mousquetaire)* 1.26 m (4 ft 1 in) mean; *(Corsaire)* 1.66 m (5 ft 5$\frac{1}{4}$ in) mean *Machinery: (Chevalier)* 2-shaft triple-expansion, 2200 ihp=24$\frac{1}{2}$ knots; *(Mousquetaire)* 2-shaft triple-expansion, 2100 ihp=24$\frac{1}{2}$ knots; *(Corsaire)* 2-shaft triple-expansion, 2500 ihp=25$\frac{1}{2}$ knots *Armament: (Chevalier* and *Mousquetaire)* 2 37-mm (1.46-in) (2×1); 2 45-cm (17.7-in) Model 1892 torpedo tubes (2×1); *(Corsaire)* 2 37-mm (1.46-in); 2 38.1-cm (15-in) Model 1887 torpedo tubes (4 torpedoes carried)

Chevalier Class name of a group of *Gearing* Class US destroyers after FRAM conversions See **FRAM,** *Gearing*

Chicago

US protected cruiser. Following the authorization by Congress in 1882 for the construc-

tion of the two small cruisers *Atlanta* and *Boston,* came the recommendation for a protected cruiser and dispatch vessel. As these were to be named *Chicago* and *Dolphin* respectively, the vessels built under this

Name and no	launched	commissioned	builder
Chicago **CA.14**	5/12/1885	17/4/1889	J Roach & Sons

programme were known as the 'ABCD' ships; the first oceangoing ships to be built for the US Navy for 30 years. The bill authorizing the commencement of the programme finally became law on March 3, 1883,

A squadron of Chieftain tanks leaguered up during a training exercise in Germany in 1976

being signed by President Chester A Arthur.

Even such a limited programme was nearly too much for the inexperienced Navy Board and the American shipbuilders. Amid suspicions of bribery and favouritism the contract for all four ships went to the yard of John Roach of Chester, Pennsylvania, but to make matters worse the firm went into liquidation with three ships still under construction and one awaiting acceptance.

The *Chicago* was eventually commissioned in April 1889, a handsome vessel with high freeboard and a three-masted barque rig. Although well armed her machinery did not compare with current practice abroad, with compound overhead beam engines and cylindrical boilers resting on brick fireboxes, 'like an old-fashioned sawmill', as one critic put it.

Towards the end of 1889 the *Chicago*, with the *Atlanta* and *Boston* and the gunboat *Yorktown*, joined the Squadron of Evolution and visited Europe, and later she was the flagship of the European Squadron. Her captain was Alfred T Mahan, the great naval historian. In 1895-98 the machinery was replaced to improve her speed and the barque rig was replaced by two light masts. The 6-in (152-mm) guns were replaced by 12 5-in (127-mm), in a new lower deck battery.

The ship spent most of her time on training, and by 1917 she had only four 5-in (127-mm) guns and two 3-in (76-mm) AA guns. She was classified as armoured cruiser *CA.14* on July 17, 1920, but on August 8, 1921, she was reclassified as light cruiser *CL.14*. She was stationed at Pearl Harbor as an accommodation ship from 1923 and was renamed *Alton* and reclassified as a hulk, *IX.5* on July 16, 1928. She was stricken in August 1935, sold for scrap the following May, but foundered in tow en route to San Francisco on July 8, 1936.

The Chieftain main battle tank, showing the driver's position and part of the fighting compartment. The thermal jacket around the gun barrel is designed to keep the barrel temperature constant when the gun is in action and so keep ammunition performance identical

Displacement: 4500 tons (normal) *Length:* 99.06 m (325 ft) wl *Beam:* 14.68 m (48 ft 2 in) *Draught:* 5.79 m (19 ft) *Machinery:* 2-shaft compound overhead beam, 5000 ihp=15 knots (new machinery=18 knots after 1898) *Protection:* 38 mm (1½ in) deck *Armament:* (As built) 4 8-in (203-mm)/30-cal (4×1); 8 6-in (152-mm)/30-cal (8×1); 2 5-in (127-mm)/30-cal (2×1); 2 57-mm (2.24-in)/30-cal (2×1); 2 1-pdr; 4 47-mm (1.85-in); 2 37-mm (1.46-in); 2 Gatling machine-guns; (After reconstruction) 4 8-in (203-mm); 14 5-in (127-mm); 7 57-mm (2.24-in) *Crew:* 409 (after reconstruction)

Chieftain

British Army main battle tank, from 1965 onwards. Chieftain can be considered as the logical progression from Centurion, with the design priority given to firepower followed by protection and then mobility. Design began in 1956 with the formulation of a specification for Centurion's successor, and Chieftain was accepted for production in May 1963. Since then it has been periodically and systematically improved. In its current version it is generally acknowledged to be the best fighting tank in the NATO armoury.

The armament of the Chieftain is a 120-mm (4.7-in) gun. This calibre was selected

Chieftain with BAOR in Germany. The tank call sign is painted on the rear of the turret, while stores and the crew's personal kit are stowed in the bins and racks on the turret sides—among the stores are lubricant oils, a cooker, and kit bags and large packs

MOD

because it was considered essential to have a tank weapon capable of a one-shot kill over ranges of up to 4000 m (4375 yards). An unusual feature of this gun is the use of separated bag-charge ammunition. Although this led to problems in the design of a sliding-block breech, it was considered to be worthwhile because by reducing the length of the units of ammunition loaded, it reduced the amount of space needed inside the turret and thus allowed a heavy gun to be mounted in a relatively small turret ring. Moreover the separate units were lighter and handier and the rate of fire comparable with lighter guns using large fixed rounds—ten rounds per minute for the first minute and six rounds per minute thereafter.

Protection is derived from a combination of armour thickness and obliquity. Although the thickness of armour has never been publicly revealed, Chieftain has a higher proportion of its weight devoted to armour than any other contemporary tank, and the sloping of the various plates is designed to deflect both shot and mine blast, while skirting plates give protection against infantry antitank weapons.

Protection is also afforded against NBC (nuclear, biological and chemical) weapons, napalm and incendiary agents. An air filtration and ventilation system allows the tank to operate for periods of up to 48 hours without the hatches being opened.

The Chieftain engine is a 2-stroke multifuel opposed-piston engine of 19 litres (311 475 cu in) capacity, which drives through a mechanical transmission, thus ensuring more useful horsepower at the drive sprocket than would be achieved with a more sophisticated fluid transmission.

Fire control in early models was performed by a ranging machine-gun mounted coaxially with the main armament, the machine-gun's bullet being ballistically matched to the 120-mm (4.7-in) HESH shell. Thus, the machine-gun was fired until the bullet struck the target, whereupon the 120-mm (4.7-in) gun was fired with a high probability of hitting. In addition, a laser rangefinder was incorporated into the gunner's sight as an alternative method of determining the range.

The 'combat improved' version of the Chieftain is equipped with an 'Improved Fire

Draped in camouflage netting a Chieftain grinds across a training area. The turret is traversed to a ten o'clock position, which allows the commander a forward view unrestricted by the gun barrel

Trailing a plume of dust, a Chieftain, fitted with a bulldozer blade, roars down a track at a camp in England. The 'white light' searchlight is on the left of the turret where it can be employed co-axially with the main armament.

Chieftain

A British Chieftain tank of the 5th Royal Inniskilling Dragoon Guards fires its 120-mm main gun during training at Suffield in Canada. The Chieftain MBT (Main Battle Tank) equips British and Iranian forces, the latter version, known as the Shir Iran, having Chobham armour and an improved Rolls-Royce engine. Chieftain has a Barr and Stroud LF2 laser rangefinder and 12.7-mm ranging machine-gun. It has 53 rounds of mixed HESH, APDS and smoke and ammunition for its three machine-guns. The crew of four have pressurized air-conditioned and filtrated NBC protection and infrared night vision equipment for driving and fighting. As well as the IR aids they have a 2kW convertible white-IR searchlight mounted on the left of the turret. In addition to the MBT there is an armoured recovery version of the Chieftain and an armoured Vehicle-Launched Bridge which can lay a scissors-type bridge without exposing the crew to enemy fire. Chieftain has gone through seven marks, though a number of these are retro-fitted models with improved engines, air cleaning, range finding and ammunition stowage

Chieftain

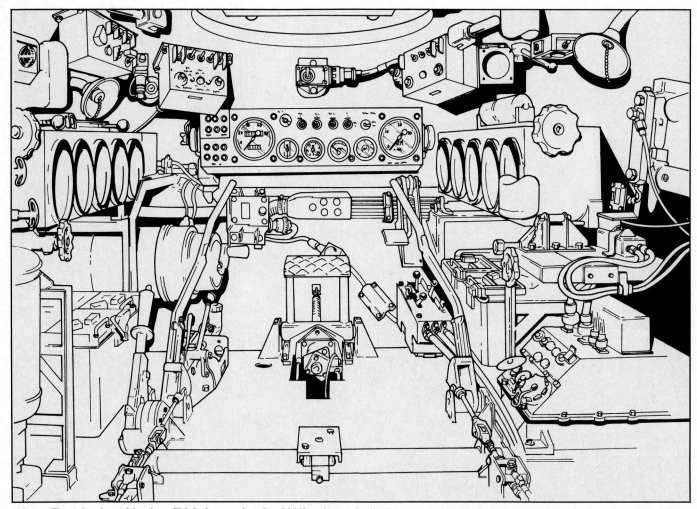

Above: **The driver's position in a Chieftain: steering, by skidding the tracks, is the same technique that was used in tanks of the First World War**

Control System' which incorporates a new laser rangefinder, laser sight, electronic fire control computer, and a variety of sensors which can measure and correct for such variables as the tilt of the tank and gun, wind speed, air humidity and barrel wear. All this, allied with full stabilization of the armament, means that the gun can be practically guaranteed to hit a stationary target at 3000 m (3280 yards) or a moving one at 2000 m (2187 yards) with the first shot.

As well as being used by the British Army, Chieftain has been offered for sale; currently an improved version is being prepared for supply to Iran. This model is believed to incorporate the new 'Chobham' armour and a new 1200-bhp Rolls-Royce engine.

The various models of Chieftain are as follows: Mk 1 Training tanks, using 585 bhp engine; Mk 2 Service tanks with 650 bhp engine; Mk 3 Improved Mk 2 with new auxiliary generator, cupola etc; Mk 3/3-MK 3 with laser rangefinder, improved sights, improved air conditioning; and the 'combat improved' version with a new 720-hp engine and improved fire control system.

Length: 10.8 m (35 ft 5 in) *Width:* 3.66 m (12 ft) *Height:* 2.9 m (9 ft 6 in) *Weight, loaded:* 54 866 kg (54 tons) *Crew:* 4 *Power Unit:* 720-bhp multifuel *Speed:* 43.4 km/h (27 mph) *Armament:* 120-mm (4.7-in) turret gun; 2×7.62-mm (0.30-in) mg *Ammunition:* 64 rounds, 120-mm (4.7-in)

A gunner in a Royal Hussars Chieftain prepares to engage a target with the 120-mm (4.7-in) gun

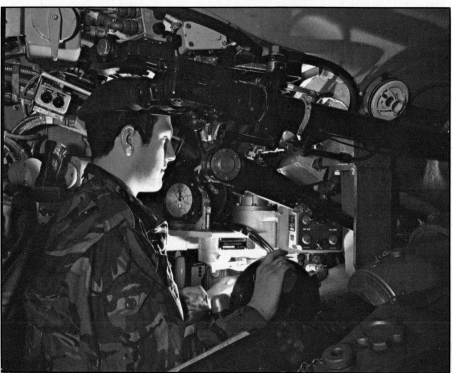

A Boeing Vertol CH-47 Chinook prepares to lift a British Army Ferret armoured car during a demonstration of its capabilities in the Far East

Chikasaw US Army name for Sikorsky S-55
helicopter   See **S-55**

Chikuma

Japanese protected cruiser class. The Japanese 2nd Class protected cruisers *Chikuma*, *Hirado* and *Yahagi* were larger and better-armed versions of the very successful 4105-ton *Tone*, built between 1906 and 1909. They were the equivalent of the British 'Town' type light cruisers, but had a much greater range, a lower freeboard, and more weight devoted to protection.

Their normal bunker capacity was 500 tons of coal, which could be increased to a maximum of 900 tons, and in addition they carried 300 tons of oil, giving them an endurance of 10 000 nautical miles at 10 knots. As with other major Japanese warships, the long range was necessitated by the long distances between bases in the Pacific.

They were handsome ships, with a swan bow, a raised forecastle and poop and four upright funnels. *Tone* could be distinguished from them by having only three raked funnels. A 6-in (152-mm) gun was mounted on the forecastle and poop, one on each broadside at the break of the poop and forecastle, and one either side between the first and second funnel. The 12-pdrs were mounted amidships. 363 tons was devoted to armament, and 439 tons to protection. The armoured deck extended from bow to stern, with a maximum thickness over boilers and machinery.

All had 16 Kanpon boilers. *Chikuma* and *Hirado* had two Curtis turbines driving two shafts, but *Yahagi* had four Parson turbines driving four shafts. *Chikuma* was built by Sasebo dockyard, *Hirado* by Kawasaki at Kobe and *Yahagi* by Mitsubishi at Nagasaki.

No more ships of this type were built by Japan, not because they were unsuccessful but because Japan's limited resources were needed to build battleships and battlecruisers. As a result, Japan had a large force of battleships, battlecruisers, large armoured cruisers and destroyers in the First World War, but very few light cruisers suitable for trade protection or commerce raiding, or for escorting and scouting for the larger ships.

During the first part of the war, they took part in the search for the German Pacific squadron and in patrols against the German surface raiders. In the 1920s they were fitted with two 3.1-in (79-mm) AA guns and their three 18-in (46-cm) torpedo tubes were replaced by four 24-in (60.9-cm) tubes. *Chikuma* herself was discarded and broken up in 1931. *Hirado* and *Yahagi* had been disarmed by the start of the Second World War. They were used as training ships during the war, and were scrapped in 1947.

Displacement: 4400 tons (normal), 5000 tons (full load) *Length:* 144.78 m (475 ft) oa *Beam:* 14.17 m (46 ft 6 in) *Draught:* 5.03 m (16 ft 6 in) *Machinery:* 2-shaft turbines, 22 500 shp=26 knots *Protection:* 76-51-mm (3-2 in) deck *Armament:* 8 6-in (152-mm); 4 12-pdr; 2 3.1-in (79-mm) AA; 2 mg; 2 24-in (61-cm) torpedo tubes *Crew:* 450

Chinook, CH-47 Boeing Vertol

US Army medium-lift helicopter. Design of the Boeing Vertol Model 114 Chinook began in 1956 to meet a US Army requirement for a medium transport helicopter able to fly in all weathers and under the most adverse conditions of temperature and altitude.

The company had grown from that of a pioneer constructor called Piasecki, so it was not unnatural that a variation of the 'Flying Banana' twin tandem-rotor layout first used by him should be chosen for the Chinook. With the two engines mounted on each side of the rear rotor pylon and over the back end of the cabin, the internal area was left unobstructed and a large rear loading ramp could be installed, essential for loading bulky freight.

Like its smaller and lower-powered predecessor the CH-46 Sea Knight, the Chinook was designed to take advantage of the new generation of light shaft-turbine engines just becoming available. Following an initial order in 1959 for five development aircraft, the first hovering flight was made in September 1961 under the power of two 1940-hp Lycoming T55 engines. By the time of the

Name	laid down	launched	completed
Chikuma	5/1910	4/1911	3/1912
Hirado	8/1910	6/1911	6/1912
Yahagi	6/1910	10/1911	7/1912

593

Chitose

first production model, the CH-47A, these had been uprated to 2200 hp and were soon uprated again, to some 2650 hp.

The US Army started receiving its first aircraft for pilot training and operational testing early in 1963, and by late that year had made the Chinook its standard medium transport helicopter. Since then, the type has had a most distinguished career, proving itself well up to the most demanding tasks particularly in the harsh operational environment of Vietnam. Here it was used for anything from rescuing no fewer (on one occasion) than 147 civilians, to carrying troops and equipment in

The CH-47C Chinook saw extensive service in Vietnam from September 1968 as a troop carrier, freight transport and heavy-lift recovery helicopter

its 9.14 m (30 ft) long cabin and hoisting a total of well over 10000 damaged aircraft back for repair or salvage. The Chinook also proved extremely reliable, each of its contra-rotating rotors being capable of being driven by either engine in case of failure.

Three main versions of the Chinook have been built, including the CH-47A already mentioned. Apart from more powerful engines, of 2850 hp, the CH-47B had a number of improvements to the rotor blades and also strakes along the rear of the fuselage for better longitudinal stability. First deliveries of this version were made in 1967.

The latest model, the CH-47C, again has much uprated engines, the T55 now producing no less than 3750 hp, which considerably enhances performance. A much-strengthened transmission is required to cope with the extra power. Deliveries of this version, which also has fuel capacity increased by over 60% to 4137 litres (1093 US gal), began in 1968.

Well over 800 Chinooks of all models were built at Vertol's Philadelphia plant before production there ended in the mid-1970s, but the type continues in licensed production at Elicotteri Meridionali in Italy and a series of product-improvement programmes are under way in the US. These already include a crashworthy fuel system and an integral spar inspection system. In addition, the steel-spar and honeycomb rotor blades of US Army aircraft are gradually being replaced with partially composite-material units which have a very much longer fatigue life.

Export customers include Australia and Iran, and the Chinook is also in use for commercial and quasi-commercial purposes.

(CH-47C) Rotor diameter: 18.29 m (60 ft 0 in) *Overall length:* 30.17 m (99 ft 0 in) *Maximum design gross takeoff weight:* 20865 kg (46000 lb) *Maximum payload:* 9843 kg (21700 lb) *Maximum speed:* 304 km/h (189 mph)

Chitose

Japanese aircraft carrier class. *Chitose* and *Chiyoda*, like *Tsurugizaki* (later *Shoho*), *Takasaki* (later *Zuiho*) and *Taigei* (later *Ryuho*) were designed to be easily convertible to high speed oilers, submarine tenders, seaplane carriers or aircraft carriers in an emergency. Japanese carrier tonnage had been limited by the London Treaty, but Japan abrogated the Treaty in 1936 when both ships were under construction and *Chitose* and *Chiyoda* were completed as seaplane car-

riers. Japan had a large force of seaplanes because of the lack of airfields in the Pacific.

As seaplane carriers they displaced about 11000 tons and had two twin 5-in (127-mm) guns forward, with 12 25-mm (1-in) light AA guns. The bulky bridge and single funnel were well forward, and there was a large box gantry amidships and a catapult at the stern. They could carry 24 seaplanes. They were powered by 44000 shp turbines and 12800 shp cruising diesels. They were ordered under the second Fleet Replenishment Law, and built at Kure dockyard. *Chitose* was launched on November 29, 1936, and *Chiyoda* on November 19, 1937.

In 1941 *Chitose* was rebuilt to carry midget submarines. Doors were fitted at the stern with rails in the aft part of the hangar leading down to the waterline. Twelve midget submarines were carried, and they could all be launched in pairs in 17 minutes. Trials were successful and *Chiyoda* was also similarly modified in 1941. The seaplane capacity was reduced to 12.

After Japan's catastrophic carrier losses at the Battle of Midway in June 1942, it was decided to convert both to aircraft carriers with a 152.5 m by 23 m (500 ft 6 in by 75 ft 6 in) flight deck. *Chiyoda* was converted during 1942/43 and *Chitose* during 1943/44. As light fleet carriers, they were flush decked, with a single funnel exhausting downward to starboard amidships. They were comparable in some ways with the American *Independence* Class, but were slower and almost completely unprotected.

At the Battle of the Philippine Sea they formed the 3rd Carrier Division, and on May 22, 1944, *Chitose* was hit by two torpedoes from the American submarine *Puffer,* neither of which exploded. They were both lost on October 25, 1944, when they formed part of Admiral Ozawa's decoy force at the Battle of Leyte Gulf.

Displacement: 11190 tons *Length:* 192.48 m (631 ft 6 in) *Beam:* 20.80 (68 ft 3 in) *Draught:* 7.47 m (24 ft 6 in) *Machinery:* turbines and diesels, 56800 shp=29 knots *Armament:* 8 5-in (127-mm); 30 25-mm (1-in) *Aircraft:* 30 *Crew:* 950 approx

Choctaw US Army name for Sikorsky S-58 helicopter   See **S-58**

Christie

US tank series. Walter J Christie was an American engineer who founded the Front Drive motor company shortly before the First World War, manufacturing a variety of trucks and fire engines. In 1916 he designed a self-propelled mounting for a 3-in (76-mm) AA gun. He appeared to have designed the gun and mounting too, for there was certainly no official manufacture of such a weapon until August 1918, and it was probably a converted coast defence gun. The mounting was a four-wheeled platform with folding outriggers and with the engine and driving controls at one end. Although the US Army

U.S. ARMY 413122

ARMY

and he neglected the SP guns to pursue his own ideas of tank design. As a result, relations between Christie and the army became somewhat strained, a situation which gradually worsened.

His first tank was the M1919 which was a failure in most respects. His attempts to armour the vehicle made the engine and transmission inaccessible, the suspension was poor, and it was underpowered. His next design, the M1921, removed the high-set turret and placed a 57-mm (2.24-in) gun in a ball mounting in the front plate and simply had a small observation cupola on top. However, the suspension was much the same, front and rear main wheels with a two-wheeled bogie in the track centre, and by this time the army had little money to spend and were not inclined to give Christie a chance to improve at their expense.

He now turned to designing amphibian tanks at his own expense, and, with a characteristic flair for publicity, plunged his M1922 into the Hudson River, sailed upstream and drove out onto a railroad track. This won him an order for six from the US Marines in 1922, and in the following year one of these vehicles made the first amphibian landing from a ship onto the shores of Puerto Rico.

With that order his military connections ended for some time; he appears to have run out of funds and occupied his time in designing. He thus developed the suspension system which was to make him famous—a double-skinned construction into which coil springs were built, these springs supporting large-diameter rubber-tyred wheels which supported the track and also acted as road wheels when the track was removed. In 1928 he received $100 000 from the US government for various patent rights and formed the US Wheel Tracklayer Corporation and built a new tank, the M1928.

bought it from him for $7800, it was found, on trial, to be overweight, and to have a poor cross-country performance; moreover the gun mounting was a bad design.

Nothing daunted, Christie then designed a tracked SP mounting to carry an 8-in (203-mm) howitzer; it had the additional feature that the tracks could be removed and the

carriage driven on its wheels on roads in order to conserve track life. Four of these SP mountings were bought by the army for $15 000 each in 1918.

The army encouraged Christie to develop his SP gun designs, and he did in fact produce a number in the period 1918-21. He had, however, become more interested in tanks

In October 1930 the M1928 was tested by the US Army, two of the assessors being Major George S Patton and Lt Col Adna R Chaffee, both destined to make their mark in US armour history. The M1928 put up an impressive performance, crossing obstacles previously considered impassable, running at 113 km/h (70 mph) on roads and 48 km/h (30 mph) cross-country. The Board of Assessors recommended immediate acceptance of the design. Christie received an order for five tanks, to be known as T3, and the first of these was delivered in September 1931.

The T3 weighed 10.5 tons and was powered by a V-12 engine which Christie 'tweaked' to produce 387 bhp. This gave it a remarkable turn of speed, but its cross-country speed was too much for both the tank and the crew. After building the T3s for the army, Christie then sold similar models to Poland and Russia, though the Poles defaulted on their order and the two tanks destined for them reverted to the US Army.

The American tanks became the basis for the Combat Car development while the Russian tanks began the long chain of designs which culminated in the T34. Christie, by this

A US T3 developed by the Wheel Track Layer corporation in 1931 using Christie suspension

Churchill

time, had fallen out with the army once again. He disagreed with the service specification and lost interest in improving the design, urging the army, once more, to wait for his next idea. There was also a violent disagreement over contracts. As a result, the US Army ceased to deal with Christie, and though his patents were still used, development was taken out of his hands.

In 1936 he sold one tank to Britain, which became the design source for the Cruiser series, and in the years after that he proposed a variety of vehicles, each more surrealistic than the last—tanks with wings to cross gaps, tanks with helicopter rotors, tanks to be delivered non-stop by aircraft. His last design, in 1943, is said to be remarkably like the postwar Swedish 'S' Tank in concept but it was never built.

Christie's strength and weakness lay in his obsession with speed and manoeuvrability to the exclusion of practically everything else. His designs were remarkable mechanical achievements but as practical tanks they were worthless, and in every case his basic ideas had to be considerably modified by practical soldiers before they could be put to use.

See also Combat Cars.

(T3) *Weight:* 11 tons *Length:* 5.49 m (18 ft 0 in) *Width:* 2.25 m (7 ft 4 in) *Height:* 2.34 m (7 ft 8 in) *Speed:* 72 km/h (45 mph) on wheels; 40 km/h (25 mph) on tracks *Armour thickness:* 16-13 mm (0.63-0.5 in) *Armament:* 1 37-mm (1.46-in) gun; 1 0.30-in (7.62-mm) mg *Crew:* 3

Churchill

British infantry tank. At the outbreak of the Second World War it was expected that the fighting would soon revert to the trench warfare of 1914-18. It was therefore thought necessary to develop a heavy infantry tank to accompany attacks over shell-torn ground, in the same fashion as the First World War tanks had operated.

The specification called for 60 mm (2.4 in) of armour to protect against the German 37-

A Carrier, Churchill, 3-in (76-mm) Gun, Mk I. This crude SP gun was an anti-invasion measure

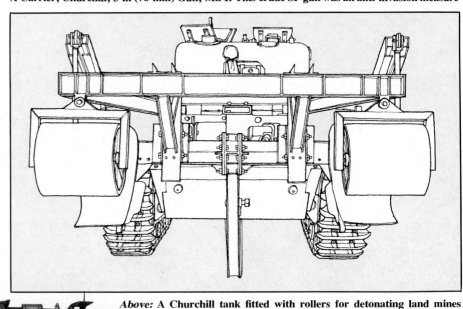

Above: A Churchill tank fitted with rollers for detonating land mines

The Infantry Tank Mk IV Churchill I armed with a 2-pdr and a 3-in (76-mm) howitzer in the hull

mm (1.46-in) gun, a speed of 16 km/h (10 mph) and an armament of one 2-pdr gun and a 7.92-mm (0.312-in) machine-gun in the turret with another 2-pdr and another machine-gun in the front of the hull. The pilot models of the '≠A20' were developed by Harland and Wolff in Belfast, using a multi-wheel suspension said to have been inspired by the French Char B1 bis and a flat 12-cylinder petrol engine by Meadows.

The first pilot was tested in the summer of

A Churchill Mk I showing fighting compartments and Bedford 12-cylinder engine with auxiliary fuel tank. The Churchill went through nine marks and a number of sub-types

Churruca

Spanish destroyer class. Before 1920, the Spanish navy concentrated on building major warships, and very few destroyers were constructed. Therefore in 1922 the first of the *Churruca*s were ordered. They were built to a British design and were closely based on the Royal Navy's *Scott* Class flotilla leaders of 1918. They had the same raised forecastle hull with two funnels and superfiring 4.7-in (120-mm) guns fore and aft. The fifth 4.7-in (120-mm) gun was between the funnels, and the British design of triple torpedo mount

1940 and proved a disappointment. The gearbox gave trouble, the engine did not produce sufficient power and the vehicle was well over the specified weight of 32 tons. The A20 design was forthwith abandoned and a new specification for 'Tank A22' was given to Vauxhall Motors in July 1940.

Their first task was to design a new 12-cylinder engine, after which the A20 design was modified to fit around the power unit. A heavier gun than the 2-pdr was desirable, but no suitable weapon was available; so the 2-pdr was retained as the turret gun and, to provide a high explosive capability for infantry support, a 3-in (76-mm) howitzer was fitted into the hull front plate. The first production tanks were delivered in June 1941, 11 months from the issue of the specification, a remarkable feat by Vauxhall, who had no previous experience of tank design or construction.

Subsequently a total of 5640 Churchill tanks were built, of a variety of variant marks and models, and many of these were further converted into special-purpose tanks. The Churchill was first used on the abortive Dieppe raid. It was then employed in Tunisia, where it demonstrated its ability to good effect, and it remained in British service throughout the war. Indeed, it remained in service in other countries until the late 1960s. Although there were several mechanical problems with the first models—of the first 1200 built, almost 1000 had to go back to be modified—most of these had been overcome by the time the tank first saw serious action and its subsequent record was of great reliability and surprising manoeuvrability.

The various marks of Churchill are:
Mk I. (Original model) Armed with 2-pdr and 3-in (76-mm) howitzer. 5 man crew. Armour base 60 mm (2.4 in).
Mk II. 3-in (76-mm) howitzer removed from hull and replaced by a 7.92-mm (0.312-in) Besa machine-gun.
Mk III. Welded turret with 6-pdr gun.

Mk IV. Cast turret with 6-pdr gun.
Mk IV/NA75. Modification to the Mark IV carried out in North Africa by removing the 6-pdr and inserting a 75-mm (2.95-in) gun and mantlet removed from a Sherman tank. 120 were so converted.
Mk V. 95-mm (3.74-in) howitzer in turret for use as a close-support weapon.
Mk VI. 75-mm (2.95-in) turret gun in place of 6-pdr.
Mk VII. (Major redesign) New hull to give frontal armour thickness of 150 mm (5.9 in), new turret of composite welded/cast construction, stronger suspension. 75-mm (2.95-in) turret gun.
Mk VIII. As for VII but with 95-mm (3.74-in) howitzer in the turret.
Mk IX. Mark III or IV with added armour and new turret with 75-mm (2.95-in) gun so as to approximate to Mk VII standard.
Mk X. Mk VI reworked as above.
Mk XI. Mk V reworked as above.

Because of a shortage of the new turrets, some of the Mks IX, X and XI had the hull modifications done but had to retain their original turrets; the letters LT (for Light Turret) were then added behind the Mk number.

The Churchill formed the basis for a wide variety of specialized armour, such as AVREs, bridging tanks, flamethrowers and so on. These are dealt with in separate entries under their code names or under the general heading.

See also AVRE.

(Mark III) *Length:* 7.670 m (25 ft 2 in) *Width:* 3.251 m (10 ft 8 in) *Height:* 2.488 m (8 ft 2 in) *Weight, loaded:* 39 625 kg (39 tons) *Power unit:* Bedford 12-cylinder petrol, 350 bhp *Speed:* 25 km/h (15.5 mph) *Armament:* 6-pdr turret gun; 2 7.92-mm (0.312-in) BESA machine-guns *Ammunition:* 84 rounds 6-pdr; 9450 rounds 7.92-mm (0.312-in) *Armour:* 88 mm (3.46 in) hull front; 88 mm (3.46 in) turret front *Crew:* 5

with raised centre tube was adopted.

Churruca, Alcala Galiano, Sanchez Barcaiztegui, Jose Luis Diez, Almirante Ferrandiz, Lepanto and *Almirante Valdez* were built at SECN's Cartagena dockyard between 1925 and 1932. *Churruca* and *Alcala Galiano* were sold to Argentina in 1927 and renamed *Cervantes* and *Juan de Garay*. They remained in service with the Argentine navy until 1960. In 1929 two more *Churruca*s were laid down at Cartagena to replace them and they were also called *Churruca* and *Alcala Galiano*.

Seven more, *Almirante Antequera, Almirante Miranda, Gravina, Escano, Ulloa, Jorge Juan* and *Ciscar*, were also built at SECN's Cartagena dockyard between 1930 and 1936. These were known as the Second Series, and differed from the first by having a tripod foremast, a cap on the forefunnel, a larger deckhouse abaft the second funnel and a 37-mm (1.46-in) AA gun between the funnels in place of the fifth 4.7-in (120-mm). Two more, *Alava* and *Liniers*, were delayed by the Civil War and completed in the early 1950s to a greatly modified design.

All the First and Second Series *Churruca*s served on the Republican side during the Spanish Civil War. On most of the ships the officers declared for the Nationalists but were overpowered by the crew and imprisoned or killed. None saw much action, but *Sanchez Barcaiztegui, Lepanto* and *Almirante Antequera* took part in the torpedoing of the Nationalist heavy cruiser *Baleares* on March 6, 1938. *Almirante Ferrandiz* was sunk in September 1936 and *Ciscar* in October 1937, but the latter was salved and refitted in 1938-39. She was later to run aground and break her back off Ferrol on October 17, 1957. *Churruca* was torpedoed by an Italian submarine but was later repaired.

The First Series *Churruca*s were discarded between 1957 and 1966 and the Second Series between 1959 and 1971. By the 1960s the AA armament of the surviving ships had been reduced to two 20-mm (0.79-in) guns, and

Chuyo

their torpedo tubes had been replaced by A/S torpedo-launching racks.

See also *Alava* and *Canarias*.

Displacement: 1536 tons (standard), 2087 tons (full load) *Length:* 101.5 m (333 ft 0 in) *Beam:* 9.7 m (31 ft 9 in) *Draught:* 5.2 m (17 ft 0 in) *Machinery:* 2-shaft steam turbines, 42 000 shp=36 knots *Armament:* 5 4.7-in (120-mm); 1 3-in (76-mm); 4 MG; 6 21-in (53-cm) torpedo tubes (2 triple mounts) *Crew:* 160

Chuyo

Japanese escort carrier class. Unlike other aircraft carriers converted from liners, *Chuyo* (ex-*Nitta Maru*) and her sisters *Taiyo* (ex-*Kasuga Maru*) and *Unyo* (ex-*Yawata Maru*) were built with spaces for lifts and hangars and other equipment so that they could easily be converted to aircraft carriers in an emergency; and the NYK shipping line, which operated from Japan to America, was paid a considerable subsidy for these ships by the Japanese navy.

All were built at Mitsubishi's Nagasaki yard, but only *Chuyo*, launched on May 20, 1939, and *Unyo*, launched on October 31, 1939 were completed as liners. *Taiyo*, launched on September 19, 1940, was completed in September 1941 at Sasebo dockyard as an aircraft carrier. *Unyo* was converted between January and May 1942 and *Chuyo* from May to November 1942 at Kure dockyard.

They were fitted with a 172 m by 23.5 m (564 ft 4 in by 77 ft) flight deck, and were the first Japanese carriers to have a funnel on the island, which was quite large. The high freeboard forward meant that the bow plating extended almost up to the flight deck. They were fitted with two lifts, but not with catapults or arrester gear. This, combined with their slow speed and complete lack of protection, meant that they were unsuitable for use as fleet carriers, as had been intended. Instead they were mainly used as aircraft ferries and for training pilots in deck landing and carrier operations.

Taiyo differed from the other two by having only four 4.7-in (120-mm) AA, and a much smaller crew. The class originally had only eight 25-mm (1-in) AA guns, but by 1943 these had been increased to 24. By mid-1944 *Unyo* had had four 4.7-in (120-mm) removed, and both *Taiyo* and *Unyo's* light AA armament had been increased to 64 25-mm (1-in) and 10 13-mm (0.51-in) AA.

The lack of underwater protection made these ships very vulnerable to underwater damage, and all were sunk by American submarines. *Chuyo* was torpedoed by *Sailfish* off Honshu on December 4, 1943, *Taiyo* was torpedoed by *Rasher* off Cuzon on August 18, 1944, and *Unyo* by *Barb* in the South China Sea on September 16, 1944.

Displacement: 17 830 tons (standard) *Length:* 180.24 m (591 ft 4 in) oa *Beam:* 22.48 m (73 ft 9 in) *Machinery:* geared turbines, 25 200 shp=21 knots *Armament:* 8 4.7-in (120-mm); 8 25-mm (1-in) *Aircraft:* 27 *Crew:* 850.

Cicogna, Fiat B.R.20

Italian bomber. After almost two decades of single-engined biplane B.R. (Bombardamento Rosatelli, the latter being chief

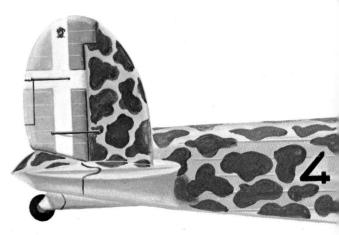

The Fiat B.R.20 Cicogna (Stork) was designed in 1934-35 and first flew in February 1936. It saw action during comparatively unopposed raids over Spain and Albania. Its debut in the Battle of Britain was disastrous, in one mission seven out of ten aircraft were shot down. The Eastern Front and Balkans were more congenial, but eventually Soviet fighters became an effective deterrent

designer) aircraft, the B.R.20 marked a complete break. Considerably larger, it was a modern monoplane with retractable landing gear, though still with typically Italian mixed construction.

The prototype was designed in 1934-35 and flew on February 10, 1936, and after quick clearance of a few faults went into production as the Cicogna (Stock) in June, entering combat service with the 13° Stormo in September 1936. Compared with the more important S.M.79 it had only two 1000 hp radials (Fiat A80 RC41) instead of three, and was closely comparable in size, yet actually carried a heavier bombload over roughly the same distance at similar speed.

Normal crew numbered five, and there were four 7.7-mm (0.303-in) machine-guns in the nose turret (2) and dorsal and ventral positions. Production was rapid, and when this original model was superseded in late 1939 some 350 had been built, including 75 for Japan (because of a delay with the Ki-21) and many for Spain and Venezuela.

After extensive operational experience in Spain and Albania the B.R.20 was modified by altering the structure, systems and even the exterior shape, the B.R.20M (Modificato) flying in late 1939. The dorsal gun was exchanged for a Breda-SAFAT of 12.7-mm (0.5-in) calibre, and the forward fuselage was wholly new. Some earlier aircraft were modified to this standard, and about 250 new B.R.20Ms had been built by the time of the Italian collapse in September 1943.

In October 1940 two Stormi with 75 aircraft—virtually all the 20M Cicogni then in service—formed the Corpo Aereo Italiano which operated from Belgium to bomb Britain. Day raids proved a disaster (seven shot down out of ten on the first mission), and after a few scattered night operations survivors were redeployed to Greece in January 1941. In 1942/43 some 250 Cicogni were operational in the Mediterranean, Balkans and Eastern Front, but increasingly proved unable to survive in the face of fighter opposition.

Fiat B.R.20M Cicogna bombers in a loose formation during a raid over Southern Russia

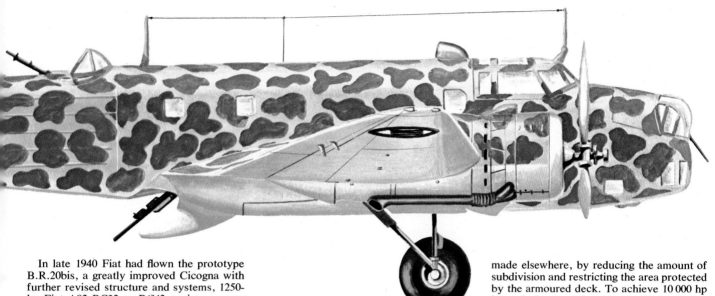

In late 1940 Fiat had flown the prototype B.R.20bis, a greatly improved Cicogna with further revised structure and systems, 1250-hp Fiat A82 RC32 or RC42 engines, a new nose (looking like that of an He 115) and considerably augmented defensive armament. Usually a 12.7-mm (0.5-in) Breda-SAFAT was aimed by hand from a blister on each side of the fuselage above the wing, and there were four to five other guns of the same calibre. Bombload was increased to 2000 kg (4410 lb), despite which the speed was also increased.

However by this time Italian industry had ceased to perform adequately, and the second B.R.20bis did not fly until 1942. Only about a dozen of these much better bombers became operational in 1943, and at the September surrender the Regia Aeronautica had only 59 serviceable Cicogni altogether, out of about 600 built. In the final year, 1942/43, these aircraft were increasingly being used as operational trainers, transports and maritime patrol aircraft.

(B.R.20M) *Span:* 21.56 m (70 ft 8¾ in) *Length:* 16.8 m (55 ft 1½ in) *Gross weight:* 10 450 kg (23 038 lb) *Max speed:* 430 km/h (267 mph)

Cincinnati

US protected cruiser class. *Cincinnati* and *Raleigh* were authorized under the 1888 Program. They were to be restricted to 3000 tons, but without sacrificing the requirement for 19 knots. The result was that sacrifices had to be made elsewhere, by reducing the amount of subdivision and restricting the area protected by the armoured deck. To achieve 10 000 hp into a hull only 12.8-m (42-ft) wide 2-cylinder low-pressure machinery had to be adopted, and coal capacity only sufficient for a theoretical maximum of 4828 km (3000 miles).

Construction was entrusted to navy yards to give them experience in shipbuilding. This gave the Navy a chance to study the problems associated with high speed at first hand. Admiral Meade commented that the *Cincinnati*s were only good for short-range operations, and had so much power that there was no room for anything else. Although 19 knots was possible in brief spurts the heat that was

Name	launched	commissioned	builder
Cincinnati	11/1892	6/1894	New York NY, Brooklyn
Raleigh	3/1892	4/1894	Norfolk NY, Portsmouth

B.R.20 Cicogna, original production version of this extremely advanced Italian light bomber

produced in the boiler-rooms when the top speed was achieved often reached the unbearable level of 95°C (200°F).

After the war against Spain both cruisers were re-engined with more efficient engines, but were relegated to 'peace cruisers', a euphemism for glorified gunboats. The 6-in (152-mm) gun forward was replaced by a 5-in (127-mm) and the above water torpedo tubes were removed.

Both ships were used for training, and by 1917 they were no longer in front-line service. Known as *Cruiser No 7* and *No 8*, they were not included in the 1920 classification system, and were sold on August 5, 1921 for scrapping. Both vessels had survived in unorthodox conditions for 29 years.

Displacement: 3213 tons (normal) *Length:* 91.44 m (300 ft) wl *Beam:* 12.80 m (42 ft) *Draught:* 5.79 m (19 ft) *Machinery:* 2-shaft triple-expansion, 10 000 ihp=19 knots *Protection:* 25 mm (1 in) deck, 63.5 mm (2½ in) slopes *Armament:* (As built) 1 6-in (152-mm)/40-cal QF; 10 5-in (127-mm)/40-cal; 8 57-mm (2.24-in); 4 1-pdr; 2 Gatling machine-guns; 4 18-in (46-cm) torpedo tubes (above water, beam); (After 1902) 11 5-in (127-mm) (later reduced to 9); 8 57-mm (2.24-in) *Crew:* 312

Circé

The French submarine *Circé* which sank the German *UC 24* in 1917 but was itself sunk by *U 47*

Name	laid down	launched	completed	built
Circé	1905	13/9/1907	1909	Toulon arsenal
Calypso	1905	22/10/1907	1909	Toulon arsenal

Circé

French submarine class. Two submarines, *Circé* and *Calypso* (Q.47-48), were ordered for the French navy in October 1904 to a Laubeuf double-hulled design. They joined the Fleet in 1909, but on July 7, 1914, they collided with one another on manoeuvres near Toulon, and the *Calypso* sank. Fortunately the loss of life was small.

Circé was stationed in the Mediterranean during the First World War. She torpedoed the German minelaying U-Boat *UC 24* on May 25, 1917, in the Adriatic, but she was herself torpedoed off Cattaro (now Kotor) by *U 47* on September 20, 1918. She was awarded the *Croix de Guerre* pennant.

Displacement: 351 tonnes/491 tonnes (surfaced/submerged) *Length:* 47.1 m (154 ft 6 in) oa *Beam:* 4.9 m (16 ft) *Draught:* 3.0 m (9 ft 10 in) *Machinery:* 2-shaft MAN diesels/electric motors, 630/460 shp=11.9/7.7 knots (surfaced/submerged) *Armament:* 2 Drzewiecki launchers, 4 external cradles, 6 45-cm (17.7-in) torpedoes carried *Crew:* 22

CL German First World War escort fighter type　　See **Halberstadt, Hannover, Junkers**

CL-13, Canadair Canadian production version of North American F-86 US jet fighter
See **Sabre**

CL-28, Canadair Canadian maritime patrol aircraft　　See **Argus**

No and name	launched	builder
DE.1033 *Claud Jones*	5/1958	Avondale Marine Ways Inc
DE.1034 *John R Perry*	7/1958	Avondale Marine Ways Inc
DE.1035 *Charles Berry*	3/1959	Avondale Marine Ways Inc
DE.1036 *McMorris*	5/1959	Avondale Marine Ways Inc

CL-41, Canadair Canadian trainer/light attack aircraft　　See **Tutor**

CL-89, Canadair

Canadian reconnnaissance drone. The CL-89, also designated AN/USD-501, is used by the armies of Britain, Germany and Italy to fly surveillance missions and to spot targets for attack by artillery. The drone can be fitted with interchangeable sensor packs containing either cameras or infrared linescan equipment. Sensors in current use are the Carl Zeiss KRb8/24 camera and the Hawker Siddeley Dynamics Type 201 linescan; additional options include an Itek twin-camera pack and a Hycon panoramic camera.

The turbojet-powered drone is launched from a vehicle with the aid of a rocket booster and follows a preprogrammed flight path. Navigation is by dead-reckoning, using a propeller-driven distance-measuring unit, directional and vertical gyros, and probably a barometric altimeter to indicate cruise height.

The cameras or linescan equipment operate automatically after a preset elapsed time, the results being recorded on film stored aboard the drone. Up to 12 flares may be ejected from the fuselage to aid night photography.

The CL-89 carries a receiver which picks up signals from a beacon at the recovery site for navigation on the return flight. Parachutes are deployed when the motor shuts down, and the drone comes to rest on two air-bags. The film is then removed and processed.

An extended-fuselage development, the CL-289 or AN/USD-502, has been proposed to carry larger payloads or extend the operating range to 400 km (250 miles). Studies have also been made of an updated variant incorporating a real-time data link, alternative sensors and an improved navigation system.

Length: 260 cm (8 ft 6 in), plus 113 cm (3 ft 8 in) for the booster *Span:* 94 cm (37 in) *Diameter:* 33 cm (13 in) *Speed:* 740 km/h (460 mph) *Range:* 160 km (100 miles) *Cruise altitude:* 300 m to 1200 m (1000 ft to 4000 ft) *Powerplant:* Williams WR2-6 single-stage turbojet plus Bristol Aerojet Wagtail solid-propellant rocket booster.

CL 834 Designation of British Sea Skua air-to-surface missile　　See **Sea Skua**

Claude Allied code-name for Mitsubishi A5M fighter aircraft　　See **A5M**

Claud Jones

US escort class, built 1957-1960. In Fiscal Year 1956 two diesel-engined escorts were authorized by Congress as successors to the *Dealey* and *Courtney* Classes, followed by a further two the following year. They were an attempt to provide the smallest and cheapest antisubmarine ships for mass production, but like their British Equivalents, the *Blackwood* Class, they proved too small to be re-equipped with modern sonar and weapons.

They were quite unlike any other DEs built for the US Navy, with diesel engines and a second diminutive funnel. The armament was light, two single 3-in (76-mm) guns, two triple A/S torpedo tubes and a depth-charge rack and two Hedgehogs. Between 1961 and 1964 *Charles Berry* and *McMorris* had the Norwegian Terne III antisubmarine rocket-launcher in place of the Hedgehogs, but later *Charles Berry* was fitted with variable-depth sonar equipment aft.

In February 1973 the *John R Perry* was transferred to Indonesia and was renamed *Samadikun*. The same navy then bought the rest of the class between January and December 1974. They were renamed *Martadinata* (ex-*Charles Berry*), *Mongisidi* (ex-*Claud Jones*) and *Ngurah Rai* (ex-*McMorris*).

Name	launched	builder
Stylet	5/1905	Rochefort dockyard
Tromblon	6/1905	Rochefort dockyard
Pierrier	2/1905	Rochefort dockyard
Obusier	3/1905	Rochefort dockyard
Mortier	3/1906	Rochefort dockyard
Claymore	3/1906	Normand, Le Havre
Carquois	6/1907	Rochefort dockyard
Trident	12/1907	Rochefort dockyard
Fleuret	12/1907	Rochefort dockyard
Coutelas	1/1907	Rochefort dockyard
Cagnée	11/1907	Toulon dockyard
Hache	2/1908	Toulon dockyard
Massue	9/1908	Toulon dockyard

No and name	launched	builder
R.98 *Clemenceau*	12/1957	Brest Arsenal
R.99 *Foch*	7/1960	Penhoët-Loire

ECP Armées

The *Clemenceau*, the first French aircraft carrier to be built after the Second World War. After lengthy trials she entered service in 1961

Displacement: 1450 tons (standard), 1750 tons (full load) *Length:* 94.5 m (310 ft) oa *Beam:* 11.3 m (37 ft) *Draught:* 5.5 m (18 ft) *Machinery:* 1-shaft diesel, 9200 bhp=22 knots *Armament:* 2 3-in (76-mm)/50-cal AA (2×1); 6 12.75-in (32.38-cm) torpedo tubes Mk 32 (2×3); 2 Hedgehog mortars/Terne III rocket-launchers (removed) *Crew:* 175

Claymore

French destroyer class, built 1904-1909. This was the fifth group of '300-tonne' type built

A Canadair CL-89 drone on its launch vehicle. The CL-89 has a range of 160 km (100 miles) and can carry cameras, sensors and up to 12 flares for illumination in night photography

Canadian Forces Photo

for the French navy. They were also the first to adopt the 45-cm (17.7-in) torpedo. Although the *caillebotis* (metal grating) deck was retained the exaggerated tumblehome of the previous class was modified, but on the whole, the class was not regarded as an improvement over the earlier 300-tonne destroyers of the *Durandal, Pique, Pertuisane* and *Arquebuse* Classes.

All the class served in the First World War, and saw action at the Dardanelles, in the Adriatic and in the North Sea. The *Tromblon, Obusier, Claymore, Carquois* and *Fleuret*

were in the English Channel in August 1914, and on November 23 the *Tromblon* attacked *U21* off Le Havre, The *Obusier* was attached to the British forces which tried to block Ostend in April 1918.

The *Mortier* escorted the battleship *Danton* during the bombardment of Pelagosa on September 17/18, 1914, while the *Hache, Coutelas* and *Cognée* escorted the *Requin* at the bombardment of Gaza on April 16, 1917. The *Massue* was escorting the *Danton* when the battleship was torpedoed by *U 64* in March 1917, and the *Claymore* was one of the French ships serving in the Baltic in 1920.

The *Stylet, Fleuret, Cognée, Coutelas, Hache, Tromblon, Pierrier* and *Obusier* were stricken and scrapped in 1920/22, but *Mortier, Massue* and *Claymore* were not stricken until 1926/27, while the *Carquois* and *Trident* lasted until 1930/31.

Displacement: 323 tonnes (normal), 356 tonnes (full load) *Length:* 58 m (190 ft 3 in) pp *Beam:* 6.2-6.53 m (20 ft 4 in-21 ft 5 in) *Draught:* 4.2 m (13 ft 9 in) max *Machinery:* 2-shaft triple-expansion, 6800 ihp=28 knots *Armament:* 1 65-mm (2.5-in)/45-cal Model 1902; 6 47-mm (1.85-in)/50-cal Model 1902; 2 45-cm (17.7-in) torpedo tubes (4 Model 1906 torpedoes) *Crew:* 60.

Clemenceau

French aircraft carrier class, built 1955-1963. Although aircraft carriers had been ordered for the Marine Nationale before the outbreak of the Second World War they had not made much progress, and so when the French Government authorized the construction of a fleet carrier (PA.54) in 1953 it marked the beginning of France's first aircraft carrier. A sister (PA.55) was authorized two years later.

As first envisaged they were to be 22 000-ton ships armed with 12 twin 57-mm (2.24-in) guns. An unusual feature was the positioning of the after end of the angled flight deck well to starboard of the centre-line. The theoretical advantage of this feature was the reduc-

Clemson

tion of the port overhang, but on the advice of US and British carrier experts it was dropped, as turbulence from funnel-gas and the island super structure would have made landings hazardous. The armament was soon revised to 12 single 100-mm (3.9-in) guns and then to eight, disposed in four quadrants at the edge of the flight deck.

The *Clemenceau* was ordered in 1954 and work started at the end of 1955, while *Foch* was laid down in a special dry dock at St Nazaire in December 1956. After lengthy trials the first ship entered service in November 1961, and the second in July 1963.

The two carriers were fitted with the latest aids, including the Mitchell-Brown BS 5 steam catapult, a deck-edge lift on the starboard side, two mirror landing-sights and an 8° angled deck. The hangar measures 151.7 m×26.5 m×8.5 m (497 ft 8 in×87 ft×28 ft) and the flight deck is 165.5 m×29.5 m (543 ft×96 ft 9 in). The lifts are 16m×11m (52 ft 6 in×36 ft) in area. The only armour provided is in the form of crowns to the machinery spaces and magazines, and splinter-proof protection to the flight deck and bridges. As considerable topweight was added during the design stage and building it is not surprising that the *Foch* needed the addition of bulges to give a greater margin of stability, and the *Clemenceau* was similarly altered during the first refit, increasing the beam by 1.8 m (6 ft).

The first air group comprised three flights of Etendard IV, Crusader and Alizé aircraft, 30 in all. Since then the ships have been modified to operate the Super-Etendard. The fuel capacity differs; the *Clemenceau* carries 1200 cu m (42 375 cu ft) of jet fuel and 400 cu m (14 125 cu ft) of avgas, while the *Foch* carries 1800 cu m, (63 566 cu ft) and 109 cu m (3848 cu ft) of each. As the French navy is showing considerable interest in V/STOL aircraft the two ships may end their days as 'Harrier carriers'.

Displacement: 27 307 tonnes (normal), 32 780 tonnes (full load) *Length:* 265 m (869 ft 5 in) oa *Beam:* 31.7 m (104 ft) over bulges; 51.2 m (167 ft 11 in) over flight deck *Draught:* 8.6 m (28 ft 2½ in) *Machinery:* 2-shaft geared steam turbines, 126 000 shp=32 knots *Protection:* Not published (see above) *Armament:* 8 100-mm (3.9-in) DP (8×1) *Aircraft:* 30 (normal), 40 (maximum) *Crew:* 1228

Clemson

US destroyer class, built 1917-1921. This was the third group of flush-decked destroyers, built after the *Wickes* Class. The only significant change made from the preceding class was to add 100 tons of bunker fuel to increase range, as the US Navy was understandably reluctant to do anything to delay rapid construction. The new destroyers were needed to meet the desperate shortage of escorts, but in the event only 44 were completed by the Armistice; six were cancelled and the rest of the programme was slowed down.

The class comprised DD.186 *Clemson;* DD.187 *Dahlgren;* DD.188 *Goldsborough;* DD.189 *Semmes;* DD.190 *Satterlee;* DD.191 *Mason;* DD.192 *Graham;* DD.193 *Abel P Upshur;* DD.194 *Hunt;* DD.195 *Welborn C Wood;* DD. 196 *George E Badger;* DD.197

The USS *Bainbridge* (DD.246), a destroyer of the *Clemson* Class built between 1917 and 1921, seen here in 1944. Though many of the class had been lost or scrapped by the time the United States entered the Second World War, one, the *Reuben James,* became the first USN vessel to be lost to enemy action when she was torpedoed by a U-Boat

Branch; DD.198 *Herndon;* DD.199 *Dallas;* DD.200-205 Cancelled 3/2/1919; DD.206 *Chandler;* DD.207 *Southard;* DD.208 *Hovey;* DD.209 *Long;* DD.210 *Broome;* DD.211 *Alden;* DD.212 *Smith Thompson;* DD.213 *Barker;* DD.214 *Tracy;* DD.215 *Borie;* DD.216 *John D. Edwards* (ex-*Stewart*); DD.217 *Whipple;* DD.218 *Parrott;* DD.219 *Edsall;* DD.220 *MacLeish;* DD.221 *Simpson;* DD.223 *Bulmer;* DD.223 *McCormick;* DD.224 *Stewart;* DD.225 *Pope;* DD.226 *Peary;* DD.227 *Pillsbury;* DD.228 *Ford;* DD.229 *Truxtun;* DD.230 *Paul Jones;* DD.231 *Hatfield;* DD.232 *Brooks;* DD.233 *Gilmer;* DD.234 *Fox;* DD.235 *Kane;* DD.236 *Humphreys;* DD.237 *McFarland;* DD.238 *James K. Paulding;* DD.239 *Overton;* DD.240 *Sturtevant;* DD.241 *Childs;* DD.242 *Kings;* DD.243 *Sands;* DD.244 *Williamson;* DD.245 *Reuben James;* DD.246 *Bainbridge;* DD.247 *Goff;* DD.248 *Barry;* DD.249 *Hopkins;* DD.250 *Lawrence;* DD.251 *Belknap;* DD.252 *McCook;* DD.253 *McCalla;* DD.254 *Rodgers* (ex-*Kalk*); DD.255 *Osmond Ingram* (ex-*Ingram*); DD.256 *Bancroft;* DD.257 *Welles;* DD.258 *Aulick;* DD.259 *Turner;* DD.260 *Gillis;* DD.261 *Delphy;* DD.262 *McDermut;* DD.263 *Laub;* DD.264 *McLanahan;* DD.265 *Edwards;* DD.266 *Greene* (ex-*Anthony*); DD.267 *Ballard;* DD.268 *Shubrick;* DD.269 *Bailey;* DD.270 *Thornton;* DD.271 *Morris;* DD.272 *Tingey;* DD.273 *Swasey;* DD.274 *Meade;* DD.275 *Sinclair;* DD.276 *McCawley;* DD.277 *Moody;* DD.278 *Henshaw;* DD.279 *Meyer;* DD.280 *Doyen;* DD.281 *Sharkey;* DD.282 *Toucey;* DD.283 *Breck;* DD.284

Isherwood; DD.285 *Case;* DD.286 *Lardner;* DD.287 *Putnam;* DD.288 *Worden;* DD.289 *Flusser;* DD.290 *Dale;* DD.291 *Converse;* DD.292 *Reid;* DD.293 *Billingsley;* DD.294 *Charles Ausburn* (ex-*Ausburn*); DD.295 *Osborne;* DD.296 *Chauncey;* DD.297 *Fuller;* DD.298 *Percival;* DD.299 *John Francis Burnes* (ex-*Swasey*); DD.300 *Farragut;* DD.301 *Somers;* DD.302 *Stoddert;* DD.303 *Reno;* DD.304 *Farquhar;* DD.305 *Thompson;* DD.306 *Kennedy;* DD.307 *Paul Hamilton* (ex-*Hamilton*); DD.308 *William Jones;* DD.309 *Woodbury;* DD.310 *SP Lee* (ex-*Branch*); DD.311 *Nicholas;* DD.312 *Young;* DD.313 *Zeilin;* DD.314 *Yarborough;* DD.315 *La Vallette;* DD.316 *Sloat;* DD.317 *Wood;* DD.318 *Shirk;* DD.319 *Kidder;* DD.320 *Selfridge;* DD.321 *Marcus;* DD.322 *Mervine;* DD.323 *Chase;* DD.324 *Robert Smith;* DD.325 *Mullany;* DD.326 *Coghlan;* DD.327 *Preston;* DD.328 *Lamson;* DD.329 *Bruce;* DD.330 *Hull;* DD.331 *MacDonough;* DD.332 *Farenholt;* DD.333 *Sumner;* DD.334 *Corry;* DD.335 *Melvin;* DD.336 *Litchfield;* DD.337 *Zane;* DD.338 *Wasmuth;* DD.339 *Trever;* DD.340 *Perry;* DD.341 *Decatur;* DD.342 *Hulbert;* DD.343 *Noa;* DD.344 *William B Preston;* DD.345 *Preble;* DD.346 *Sicard;* DD.347 *Pruitt.*

None of the class served in the First World War, the *Clemson* herself only commissioning in December 1919. Several were lost in peacetime accidents. The *Graham* was damaged beyond repair in a collision with a merchant ship on December 16, 1921, but

US Navy

before she was scrapped her bow section was used to repair her sister *Huebert*. The *Chauncey, Fuller, Woodbury, Nicholas, Young, Delphy, S P Lee, Farragut, Percival, Somers, Kennedy, Paul Hamilton, Stoddert* and *Thompson* of Destroyer Squadron (DesRon) 11 of the Pacific Fleet were on a 24-hour trial run from San Francisco to San Diego on Saturday September 8, 1923. Shortly before midnight the entire squadron ran into shallow water near Honda, north of Point Arguella, near the Santa Barbara Channel. Only five out of the 14 destroyers failed to run aground; the *Somers* and *Farragut* touched bottom and managed to pull clear, but the *Delphy, S P Lee, Young, Woodbury, Nicholas, Fuller* and *Chauncey* ran hard aground on the rocks at 20 knots.

In all 23 men were lost, mostly when the *Young* capsized in the heavy surf. The immediate cause of the disaster was the misinterpretation of a radio compass bearing but it is believed that DesRon 11 was probably off course as a result of abnormal currents caused by the Tokyo earthquake a week earlier. The seven flush-deckers were total losses, and in 1925 a salvage company bought the wrecks for $1035.

Several of the class served as tenders to naval airships and seaplanes, with after torpedo tubes replaced by fuel tanks. In 1923 the *Charles Ausburn* carried out experiments with a floatplane (a TS-1) on a platform on the forecastle, and she was one of the destroyers stationed off Greenland as a rescue ship during the 1924 round-the-world flight by the US Army.

In 1929 the annual report of the Secretary of the Navy indicated that 60 of the flush-deckers had reached the end of their useful lives, and it was recommended that

they be decommissioned as a preliminary to scrapping. To avoid the loss of so many active destroyers the Fleet undertook to rehabilitate as many of the condemned destroyers as possible, with its own resources. The work involved rewiring, retubing condensers, machinery overhauls and shifting masts, searchlight towers and bridges.

To reduce cost a great deal of cannabilization was resorted to, and as a result the following destroyers were scrapped or stricken: 1930—*Henshaw, Doyen, Wood, Corry, Sinclair, Stoddert;* 1931—*McCawley, Sharkey, Toucey, Breck, Isherwood, Case, Lardner, Flusser, Converse, Reid, Billingsley, Charles Ausburn, Osborne, Percival, John Francis Burnes, Farragut, Somers, Reno, Thompson, Kennedy, Paul Hamilton, Zeilin, Yarborough, La Vallette, Selfridge, Mervine, Robert Smith Mullany, Coghlan, Lamson, Hull, MacDonough, Farenholt, Melvin, Moody;* 1932—*Meyer, Farquhar, William Jones, Preston, Bruce;* 1934—*Sumner;* 1936—*Morris, Tingey, Turner.*

In addition six were lent to the Coastguard: *Abel P Upshur, George E Badger, Herndon, Hunt, Semmes* (CG.15-20) and *Welborn C Wood* (CG.19) to replace older destroyers. Nine were converted to Destroyer Minesweepers: (DMS.9-17) *Chandler, Southard Havey, Long, Hopkins, Zane, Wasmuth, Trever,* and *Perry;* and four to light minelayers: (DM.19-22) *Tracy, Preble, Sicard* and *Pruitt.*

In September 1940 20 were transferred to the Royal Navy, *DD.190, DD.191, DD.193, DD.194, DD.195, DD.197, DD.198, DD.252, DD.253, DD.254, DD.256, DD.257, DD.258, DD.263, DD.264, DD.265, DD.268, DD.269, DD.273,* and *DD.274.*

The survivors in the USN were converted for escort work or as seaplane tenders and

fast transports. By 1945 all were reduced to some form of auxiliary service. Most of those serving as escorts lost the after funnel and boiler to leave room for added fuel, and many were rearmed with 3-in (76-mm) AA guns. The *Leary* was the first USN ship equipped with radar before the war.

The following ships were sunk: *Borie, Edsall, Pope, Peary, Pillsbury, Truxton, Overton, Reuben James, Barry* and *Noa.* The *Reuben James* had the dubious distinction of being torpedoed by a German U-Boat more than a month before the United States entered the war. The strangest story is that of the *Stewart.* She was refitting at Soerabaya in March 1942, and was scuttled in dock when the Japanese overran Java. Unknown to the US Navy she was salved and used by the Japanese as Patrol Boat *No 102,* and eventually fell into American hands in August 1945. But by now there was a new USS *Stewart,* and so she had to be recommissioned as *DD.224,* but without a name, for the last voyage back to San Francisco.

Four became fast banana-carriers, called *Teapa* (ex-*Putnam*), *Tabasco* (ex-*Worden*), *Masaya* (ex-*Dale*) and *Matagalpa* (ex-*Osborne*); the last of these was not scrapped until 1955. The rest of the class were scrapped in 1946/47.

See also Belmont, Wickes.

Displacement: 1190 tons (normal), 1590 tons (full load) *Length:* 95.86 m (314 ft 6 in) oa *Beam:* 9.37 m-9.68 m (30 ft 9 in-31 ft 9 in) *Draught:* 2.82 m (9 ft 3 in) *Machinery:* (As built) 2-shaft geared steam turbines, 26 000-27 000 shp=35 knots *Armament:* 4 4-in (102-mm)/50-cal (4×1); 1 3-in (76-mm)/23-cal AA; 2 0.5-in (12.7-mm) machine-guns (2×1); 12 21-in (53-cm) torpedo tubes (4×3) *Crew:* 136-153.

Cleveland

Cleveland

US light cruiser class. The 27 ships of this class were developed from the earlier *St Louis* Class (themselves modified *Brooklyns*, but they sacrificed one triple 6-in (152-mm) turret forward for an improved AA armament. This triple turret had only been carried by the *Brooklyns* and the *St Louis* Class to match the Japanese *Mogamis*, and the *Cleveland*'s main armament was more than adequate to cope with surface targets. They were a better-balanced design than the earlier US light cruisers, and they were at least the equal of any foreign contemporary.

The hull was slightly broader than that of the *St Louis* Class, and the main belt was shorter. There were no openings in the hull, which was mechanically ventilated through-out. It was excellently subdivided. Like the *St Louis* Class, the after superstructure was closed up to the second funnel, giving good sky arcs for most of the AA armament. The 5-in (127-mm) turrets were arranged in lozenge fashion about the superstructure, with the light AA guns fore and aft and on either side of the funnels. The seaplanes were carried in a hangar aft, with a catapult and prominent aircraft handling crane. The *Cleve-lands* were completed with gunnery control and air-search radar.

They were the largest class of cruiser ever built, despite nine being converted into *Independence* Class light fleet carriers and three being cancelled. Twenty-seven were completed to the original design, and they were built by only four firms.

Youngston (CL-94) was cancelled on August 11, 1945, and CL-84 and CL-88 were never commenced. The excellence of the design is shown by the fact that none were sunk, although *Birmingham* (CL-62) was severely damaged by the explosion aboard the carrier *Princeton* (CVL-23) in October 1944 and again by a Japanese kamikaze aircraft off Okinawa in May 1945, and *Houston* was very badly damaged by a torpedo from a Japanese aircraft off Formosa in October 1944.

By the time the Americans had worked out the correct methods of using radar fire control, the *Clevelands*, with the stream of fire from the power-worked triple 6-in (152-mm) turrets, were very formidable surface warships. They saw extensive action during the Second World War, and mostly served in the Pacific as escorts to the fast carrier Task Forces. Eleven more were redesigned as a result of wartime experience with a single funnel and a more compact superstructure to give better sky arcs for the AA guns. These were known as the *Fargo* Class, but only two were completed.

By the mid-1950s it was obvious that the all-gun armed cruiser was obsolete, and it was intended to convert 13 *Clevelands* into single-ended guided missile cruisers. However, these conversions took so long and were so expensive for the results achieved that only six were rebuilt in this way.

All had their aft superstructure completely rebuilt, and *Galveston* (CLG-3), *Little Rock* (CLG-4) and *Oklahoma City* (CLG-5) had a twin Talos SAM launcher fitted aft in place of the two triple 6-in (152-mm) turrets. *Providence* (CLG-6), *Springfield* (CLG-7) and *Topeka* (CLG-8) had a twin Terrier SAM instead. *Little Rock*, *Oklahoma City*, *Providence* and *Springfield* also had their forward bridge enlarged and the forward superfiring 6-in (152-mm) turret removed to provide suffi-cient office space, accommodation and com-munications facilities to enable them to be used as fleet flagships.

The two not fitted as flagships were dis-carded in the early 1970s, and the four flagships were also being phased out by the late 1970s. The unconverted *Clevelands* were scrapped from 1959 onwards. The USN had so many light cruisers after the Second World War that they had all been mothballed since 1950 with the exception of *Manchester* (CL-83), which was put in reserve in 1956.

CL-55-61, 76-79, 85, 99-100 and 103-105 were built by New York Shipbuilding; CL-62-63, 80-81, 86-87 and 101-102 by Newport News; CL-64-67 and 82-83 by Bethlehem (Quincy); and CL-89-94 by Cramp. Other numbers were cancelled.

No and name	laid down	launched	completed
CL-55 *Cleveland*	7/1940	11/1941	6/1942
CL-56 *Columbia*	8/1940	12/1941	6/1942
CL-57 *Montpelier*	12/1940	2/1942	9/1942
CL-58 *Denver*	12/1940	1/1942	10/1942
CL-60 *Santa Fe*	6/1941	6/1942	11/1942
CL-62 *Birmingham*	2/1941	3/1942	1/1943
CL-63 *Mobile*	4/1941	5/1942	3/1943
CL-64 *Vincennes*	3/1942	7/1943	1/1944
CL-65 *Pasadena*	2/1943	12/1943	6/1944
CL-66 *Springfield*	2/1943	3/1944	9/1944
CL-67 *Topeka*	4/1943	8/1944	12/1944
CL-80 *Biloxi*	7/1941	2/1943	8/1943
CL-81 *Houston*	8/1941	6/1943	12/1943
CL-82 *Providence*	7/1943	12/1944	5/1945
CL-83 *Manchester*	9/1944	3/1946	10/1946
CL-86 *Vicksburg*	10/1942	12/1943	6/1944
CL-87 *Duluth*	11/1942	1/1944	9/1944
CL-89 *Miami*	8/1941	12/1942	12/1943
CL-90 *Astoria*	9/1941	3/1943	5/1944
CL-91 *Oklahoma City*	12/1942	2/1944	12/1944
CL-92 *Little Rock*	3/1943	8/1944	6/1945
CL-93 *Galveston*	2/1944	4/1945	5/1946
CL-101 *Amsterdam*	3/1943	4/1944	1/1945
CL-102 *Portsmouth*	6/1943	9/1944	6/1945
CL-103 *Wilkes-Barre*	12/1942	12/1943	7/1944
CL-104 *Atlanta*	1/1943	2/1944	12/1944
CL-105 *Dayton*	3/1943	3/1944	1/1945

Displacement: 10 000 tons (standard); 13 755 tons (full load) *Length:* 185.9 m (610 ft) *Beam:* 20.3 m (66 ft 6 in) *Draught:* 7.6 m (25 ft) *Machinery:* 4-shaft geared steam turbines, 100 000 shp=33 knots *Protection:* 38-127 mm (1.5-5 in) sides; 51-76 mm (2-3 in) decks; 76-127 mm (3-5 in) main turrets *Armament:* 12 6-in (152-mm); 12 5-in (127-mm); 8 40-mm (1.57-in); 10 20-mm (0.79-in) *Aircraft:* 4 *Crew:* 1200

Cleveland RAF name for Curtiss SB2C US Navy dive-bomber   **See Helldiver**

CLGP US Cannon Launched Guided Projec-tile   **See Copperhead**

US Navy

USS *Cleveland* photographed in Cape Cod Bay in March 1946. She was the first of 27 light cruisers laid down between 1940 and 1944 and which saw action largely in the Pacific as fast escorts for carrier task forces. After the war six were equipped with Terrier or Talos guided missiles

Clive, Handley Page

British bomber. Originally named Chitral, the Clive was a traditional bomber/transport for the RAF, built to Specification C. 20/27. The wooden prototype (19126) flew in February 1928, combining the Hyderabad airframe (with the swept-back wings of the Hinaidi II) with two reliable and efficient Bristol Jupiter VIII F radial engines, rated at 460 hp each. This aircraft became a civil airliner, and the RAF ordered two Clive II production versions with a metal airframe, though still with fabric covering. Clives served with Heavy Transport Flight at Lahore, carrying 17 troops, external bombs and two Lewis guns.

Span: 22.86 m (75 ft) *Length:* 19.15 m (62 ft 10 in) *Gross weight:* 6577 kg (14 500 lb) *Maximum speed:* 178.6 km/h (111 mph)

Clod, Antonov An-14

Soviet light transport aircraft. Clod is a small twin-engined utility aircraft used by Aeroflot and for liaison by the Soviet air force. The first prototype flew in 1958, but development difficulties and concentration on the An-10 delayed service entry until 1965. The first military example was seen in 1967.

The pod-like fuselage can accommodate up to six stretchers and a medical attendant or may be fitted out for freight-carrying. Clamshell rear doors give access to the fuselage. The two engines are carried on the high-mounted wing, which is braced by struts to stub wings on each side of the lower fuselage. Twin fins and rudders are mounted on the ends of a tailplane carried on a boom extending from the rear of the fuselage.

A turboprop development, the An-14M, has accommodation for up to 15 passengers, and a heavier variant—the An-28—has also been flown.

Span: 22 m (72 ft 2 in) *Length:* 11.4 m (37 ft 5 in) approx *Height:* 4.63 m (15 ft 2½ in) *Max takeoff weight:* 3600 kg (7935 lb) *Powerplant:* 2 AI-14RF piston engines, 300 hp each (An-14M has two TVD-650 turboprops, 810 ehp each) *Cruising speed:* 180 km/h (112 mph) *Range:* 650 km (404 miles) with max payload

Clorinde

French submarine class, built 1910-17. Two submarines, *Clorinde* and *Cornélie*, were ordered under the 1909 Programme to a Hutter design. They were officially described as being intended for coastguard and blockade duties, but were not unduly restricted in range.

The design resembled that of the *Brumaire* type, but in place of the elliptical cross-section the circular form was adopted, with a double hull on the lines of the Laubeuf designs. The outbreak of war delayed construction considerably, but as a result the two boats benefited from war experience.

The *Clorinde* was completed in October 1916 but her sister did not join the fleet until the following September. Both were based on Brest and operated in the Atlantic. *Clorinde* was stricken in January 1926, and *Cornélie* in December the same year.

Displacement: 413 tonnes/567 tonnes (surfaced/submerged) *Length:* 53.95 m (177 ft) oa *Beam:* 5.1 m (16 ft 9 in) *Draught:* 3.41 m (11 ft 2 in) *Machinery:* 2-shaft MAN-Loire diesels/electric motors, 800 bhp/700 ehp = 13/9 knots (surfaced/submerged) *Armament:* 8 45-cm (17.7-in) torpedo tubes (2 external launching cradles forward and 6 Drzewiecki collars); 75-mm (2.95-in) gun added in 1917-18 *Crew:* 29

CM.170, Potez/Aerospatiale French trainer aircraft **See Magister**

CM.175, Potez French navy trainer aircraft **See Zephyr**

No and name		launched	builder
Q.90	*Clorinde*	10/1913	Rochefort dockyard
Q.91	*Cornélie*	10/1913	Rochefort dockyard

Replacing the American DC-3/C-47, the Soviet Il-12 (Coach) could carry 32 passengers in its civilian form, and was also used by the armed forces

Coach, Ilyushin Il-12

Soviet transport aircraft. The Il-12 was designed during the Second World War as a successor to the Douglas DC-3/C-47 and its Russian licence-built version, the Li-2. The type made its maiden flight in 1946 and entered service with Aeroflot the following year. The Il-12 was the first transport aircraft other than the Li-2 to be built in Russia since 1937, and was crude by Western standards; it was, however, the first Soviet transport to have a nosewheel undercarriage and feathering propellers.

Variants of Coach supplied to the Soviet air force from 1947 were used for dropping paratroops and towing gliders as well as for normal freighting duties. Military versions had large cargo doors in the port side of the rear fuselage in addition to the standard door on the opposite side, and some were fitted with light machine-guns in the cabin windows. Coach was supplanted by the Il-14 Crate from 1953.

Span: 31.7 m (107 ft) *Length:* 21.31 m (69 ft 11 in) *Max takeoff weight:* 17 250 kg (38 030 lb) *Powerplant:* 2 ASh-82FNV piston engines, 1650 hp each at normal power *Cruising speed:* 350 km/h (217 mph) *Range:* 1250 km (777 miles) with 32 passengers

Cobra

Austro/Hungarian torpedo boat class, built 1897-1900. In 1897 four 1st Class torpedo boats were ordered from the Yarrow yard at Poplar, London. They were similar to other Yarrow torpedo boats, with two funnels, a bow torpedo tube (except in *Kigyo*), two deck tubes and two single 3-pdr guns.

The class, in common with other torpedo boats of the KuK navy, was given numbers in 1910; *Cobra* became *No 16, Boa No 15, Kigyo No 14* and *Python No 13.* In 1914 *No 14* was serving as a seaplane tender, and all four survived the war. Under the Peace Treaty of 1920 *Nos 13, 15* and *16* were allocated to France, while *No 14* went to Great Britain, but in fact all four were scrapped locally in the same year.

Displacement: 115 tons (normal), 135 tons (full load) *Length:* 45.9 m (150 ft 6 in) pp *Beam:* 4.6 m (15 ft 1 in) *Draught:* 2.3 m (7 ft 6½ in) *Machinery:* 2-shaft triple-expansion, 1800 ihp = 24 knots *Armament:* 2 47-mm (1.85-in)/33-cal QF (2×1); 3 45-cm (17.7-in) torpedo tubes (3×1) (2 in *Kigyo*) *Crew:* 21

Name	launched
Cobra	1898
Boa	9/1898
Kigyo	4/1899
Python	4/1899

Cobra

British destroyer. The *Cobra* was one of the first two warships (the other being the destroyer *Viper*) to be fitted with steam turbine machinery. She was laid down in 1898 as a speculative venture by Armstrong Whitworth at Elswick and launched on June 28, 1899.

She was ready for preliminary trials in the following month but was damaged by another ship while fitting out and her completion was delayed for over six months.

In December 1899, Armstrongs offered her to the Admiralty who purchased the ship in 1900 with the proviso that her hull be strengthened. This latter was the result of a somewhat critical Admiralty survey of the hull and in the light of later events it is a pity that even greater strengthening was not asked for. Had it not been for a need to evaluate the steam turbine it is probable that the Admiralty would never have purchased the ship.

The *Cobra* was of the same general configuration and had the same armament as the standard '30-knotter' destroyers of the time. She was powered by two low-pressure and two high-pressure Parsons turbines which drove no less than 12 propellers, three on each shaft. Her preliminary trials were somewhat disappointing as it was found that her fuel consumption was high and that the number of stokers required to achieve full speed was excessive. However, after some modifications and an increase in her boiler-room personnel, she made 34.89 knots on the measured mile in June 1900.

She was accepted for service in 1901 and on September 17 she left the Tyne for Portsmouth where she was to be fitted with her armament. Shortly after departing she encountered heavy weather and began to roll badly, so speed was reduced to 10 knots. At dawn on the following day when the *Cobra* was nearing the Outer Dowsing Light Vessel she suddenly broke in two and sank. Her back had broken between the two aftermost boilers about 45 m (150 ft) from the bows. There were 12 survivors.

There being no obstructions in the area where the ship was lost, it was concluded by the subsequent court martial and committee of enquiry that her loss was due to structural weakness and was in no way due to her being fitted with turbines. Nevertheless, there was subsequently some reaction against turbine machinery and very high-speed destroyers which delayed the general adoption of such machinery. The *Cobra* was the only British destroyer to be lost due to weather stress.

Displacement: 375 tons (normal) *Length:* 68.17 m (223 ft 8 in) *Beam:* 6.27 m (20 ft 7 in) *Draught:* 1.98 m (6 ft 6 in) *Machinery:* 4-shaft steam turbines, 11500 shp = 34 knots *Armament:* (not fitted) 1 12-pdr; 5 6-pdr (5 × 1); 2 18-in (46-cm) torpedo tubes (2 × 1) *Crew:* 77

Cobra

British flame-throwing tank developed in 1944/45. Originally called 'Mamba' it was devised as a cheap and easily transportable 'add-on' kit which could be fitted to Churchill tanks in the field by regimental fitters.

Officially called the 'Flamethrower Transportable No 6' it consisted of an armoured container fitted to the outside of the tank and holding 364 litres (80 gallons) of flame-thrower fluid, plus the necessary pressure bottles and valves. The flame projector was mounted on a turntable at the front of the tank, controlled by the codriver or hull gunner, the fluid and gas being piped from the container by pipelines along the side of the tank which were protected by an armoured sheathing.

See also Churchill.

Cobra 2000, Messerschmitt-Bölkow-Blohm

German antitank missile. The 2000 m (2187 yards) range development of the Bö810 Cobra replaced the Cobra 1600 on the MBB production line in 1971 and is built under licence in Brazil, Italy, Pakistan and Turkey. Cobra is a first-generation wire-guided antitank missile and is unusual in being launched directly from the ground rather than from a box container.

The missile is placed in a suitable firing position and connected by cable to a control box; up to eight rounds may be operated from the same box, being selected and fired in turn. A booster motor with a downward-deflected nozzle jumps the missile clear of obstructions after launch, and cruise propulsion is then assumed by a sustainer motor.

The operator sights his target and steers the missile by means of a joystick on the control box. Commands are transmitted to the round via trailing wires, the weapon being manoeuvred by means of spoilers in the wings. Flares mounted at the rear of the missile allow the operator to maintain visual contact throughout the attack.

More than 170000 Cobras have been built and the improved Mamba is in production.

Length: 95 cm (37.4 in) *Span:* 48 cm (18.9 in) *Diameter:* 10 cm (3.9 in) *Weight:* 10.3 kg (22.7 lb) *Range:* 400-2000 m (1300-6550 ft) *Speed:* 85 m/sec (280 ft/sec) *Warhead:* interchangeable hollow-charge and antitank shrapnel, 2.7 kg (6 lb) each

Messerschmitt-Bölkow-Blohm

Cobras in position with their operator and controller. The missiles rest on their stubby flights and do not need a launch box. The controller can operate up to eight of the wire-guided missiles from one control unit and fire the Cobras in relays as targets appear

Cock

Above and Below: Front and rear of the Antonov An-22 (Cock) transport aircraft. The Cock has rear clam doors which give access to a cargo hold measuring 33 m×4.4 m×4.4 m (108 ft×14 ft 5 in×14 ft 5 in) with a non-slip titanium floor. It can lift 100 000 kg (220 462 lb) to 7848 m (25 748 ft)

An Antonov An-22 Cock in Aeroflot markings; Aeroflot use military transport types to lift stores and equipment to remote areas like Siberia

Novosti

Cock, Antonov An-22

Russian transport aircraft. The An-22 was, at the time of its maiden flight in 1965, the largest aircraft in the world. This title has since been assumed by the Lockheed C-5A Galaxy (although the commercial Boeing 747 has taken off at higher gross weights). However, the Cock is still the largest propeller-driven type.

The An-22 entered service in 1967 and has been supplied to Aeroflot (about 50 aircraft) as well as the Soviet air force (more than 70 examples). The type is used for transporting oil-rig equipment and other bulky cargoes in the civil role, but the Aeroflot aircraft are equipped to military standards and form a strategic reserve for the air force.

Permanent accommodation for 28 or 29 passengers is provided behind the flight deck, but the majority of the fuselage is devoted to a freight hold measuring 33 m ×4.4 m ×4.4 m (108 ft 3 in × 14 ft 6 in × 14 ft 6 in). Four travelling gantries run on rails in the roof of the hold, and these continue along the underside of the rear door to assist loading large cargoes. Two winches rated at 2500-kg (5511-lb) pull each are also installed. The reinforced nonslip floor is constructed from titanium.

Typical military loads include a tracked vehicle carrying twin SA-4 Ganef surface-to-air missiles, together with a command car, or two launchers for Frog 5 artillery rockets, also with a command car. Armoured personnel carriers and self-propelled guns are amongst other vehicles which are transported by An-22.

Amongst Cock's achievements is a world payload-to-height record of 100 000 kg (220 000 lb) lifted to 7848 m (25 748 ft). Despite its bulk and weight, however, an An-22 can take off fully loaded in 1300 m (4265 ft)

and land in 800 m (2625 ft). The levered-suspension undercarriage, with 14 wheels fitted with low-pressure tyres, allows the aircraft to operate even from wet grass.

Span: 64.4 m (211 ft 3½ in) *Length:* 57.31 m (188 ft) *Height:* 12.53 m (41 ft 1 in) *Max takeoff weight:* 250 000 kg (550 000 lb) *Powerplant:* 4 Kuznetsov NK-12 turboprops, 15 000 shp each *Cruising speed:* normally 560-640 km/h (350-400 mph) *Range:* 5000 km (3100 miles).

Cockatrice

British Army flame-thrower, developed in 1941/42. Developed by the Petroleum Warfare Department, it was a pressure-operated projector mounted on an armoured Bedford truck chassis. Additional armament consisted of two Lewis machine-guns on an AA mounting at the rear end of the truck. Only a handful were made, since its principal object was to prove the viability of the PWD's pressure-operated projector rather than to go into service as a serious weapon.

As a result of the success of this vehicle in demonstrations, the PWD device was selected over various competing systems and went on to become the principal flame-thrower used in the Churchill and other armoured vehicles. The Cockatrices which were built were retained in Home Defence units for some time before being scrapped.

Codrington

British destroyer leader. The *Codrington* was the leader of the *Acasta* Class destroyers of the 1927 Programme. She was the first leader to be designed after the First World War and set the pattern for all the leaders of the 'A' to 'I' Class destroyers.

Basically she was an expanded version of the *Acasta* design, being of 200 tons greater displacement to provide the space required for the Captain ('D') and his staff and the additional communications equipment required by her function as flagship. Her appearance was much the same as that of the destroyers, but she carried an additional 4.7 in (120-mm) gun between the two funnels and her bridge was somewhat larger.

As designed she would have mounted four guns with 40° elevation and one with 60° elevation for use against aircraft but difficulties encountered in the design of these weapons led to them being abandoned so she was fitted with the same guns as the destroyers; the 4.7-in (120-mm) Mk IX on 30° CP XIV mountings.

The *Codrington* was laid down by Swan Hunter at Wallsend on June 20, 1928, launched on August 9, 1929, and completed on June 6, 1930. She served in the Mediterranean for the majority of her peacetime career but in September 1939 was operating out of Dover as leaders of the 19th ('B' Class) Destroyer Flotilla and in March 1940 transferred to Harwich as leader of the 1st ('G' Class) Destroyer Flotilla. At about this time her after bank of torpedo tubes was replaced by a 12-pdr (3-in) AA gun and the mainmast was removed. In 1940, she took part in the Norwegian Campaign and the evacuation from Dunkerque. In July 1940 she was sunk during an air raid on Dover harbour.

Displacement: 1540 tons (standard), 2012 tons (full load) *Length:* 104.55 m (343 ft) *Beam:* 10.29 m (33 ft 9 in) *Draught:* 2.59 m (8 ft 6 in) *Machinery:* 2-shaft geared steam turbines, 30 999 shp=35 knots *Armament:* 5 4.7-in (120-mm) (5×1); 2 2-pdr (2×1); 8 21-in (53-cm) torpedo tubes (2×4) *Crew:* 185

Coke, Antonov An-24

Russian transport aircraft. The An-24, similar in appearance to the Dutch Fokker-VFW F.27 Friendship, is used in general transport roles by the Soviet air force in addition to its widescale operation by Aeroflot. The type is also used by the air forces of many Soviet Bloc and Russian-orientated countries.

The Coke made its maiden flight in 1959 and has been built in a number of variants with accommodation for up to 50 passengers or in a freight layout. The An-24TV version is fitted with a cargo door which hinges upwards and folds back into the cabin roof; this door can be opened in flight for air-drops. Cargo is loaded with the aid of a sliding roof-mounted winch of 1500 kg (3307 lb) capacity and a floor-mounted conveyor system. The An-26 Curl, which has a variety of military applications, is a development of the An-24. Another is the very powerful An-32 with AI-20 turboprops of over 500 shp which has exceptional STOL performance but the same carrying capacity.

Span: 29.2 m (95 ft 9½ in) *Length:* 23.53 m (77 ft 2½ in) *Height:* 8.32 m (27 ft 3½ in) *Max takeoff weight:* 21 000 kg (46 300 lb) *Powerplant:* 2 Ivchenko AI-24 Seriiny II turboprops, 2550 ehp each *Cruising speed:* 450 km/h (280 mph) *Range:* 550 km (330 miles) with max payload and reserves

Colbert

French cruiser, built 1953-59. Under the 1953 Programme a new antiaircraft cruiser was ordered, similar in design to the revised plans drawn up for the *de Grasse*. Nothing has been revealed about the system of armouring, but it has been officially stated that the new ship has a different scheme to the *de Grasse*.

As completed the *Colbert* has an extremely heavy armament of antiaircraft guns, eight twin 127-mm (5-in) guns and ten twin 57-mm (2.24-in) guns, disposed on four levels. The 127-mm (5-in) guns were French-designed, but chambered to take US-pattern 5-in (127 mm) ammunition; the 57-mm (2.24-in) guns were designed by Bofors.

The ship was laid down in a dry dock at Brest arsenal in December 1953, floated out on March 24, 1956, and began her trials the following year.

From April 1970 the ship was in dockyard hands for a complete reconstruction and conversion to a guided-missile cruiser. In the process she was rearmed with a twin Masurca SAM-system, with a double-arm launcher on the quarterdeck and a completely new radar array. At the same time the armament was revised, with all 127-mm (5-in) guns replaced by two of the new 100-mm (3.9-in) dual-purpose guns forward. Six of the original 57-mm (2.24-in) twins were retained, on two levels on either side of the superstructure. The bridge was rebuilt to accommodate new radar, fire control and command facilities.

The sketch design published in 1970 showed a more ambitious rearmament scheme, with six Exocet surface-to-surface missiles and six 100-mm (3.9-in) guns. However, it was later admitted that the scale of armament had been reduced, cutting 80 000 million francs from the estimated cost of 350 000 million francs. By late 1977 only the

Top: **The French cruiser *Colbert* prior to her conversion in 1972** *Above:* **The *Colbert* after 1972 fitted with twin Masurca SAM-system on the quarterdeck and a modernized radar array**

bedplates for four MM38 missiles had been installed, but the missiles were due to be fitted at the next refit. The Mk 2 Mod 3 Masurca is fitted, and 48 missiles similar to the US Terrier are carried in stowage.

Machinery and boilers are in separate compartments on the unit system, two boilers to each set of turbines. The port and starboard turbine rooms are divided by an 18 m (59 ft) watertight bulkhead.

Radar and fire control are entirely French, DRBV 51 guidance radars for the Masurca, DRBV 20 for long-range air warning and surveillance, DRBC 32C for gunnery, etc. The ship is also fitted with the British Knebworth Corvus chaff-rocket system and can operate a helicopter, although no hangar is provided. Extensive command and communications facilities enable her to act as a headquarters ship for combined operations.

PARTICULARS OF GUNS

Gun	127-mm/54-cal	57-mm/60-cal
Elevation	80°	80°
Projectile weight:	32 kg (70.5 lb)	2.6 kg (5.7 lb)
Muzzle velocity:	850 m/sec (2789 ft/sec)	920 m/sec (3018 ft/sec)
Rate of fire: (per barrel)	15 rds/min	65 rds/min
Range:	22 km (14 miles)	14.5 km (9 miles)
Altitude:	13 000 m (42 657 ft)	9000 m (29 527 ft)

Displacement: 8500 tonnes (standard), 11 300 tonnes (full load) *Length:* 180.8 m (593 ft 2 in) oa *Beam:* 18.9 m (62 ft) *Draught:* 7.7 m (25 ft 3 in) max *Machinery:* 2-shaft geared steam turbines, 86 000 shp=31½ knots *Protection:* 50-80 mm (1.97-3.1 in) belt; 50 mm (1.97 in) deck *Armament:* (As built) 16 127-mm (5-in)/54-cal (8×2); 20 57-mm (2.24-in)/60-cal (10×2); (After 1972) 2 100-mm (3.9-in) DP (2×1); 12 57-mm (2.24-in) AA (6×2); 1 twin Masurca surface-to-air missile system; 4 MM38 Exocet surface-to-surface missiles (to be fitted) *Aircraft:* 1 helicopter *Crew:* 777 as built, 560 after reconstruction

No and name	laid down	launched	completed
BB-45 *Colorado*	5/1919	3/1921	8/1923
BB-46 *Maryland*	4/1917	3/1920	7/1921
BB-47 *Washington*	6/1919	9/1920	—
BB-48 *West Virginia*	4/1920	11/1921	12/1923

Colorado

US battleship class. The *Colorado* Class were the last US battleships to be completed before the battleship building 'holiday' imposed by the Washington Treaty of 1922. They were the final development of the 1913 *Pennsylvania* Class to be constructed, and were almost identical to the preceding *Tennessee* Class except that they had twin 16-in (406-mm) turrets in place of the *Tennessees* triple 14-in (356-mm), and a slightly thicker main armour belt.

The Americans laid great stress on the ability of their battleships to operate together as a fleet, and as far as possible successive designs were given identical speeds and handling qualities. Therefore, when in 1916 they came to design a battleship that would outclass in armament at least the latest British and German ships—the 15-in (381-mm) gunned *Queen Elizabeths*, *Royal Sovereigns* and *Badens*—they naturally turned to the *Tennessee* design. Like the *Tennessee* Class, the *Colorado* Class had turbo-electric drive, and great use was made of electric motors for the auxiliaries.

Four *Colorados* were laid down, and they were intended to be the first of 16 16-in (406-mm) gunned US battleships.

Under the terms of the Washington Treaty, the Americans were not permitted to complete *Washington*. Her three-quarters complete hull was used as a target to determine the value of her protection against bombs and shell-fire. The next class of 16-in (406-mm) gunned battleships were the six *South Dakotas*, laid down in 1920-21. These too were not permitted to be completed and were broken up on their slips. No more US battleships were to be built until the *North Carolinas* were laid down in 1937-38.

For most of the interwar period *Colorado* and her sisters were based in the Pacific, and apart from the addition of two catapults aft (one on X turret and one on the quarterdeck), they were hardly changed until 1941. They were to have been modernized in 1939 but the outbreak of war in Europe made it unwise to withdraw battleships from the fleet at that time. Eventually *Colorado* was docked in June 1941 and by March 1942 she had been refitted with a new fore and aft superstructure and an AA armament of eight single 5-in (127-mm)/38-cal, 16 (later increased to 40) 40-mm (1.57-in) and a number of 20-mm (0.79-in). She also had torpedo bulges added.

Colorado was in dock at the time of Pearl Harbour, but her two sisters were both damaged there. *Maryland* only had two bomb hits and was refitted in the same manner as *Colorado*, but *West Virginia* was sunk. After she had been raised she was completely rebuilt with a single funnel and large superstructure, and her casemate guns removed. Like the other old US battleships, *Colorado* was used mainly for shore bombardment, and she took part in many of the Pacific islands landings. She was damaged by shore batteries at Tinian and Lingayen Gulf, and on November 20, 1944, she was hit by two Japanese kamikaze aircraft in Leyte Gulf. In January 1947 she was mothballed at Bremerton, and was scrapped in 1959.

Displacement: 32 600 tons (normal), 33 950 tons (full load) *Length:* 190.35 m (624 ft 6 in) *Beam:* 29.72 m (97 ft 6 in) *Draught:* 9.29 m (30 ft 6 in) *Machinery:* 4-shaft steam turbo-electric drive, 28 900 hp=21 knots *Protection:* 203-406 mm (8-16 in) side; 64-89 mm (2.5-3.5 in) decks; 229-457 mm (9-18 in) turrets *Armament:* 8 16-in (406-mm); 12 5-in (127-mm)/51-cal; 4 3-in (76-mm); 2 21-in (53-cm) torpedo tubes (submerged)

Colossus

British light fleet carrier. By the middle of the Second World War, it had become obvious to the British Admiralty that it was not possible to produce sufficient numbers of fleet aircraft carriers with their high speed, armoured flight deck and relatively large aircraft capacity, whilst the escort carriers were too small, too slow and could not carry sufficient aircraft to act as substitutes. What was needed was a design that could be built quickly by large

The radar array of the ex-*Colossus* Class Argentine carrier *Vienticinco de Mayo*. **A** HSA S-band height-finders **B** Navigation or target-indication scanner **C** HSA LW02 L-band surveillance radars **D** TACAN dome for homing and navigation signals **E** Target indication HSA radar **F** One ZW01-SGR 103

John A Roberts

Colossus

numbers of shipyards, that could carry a reasonable number of aircraft and that had sufficient speed at least to keep up with the older battleships.

The result was the light fleet carriers. The first to be built were the ten *Colossus* Class. To fulfill the requirements a number of the qualities of the fleet carriers had to be sacrificed, and the *Colossus* Class was designed to mercantile specifications to enable them to be built by yards unaccustomed to building large warships. They were completely unprotected, though they were moderately well subdivided, and their machinery was arranged en echelon. A maximum speed of 23 knots at full load was accepted as adequate, and as a result they were able to use standard destroyer machinery. A single large hangar with sufficient headroom to accommodate the latest US carrier aircraft was served by two lifts. There was a shortage of twin 4.5-in (114-mm) turrets, and in any case long-range AA defence was seen as a job for the escort and carrier aircraft rather than for the carrier herself, so the *Colossus* Class only had close-range AA guns.

In the same way that a number of Japanese liners had been designed to be converted into aircraft carriers in time of war, the *Colossus* Class were intended to be converted easily into merchant ships at the end of hostilities. However, they proved to be far too valuable as warships, and none were ever converted in this way.

None were completed in time for active service during the Second World War. *Colossus* herself was loaned to the French in 1946 as *Arromanches*. She was used extensively in French Indo-China in the late 1940s, and in 1951 the French purchased her outright. She was rebuilt in 1957-58 with an angled deck and improved electronics, and like all surviving *Colossus* Class carriers had her deck strengthened to operate the heavier modern aircraft. She survived until the early 1970s as a training and helicopter carrier.

Name	laid down	launched	completed
Colossus	6/1942	9/1943	12/1944
Glory	8/1942	11/1943	2/1945
Ocean	11/1942	7/1944	6/1945
Perseus	6/1942	3/1944	10/1945
Pioneer	1942	5/1944	1946
Theseus	1/1943	7/1944	1/1946
Triumph	1/1943	10/1944	4/1946
Venerable	12/1942	12/1943	1/1945
Vengeance	11/1942	2/1944	1/1945
Warrior	12/1942	5/1944	1/1946

Glory, Ocean and *Theseus* remained in service with the RN as light fleet carriers, taking part in the Korean War and the Suez campaign. They were discarded in 1960-61. *Perseus* and *Pioneer* were completed as aircraft maintenance carriers after the success of the purpose-built *Unicorn*. However, unlike the older ship they could not operate aircraft themselves because they had two large deckhouses on the flight deck. *Triumph,* after serving as a light fleet carrier, was converted into a heavy repair ship in 1964. She has large cranes and deckhouses on the flight deck, and she still exists in reserve.

Venerable became the Dutch *Karel Doorman* in 1948. She was completely rebuilt during 1955-58 with an angled deck and a revised superstructure with a tall lattice mast and capped funnel. She also received modern radars. After a small fire in 1968 she was sold to Argentina, where she remains as the *25 de Mayo*. *Vengeance* served in the Royal

Australian Navy between 1952 and 1955, and was sold to Brazil in 1957. She was completely rebuilt in Holland during 1957-60 with a new lattice mast and funnel, new electronics and an angled deck. She is still in service, and is named *Minas Gerais*. *Warrior* served in the Royal Canadian Navy between 1946 and 1948. She was used for deck landing trials by the RN, and was sold to Argentina as *Independencia* in 1958. She was discarded in the early 1970s.

This excellent class and its successors was one of the most successful improvizations of the Second World War.

Displacement: 13 190-13 350 tons (standard), 18 000-18 200 tons (full load) *Length:* 211.7 m (694 ft 6 in) *Beam:* 24.5 m (80 ft 3 in) *Draught:* 7.2 m (23 ft 6 in) *Machinery:* 2-shaft steam geared turbines, 40 000 shp = 25 knots *Armament:* 24 2-pdr (40-mm); 21 20-mm (0.79-in) *Aircraft:* 48 *Crew:* 1076

A de Havilland Sea Vampire makes a wheels up landing on the specially designed flexible deck of HMS *Warrior* in 1948. These experiments with a deck of rubber type material fixed 0.75 m (2¼ ft) above the flight deck were carried out in an attempt to test the viability of using a wheel-less aircraft. The aircraft was lightened by 4–5%, but they were restricted to using special carriers or airfields and so the project was discontinued

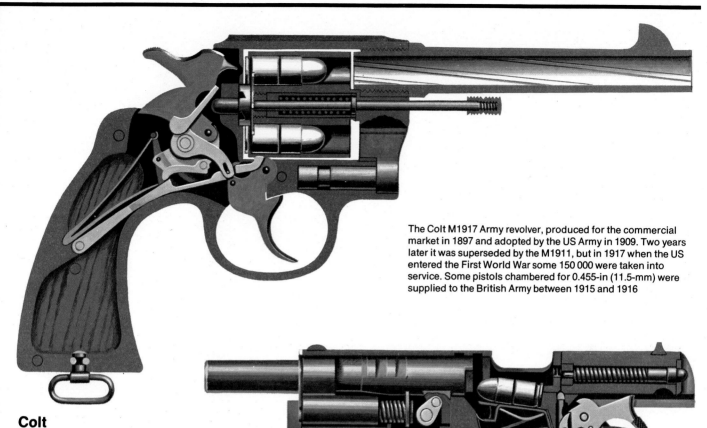

The Colt M1917 Army revolver, produced for the commercial market in 1897 and adopted by the US Army in 1909. Two years later it was superseded by the M1911, but in 1917 when the US entered the First World War some 150 000 were taken into service. Some pistols chambered for 0.455-in (11.5-mm) were supplied to the British Army between 1915 and 1916

Colt

US small arms manufacturer. Colt's Patent Firearms company was founded in Hartford, Connecticut, in 1848. Its early fortunes were founded on the famous Colt revolver, but its larger connection with military weapons came about by virtue of its alliance with John M Browning, the famous designer. As a result, several of the weapons have been unofficially known as 'Colt-Browning' guns, though the actual official designation has favoured either one name or the other.

The weapons attributed to Browning, notably his machine-guns and automatic rifle, have been described under the 'Browning' entry and need not be further considered here. But note that the Browning 0.30-in (7.62-mm) machine-gun, as adopted by the RAF, was frequently called the 'Colt-Browning' in official British documents.

The first design under the Colt name was the Browning-designed Machine-Gun M1895, more commonly called the 'Colt Potato-Digger'. This was among the first successful gas-operated machine-guns, but instead of the now-familiar horizontal gas cylinder with a piston reciprocating inside it, the action was driven by an arm hinged beneath the barrel. As the gun was fired, gas escaped through a port beneath the barrel and impinged on the end of this arm, driving it downward. By suitable linkage, this movement operated the breech mechanism.

So long as it was mounted on a tripod it was satisfactory, but inadvertently mounting it too close to the ground led to the arm striking the earth—hence the nickname. The M1895 was purchased by the US Navy in 6-mm (0.236-in) calibre and later, as the M1906, by the US Army in 7.62-mm (0.30-in) calibre, and it was widely sold abroad. The design was then modified in 1917 to become the Marlin machine-gun.

The most famous and long-serving military

The M1911A1 Colt .45 showing the slide at full recoil. A round is fed up from the magazine in the handle and carried forward into the breech as the slide moves back into position. Pressure on the trigger releases the sear which sends the hammer forward to hit the firing pin which strikes the base of the .45 ACP cartridge

A Colt .45 showing the magazine with its full capacity of seven rounds—in practice a load of six is more common—before the slide is pulled back to cock the gun. The Government Colt, Colt .45 or M1911A1 has armed US forces through two World Wars, Korea and Vietnam as well as the American intervention in Mexico in 1916. Improvements were made after the First World War, but since then it has not changed

Colt, Antonov An-2

An Antonov An-2 (Colt) in Aeroflot markings working with the Soviet agricultural service. Military Colts can carry 14 paratroops or six stretchers

design of the Colt company is the US Army 0.45-in (11.4-mm) Automatic Pistol M1911A1. Another Browning design, this originated in 1900 as a commercial weapon in 0.38-in (9.65-mm) calibre, introducing the 'swinging link' locking system. The barrel was supported in the frame by two hinged links, one beneath the muzzle and one beneath the breech. An enveloping slide covered the barrel and also formed the breech block. When the slide was forced forward by the return spring, the breech portion, pressing against the base of the cartridge in the chamber, forced the barrel forward and, by the action of the links, upward. This brought two ribs on top of the barrel into engagement with two grooves inside the slide and thus locked breech and barrel together while the pistol was fired. As the slide recoiled, so the barrel was dragged back, still locked, but as the links hinged, so the barrel was pulled down to free the lugs; the barrel then stopped and the slide continued to recoil, ejecting the spent case and reloading the chamber on the return stroke.

In 1907 the US Army carried out an exhaustive trial into competing handguns, stipulating that all must fire a 0.45-in (11.4-mm) cartridge with 230 grain bullet. The Colt was the most successful and, after some small modifications, the design was accepted as the M1911 pistol. The principal change was the removal of the front link, replacing it by allowing the barrel to slide in a bushing. Some further small modifications were made as a result of First World War experience, and it became the M1911A1 in 1926. It has served without alteration ever since, as well as being widely sold commercially. It is without doubt the finest combat pistol ever made.

The Colt company manufactured, of course, the Browning machine-guns, and they also, as contractors, manufactured many other well-known weapons such as the Thompson submachine-gun and the Vickers machine-gun. In recent years the company

has taken over the manufacture of the Armalite rifle and its derived submachine-gun the Colt 'Commando'.

See also Marlin machine-gun, Armalite and Colt Commando.

Length: 216 mm (8½ in) *Weight, unloaded:* 1.13kg (2 lb 7½ oz) *Barrel length:* 127 mm (5 in) *Magazine:* 7-round detachable box *Muzzle velocity:* 262 m/sec (860 ft/sec)

Colt, Antonov An-2

Soviet utility light transport. The An-2 has, with the possible exception of the MiG-15, been built in larger numbers than any other post-Second World War Soviet aircraft. The fact that the type is a biplane makes this unusual in a world which has moved almost universally to monoplane layouts. The An-2 (NATO code name, Colt), the first product of the Antonov design bureau, made its maiden flight in 1947. Production in the Soviet Union and Poland has since exceeded 10 000, and several thousand have been built in China.

The Colt is operated in more than 30 civil and para-military roles, including tactical logistic support, paratroop training, casualty evacuation, and radio and navigation instruction. Up to 14 parachutists can be accommodated on lightweight folding seats, or six stretcher casualties and a medical attendant may be carried: these versions are designated An-2TD and An-2S respectively.

An armed variant, the An-2NRK or An-2K, was test-flown but did not enter production. A twin-fin arrangement was adopted and a substantial section of the fuselage was glazed for the roles of night reconnaissance and airborne observation. A 23-mm (0.9-in) cannon was installed in a dorsal turret.

Span: 18.18 m (59 ft 8 in) *Length:* 12.4 m (40 ft 8 in) *Max takeoff weight:* 5500 kg (12 125 lb) *Powerplant:* Shvetsov ASh-62IR piston engine, 1000 hp at take-off *Cruising speed:* 170-190 km/h (106-118 mph) *Range:* 845 km (525 miles)

Columbia

US cruiser class, built 1890-1894. The success of Confederate commerce-raiders in the Civil War had established a tradition of fast cruisers in America, and when the US Navy began to expand in the late 1880s it was inevitable that fast commerce-raiders would be part of the new fleet.

In 1890 Congress authorized the construction of *Cruiser No 12,* and a second one, *No 13,* the following year. They were an expansion of the *Olympia,* with long hulls and powerful machinery for high speed. As they were intended to overhaul fast liners, they were given two 6-in (152mm) bowchasers, and an 8-in (203-mm) gun aft to deal with any pursuing warship.

Although designed to the same specification, the two ships were totally different in appearance, the *Columbia* having four tall funnels and the *Minneapolis* two short ones.

The powerplant was unusual for the time, three shafts, with a cruising engine coupled to the centre shaft for economy. The American public was proud of the *Columbia* when she appeared, and she was known as the 'Pirate' because of her alleged invincibility, possibly against the British mercantile marine. She made 22.8 knots on trials and her sister *Minneapolis* exceeded 23 knots and won the builders a bonus of $414 000. However, these speeds were obtained under forced draught and they would never have been able to maintain such a speed at sea. In fact the *Columbia* maintained 18 knots in a seven-day passage from Southampton to New York in July 1895, and for part of the way she showed that she could beat the Hamburg-Amerika liner *August-Victoria.*

The two big cruisers were expensive to run, and before the Spanish-American War they were laid up, only to be hurriedly recommissioned. In 1901 the *Columbia* replaced the old 74-gun ship *Vermont* as a receiving ship at New York navy yard; the *Minneapolis* was laid up in 1906 and did not

Name and no	launched	builder
Columbia (12)	7/1892	Wm Cramp & Sons, Philadelphia
Minneapolis (13)	8/1893	Wm Cramp & Sons, Philadelphia

recommission until 1917. Her torpedo tubes were removed in 1910, and in 1915 the 8-in (203-mm) sternchase gun was replaced by a 6-in (152-mm). In July 1920 they were re-classified as armoured cruisers *CA.16* and *CA.17* respectively, and on November 17, 1921 the *Columbia* was renamed *Old Columbia* to avoid confusion with the Fleet Administrative Flagship *(AG.9),* acquired three months before. The *Minneapolis* was sold in 1921 and the *Old Columbia* in 1922.

Displacement: 7375 tons (normal) *Length:* 125.8 m (413 ft) oa *Beam:* 17.75 m (58 ft 3 in) *Draught:* 6.86 m (22 ft 6 in) mean *Machinery:* 3-shaft vetical triple-extension, 18 000 ihp =21 knots *Protection:* 2½-in (64-mm)/40-cal BL; 2 6-in (152-mm)/40-cal QF (2×1); 8 4-in (102-mm)/40-cal QF (8×1); 4 14-in (35.6-cm) torpedo tubes (above water, beam) *Crew:* 459

Comandante Cappellini

Italian submarine class. *Comandante Cappellini* was one of a class of 11 oceangoing submarines which formed two distinct sub-groups known as the *Marcello* and *Cappellini* Classes. The *Comandante Cappellini* and her sister ship *Faà di Bruno* were built by OTO Muggiano and differed from the other submarines internally in a number of minor ways. The remainder of the class were built by CRDA Monfalcone. The submarines incorporated a large conning tower equipped with a small galley and WC for the watch-keepers. The partially single-hull design incorporating internal ballast tanks was capable of withstanding a fairly severe depth-charging and underwater the submarines were very manoeuvrable, but suffered to some extent from instability. The design was

Name	laid down	launched	completed
Barbarigo	2/1937	6/1938	9/1938
Comandante Cappellini	4/1938	5/1939	9/1939
Comandante Faà di Bruno	4/1938	6/1939	10/1939
Dandolo	6/1937	11/1937	3/1938
Emo	2/1937	6/1938	10/1938
Marcello	1/1937	11/1937	3/1938
Mocenigo	1/1937	11/1937	8/1938
Morosini	3/1937	7/1938	11/1938
Nani	1/1937	1/1938	9/1938
Provana	2/1937	3/1938	6/1938
Veniero	1/1937	2/1938	6/1938

The Italian submarine *Comandante Cappellini* operated by the Italians, Germans and Japanese

Italian Naval Attaché

considered to be one of the best produced by Italy up to that time.

Like many other Italian submarines they were really too large to be of great value in the shallow confined waters of the Mediterranean and in 1940 they were transferred to the German submarine base at Bordeaux on the French Atlantic coast. They carried out numerous patrols in the Atlantic sinking a total of 28 ships (136 020 gross tonnage). The *Comandante Cappellini* achieved distinction when she was involved in the mid-Atlantic rescue of a large number of POWs from the British liner *Laconia* sunk by *U 156* in September 1942.

Comandante Cappellini was converted to a transport submarine in 1943 and sailed for the Far East on May 11, 1943 to bring home a valuable cargo of rubber and wolfram. When Italy surrendered she was taken over by the Japanese at Sabang on September 10, 1943. She was handed over to the Germans who rearmed her with a 4.1-in (105-mm) gun instead of the two 3.9-in (100-mm) and renumbered her *UIT 24.* She was then used as a supply ship for German submarines operating in the Indian Ocean. Being unable to force her way back home with other German U-Boats from the Far East *Comandante Cappellini* had to return to Penang and was taken over by the Japanese as *I 503* on Germany's capitulation on May 7, 1945. She was subsequently surrendered and sunk by the USN off Kobe on April 15, 1946.

Displacement: 955/1313 tons (surfaced/submerged) *Length:* 72.99 m (239 ft 6 in) oa *Beam:* 7.16 m (23 ft 6 in) *Draught:* 5.22 m (17 ft 1½ in) *Machinery:* 2-shaft diesel/electric motors, 3600/1100 hp=17½/18 knots (surface/submerged) *Armament:* 2 3.9-in (100-mm)/47-cal (2×1) 4 13.2-mm (0.52-in) mg 8 21-in (53-cm) torpedo tubes (4 bow, 4 stern—fixed) *Crew:* 58

Comandante Margottini

Italian destroyer class. This class of 18 vessels, otherwise known as the 'Comandanti Medaglie d'Oro' Class, were the last destroyers to be designed for the Italian navy before the Armistice in 1943. Only nine of the destroyers had been laid down by the time of the Armistice and they were taken over by the Germans and subsequently broken up on the slipways. The *Comandante Margottini* was in fact launched by the Germans and was found broken in two at La Spezia in 1945 when the Allies took over the port. None of the other ships had been laid down and four were neither named nor ordered. All built were named after late honoured officers.

In appearance the ships would have closely resembled the 'Soldati' Class but were much larger and differed in armament. A much more powerful gun was adopted for the main armament; it was originally planned to have five of these guns displaced as in the 'Soldati' Class. A twin mount in A and X positions and a single mount amidships were planned but it was found that the increased weight of the new mounting would have created stability problems, and so it was decided to mount four single 135-mm (5.3-in) in A, B, X and Y positions. The arrangement of the machinery would have been as in the 'Soldati' Class, with the two boiler rooms forward, exhausting into a single trunked funnel, and the

Combat Car

Name	laid down	builder
Commandante Baroni	2/1943	Odero-Terni-Orlando, Leghorn
Comandante Borsini	4/1943	Odero-Terni-Orlando, Leghorn
Comandante Botti	8/1943	Cantieri Riuniti dell'Adriatico, Trieste
Comandante Casana	2/1943	Cantieri Navali Riuniti, Ancona
Comandante Corsi	N/A	Cantieri Riuniti dell'Adriatico, Trieste
Comandante de Cristofaro	2/1943	Cantieri del Tirreno, Riva Trigoso
Comandante Dell'Anno	2/1943	Cantieri Navali Riuniti, Ancona
Comandante Esposito	N/A	Cantieri Riuniti dell'Adriatico, Trieste
Comandante Fiorelli	N/A	Cantieri Riuniti dell'Adriatico, Trieste
Comandante Fontana	N/A	Oder-Terni-Orlando, Leghorn
Comandante Giannattasio	N/A	Cantieri Riuniti dell'Adriatico, Trieste
Comandante Giobbe	N/A	Cantieri del Tirreno, Riva Trigoso
Comandante Giorgis	N/A	Cantieri del Tirreno, Riva Trigoso
Comandante Margottini	3/1943	Oder-Terni-Orlando, Leghorn
Comandante Milano	N/A	Cantieri Riuniti dell'Adriatico, Trieste
Comandante Moccagatta	N/A	Odero-Terni-Orlando, Leghorn
Comandante Novaro	N/A	Cantieri Riuniti dell'Adriatico, Trieste
Comandante Rodocanacchi	N/A	Odero-Terni-Orlando, Leghorn
Comandante Ruta	8/1943	Cantieri Riuniti dell'Adriatico, Trieste
Comandante Toscano	12/1942	Cantieri del Tirreno, Riva Trigoso

Combat Car

US light tanks. 'Combat Car' was the American name for a light tank in the 1930s, a police fiction brought about by the wording of the National Defense Act of 1920 which specifically said that only the infantry could operate tanks. When, therefore, the US Cavalry became interested in the tank, they had to call their equipments combat cars so as not to come into conflict with Congress.

The development of the combat cars began when the US Army took delivery of the Christie T3 tanks. Four were delivered to the Cavalry at Fort Knox and were designated Combat Car T1. They were armed with a single 0.50-in (12.7-mm) Browning machine-gun in the turret and could move on wheels or tracks at high speed. A T1E3 model had a Ward LaFrance engine installed to give even higher speeds.

In 1932, however, Christie and the Army had one of their periodical estrangements, and armoured vehicle development passed to Rock Island arsenal, and they immediately abandoned Christie's suspension in favor of a system of small bogie wheels and leaf springs very similar to the contemporary Vickers system. With the engine at the rear and drive sprockets at the front, the new T2 design also adopted a radial aircraft engine as being the only way to generate sufficient power in a small space and without excessive weight.

The hull was originally fitted with a revolving turret mounting a machine-gun, but in the T2E1 improvement, the turret was dropped and a fixed barbette structure used, mounting two forward-firing machine-guns. The Vickers suspension was also abandoned in favour of a 'vertical volute spring' suspension which used two-wheel bogies in each track with a single vertical spring in the bogie mounting. Next came the T2E2 with two small fixed turrets on top of the hull.

The T2 was designed as an infantry tank but the Cavalry demanded rotating turrets

A *Combattante II* French patrol boat of the Greek *Kimothoi* Class with her four Exocet MM.38 missile-launchers amidships. The MM.38 has a 32-km (20-mile) range which gives *Combattante* Class vessels the ability to deliver a considerable weight of fire from a useful range. Gun armament consists of a twin 35-mm fore and aft; two wire-guided torpedo tubes are positioned aft

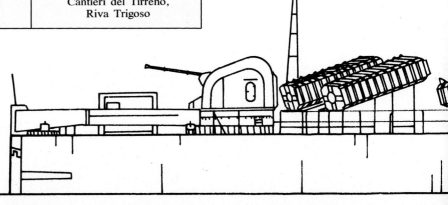

engine rooms aft. *Comandante Esposito*, however, was to have associated boiler and engine rooms together, necessitating two separate funnels.

See also 'Soldati' Class.

Displacement: 2100 tons (standard) *Length:* 120.7 m (396 ft) oa *Beam:* 12.27 m (40 ft 3½ in) *Draught:* 3.58 m (11 ft 9½ in) *Machinery:* 2-shaft geared turbines, 60000 shp=35 knots (projected) *Armament:* 4 5.3-in (135-mm)/45-cal (4×1); 12 37-mm (1.46-in)/54-cal; 6 21-in (53-cm) torpedo tubes (2×3); 52 mines

instead of the fixed barbettes, and so a further variant, the T2E3 Combat Car now appeared, using a simple hand-operated turret. This fulfilled the requirement and the T2E3 was standardized as the Combat Car M1 while the T2E2 became the Light Tank M2A2. 170 combat cars and tanks were built, the order being completed in 1937.

After some experience with these, a fresh design was made, the Combat Car M2. In this the suspension was improved by fitting better springs and spacing the bogies further apart and, most important, by bringing the rear idler wheels down to touch the ground and thus give a longer wheelbase and a better ride. The engine was changed to an air-cooled diesel. About 50 of these were built, and some of the suspension improvements were fitted retrospectively to M1 cars, whereupon they became M1A1.

By early 1939 Rock Island had perfected a 37-mm (1.46-in) gun and turret combination and mounted it on to a chassis to produce the Light Tank M2A4. There is little doubt that this would have been followed by a combat car version, but before this could happen, in 1940 the need for deceit was ended and all tracked armoured vehicles were designated 'Tanks' once more, irrespective of who drove them. The Combat Car M2 now became the Light Tank M1A1, while the M2A4 tank became the origin of the highly successful light tank series which culminated in the M3 and M5 'Stuart' designs.

(T1 Combat Car) *Weight:* 10.5 tons *Length:* 5.58 m (18 ft 4 in) *Width:* 2.22 m (7 ft 4 in) *Height:* 2.28 m (7 ft 6 in) *Engine:* V-type Liberty *Armament:* 0.5-in (12.7-mm) machine-gun

Combat Engineer Tractor

Specialized British armoured vehicle, developed after 1966 and in service by 1974.

Since the adoption of the tank, various modified types have been produced in order

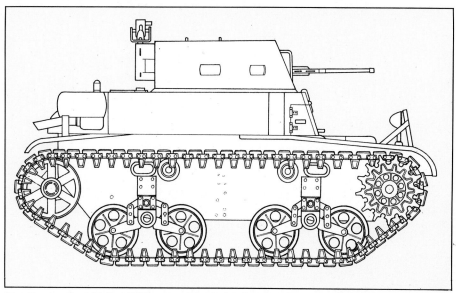

The Combat Car M1, the AFV operated by the US Cavalry, which was a light tank in all but name

to permit combat engineers to carry out their tasks in company with advanced armoured units—tasks such as improving routes and operational positions, assisting at water crossings and rescuing or assisting tanks by towing or winching them. However, all the expedients produced, notably the various AVRE vehicles, have been a second-best solution, since they were primarily designed as tanks, and in the 1960s the British army decided to develop a specially-designed and purpose-built vehicle for combat engineers.

In 1966 a development programme shared between Britain, France and West Germany was set up, but by 1970 the German army had decided to move in the direction of a modified tank and the French army were not enthusiastic. Britain subsequently developed the tractor alone.

As finally produced, the CET is a fully armoured vehicle, manned by a two-man crew, and fitted with a rear-mounted bucket which can be used for shovelling or bulldozing and a powerful winch. It is amphibious, after short preparation by the crew, and has water-jet propulsion giving a speed of 5 knots. To assist in beaching on steep river banks, a rocket-propelled anchor is stowed on the roof and can be fired onto the river bank, after which the tractor can winch itself out of the water. Additional equipment can be fitted which will allow the tractor to function as a 4-ton crane, launch bridge pontoons, lay trackway roads and tow a variety of trailers and items of construction plant.

Length, with bucket: 7.5 m (24 ft 9 in) *Width, with bucket:* 2.9 m (9 ft 6 in) *Height:* 2.6 m (8 ft 6 in) *Weight, fully loaded:* 17.1 tonnes (37 700 lb) *Road speed:* 60 km/h (37 mph) *Range:* 482 km (300 miles) *Swimming speed:* 5 knots *Wading depth:* 1.8 m (6 ft) *Draft when swimming:* 2.3 m (7 ft 6 in) *Earthmoving capacity:* 336 cu m per hour (440 cu yds) *Crew:* 2 *Engine:* Rolls-Royce 6-cylinder turbo-charged diesel, 12.2 litres, 320 bhp

Combattante

French patrol boat, built 1962 onwards. Under the 1960 Programme, an experimental patrol boat was authorized, and built by Constructions Mécaniques de Normandie in 1962-64. She was named *La Combattante*, thus commemorating a Free French destroyer (ex-HMS *Haldon*) sunk in the Second World War. She was built of laminated wood and plastic, and had a speed of only 23 knots.

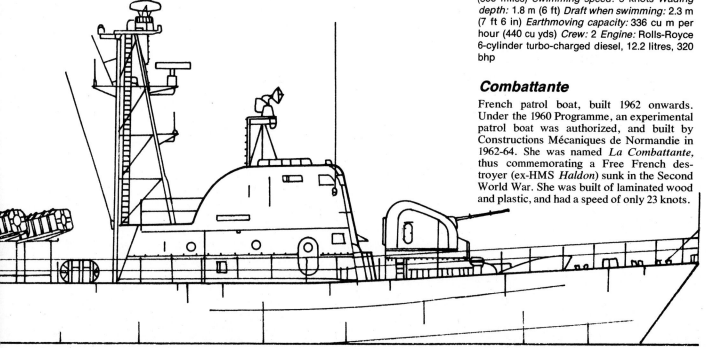

ECP Armées

La Combattante, the original vessel of this class mounting a quadruple SS.11 antiaircraft missile launcher and a rack for 14 flares. She can also carry a raiding force of 80 men, but only for short runs

P 221

The Iranian fast attack craft *Kaman*, a *Combattante II* Class vessel built by Constructions Mécanique de Normandie. The egg-like fairing on her mast protects a Hollandse Signaalapparaten WM 28 tactical fire and control radar. She is to be armed with two twin Harpoon missile launchers (not at the time this photograph was taken) and has one 76-mm (3-in) OTO-Melara and one 40-mm (1.57-in) Bofors gun. Iran ordered 12 boats which were due to be delivered by April 1979. The *Kaman* Class boats differ considerably from the original *Combattante I*, and like the Greek *Calypso* Class are *Combattante II*s with Thomson CSF Triton radar and Plessey IFF Mk 10. The complement of the original French boat was 25, the Iranian is 30, while the Greek boats have a crew of 40—though the French boat was slightly smaller and did not have the full armament of missiles and guns deployed on later versions of the class

CMN

Comet

The *Combattante* was used to test the feasibility of carrying and firing surface-to-surface missiles in minor warships, and fired Exocet MM.38 missiles. She was later fitted with a quadruple launcher for SS.11 missiles and an optical director, but the type has not been repeated.

The next step came in 1970, when the West German navy reached a decision to arm its Baltic forces with missile-armed patrol craft. The world-famous Lürssen firm of Vegesack, near Bremen, had produced a steel-hulled design capable of 35 knots for the Israeli navy, but for political reasons the contract was produced in France. A revised version was produced for the Federal German navy, to be armed with the Aerospatiale Exocet surface-to-surface missile. However, the French government was reluctant to give permission to the Germans to buy the weapon until French shipyards had been offered a fair chance to compete with the Germans for the hulls. By a very strange coincidence, the French shipyards produced a steel-hulled design called *La Combattante II*, and as it was 7 m (23 ft) longer than the original Lürssen design it fell outside the scope of any licensing agreement. To add to the Germans' discomfiture, the French government still refused to sell Exocet unless more than half the initial order was placed with a French yard, and the entire fitting out was done in France.

This has meant that Constructions Mécaniques de Normandie have been placed in the forefront of the fast patrol boat market, and since 1970 they have built the following:
20 *S.41* Class for West Germany (8 subcontracted in Germany);
4 *Kimothoi* Class for Greece;
4 *Perdana* Class for Malaysia;
12 *Kaman* Class for Iran.

The *Combattante II* is 47 m (154 ft) in length, has 4-shaft MTU diesels, and the usual armament is a 76-mm (3-in)/62 OTO-Melara Compact gun forward and four Exocet MM.38 launchers angled out amidships, though the Iranian, Greek and Malaysian boats have varying armament.

From this design was developed the 56-m (184-ft) *Combattante III*. The first of four for Greece, called *Antipliarchos Laskos*, ran her acceptance trials off Cherbourg in September 1976. She is armed with two 76-mm (3-in) OTO-Melara guns, four Exocets and two AEG T4 wire-guided torpedoes aft, plus two Emerlec twin 30-mm (1.18-in) guns, mounted on either side of the superstructure.

(Combattante II) Displacement: 234 tonnes (standard), 265 tonnes (full load) *Length:* 47 m (154 ft 2 in) oa *Beam:* 7 m (23 ft) *Draught:* 2 m (6 ft 6 in) *Machinery:* 4-shaft diesels, 12 000 bhp = 35½ knots *Armament:* 4 Exocet MM.38 missile-launchers (4 × 1), (2 in Malaysian *Perdana* Class); 1 76-mm (3-in); 1 40-mm (1.57-in) gun; (4 35-mm (1.38-in) (2 × 2) in Greek *Kimothoi* Class), (1 57-mm (2.24-in); 1 40-mm gun in *Perdana* Class)

(Combattante III) Displacement: 392 tonnes (mean), 425 tonnes (full load) *Length:* 56.15 m (184 ft 3 in) *Beam:* 8 m (26 ft 3 in) *Draught:* 2.5 m (8 ft 2 in) max *Machinery:* 4-shaft diesels, 20 000 bhp = 35.7 knots *Armament:* 3 MM.38 Exocet missiles; 2 76-mm (3-in) (2 × 1); 4 30-mm (1.18-in) (2 × 2); 2 53-cm (21-in) torpedo tubes

Comet

British tank. The Comet, of 1944-45, was the last of the 'cruiser' series and generally conceded to have been the best British wartime tank design.

In late 1941 the General Staff asked the Tank Board for a cruiser tank mounting the most powerful possible gun, capable of defeating any German tank. The first response to this was Challenger, a modified Cromwell chassis with a large turret carrying a 17-pdr gun. This was not particularly successful, and the Tank Board turned to the development for an alternative, a Cromwell chassis mounting a high-velocity 75-mm (2.95-in) gun.

This gun had been privately developed by Vickers-Armstrong as a 50-calibre weapon to give 808 m/sec (2651 ft/sec) with a 7-kg (15-lb) shot. For the sake of production convenience it was redesigned in 3.03-in (77-mm) calibre to take the same projectile as the 17-pdr gun and to use the cartridge case of the latter, the two components being married together and called the 77-mm (3.03-in) round. The result was the 77-mm gun which was, in effect, a detuned 17-pdr, the principal advantage being that the ammunition was smaller and the gun took up less room.

The Comet tank was thus based on the Cromwell hull, with extra armour, and had a wider turret ring to accept the larger turret with the bigger gun. The first production models were delivered in September 1944 and, after units had retrained, the tank was used in action for the first time in March 1945.

Apart from some disappointment over the reduced armour-piercing capability of the gun when compared with the 17-pdr, the Comet was well-liked and soon built up a good reputation for reliability and speed. After the war it became the principal British tank until replaced by the Centurion, a process which was completed in about 1950.

Length, gun stowed: 6.553 m (21 ft 6 in) *Width:* 3.073 m (10 ft 1 in) *Height:* 2.673 m (8 ft 9½ in) *Weight, combat loaded:* 33 224 kg (32½ tons) *Power unit:* Rolls-Royce V-12m 600 bhp *Speed:* 51 km/h (32 mph) *Armament:* 77-mm (3.03-in) gun; 2×7.92-mm (0.312-in) Besa machine-guns *Armour thickness:* 76-mm (3-in) hull; 102-mm (4-in) turret *Crew:* 5

Comet, Hawker Siddeley

British transport and EW aircraft. In 1956 the C.2 entered service with the Royal Air Force. The Comet II (military designation C.2) was a longer-range development of the Comet I, which had suffered catastrophic structural failures prior to 1954. In 1955 therefore the CIIs were completely rebuilt with new fuselages having elliptical passenger windows and many systems changes.

From 1956 the RAF operated one Comet T.2 crew trainer, eight C.2 transports (216 Sqn) and three E.2 electronic aircraft (51 and 192 Sqns). The C.2 carried 384 000 passengers to every part of the globe before withdrawal in April 1967, after 60 600 hours of faultless operation. The E.2 and 2R, some converted from C.2, remained in special missions at Wyton until 1974.

In February 1962 the RAF (216 Sqn) received the first of five much larger Comet C.4 transports, with more powerful Rolls-Royce Avon engines. Seating 94 passengers instead of 44, and with longer range, these again set an exemplary record in service over long intercontinental routes. At least four other Comets of this size and power have served with the RAF and Ministry of Defence, notably XS235, the Boscombe Down aircraft used in remote areas for advanced development of navigational systems, and XV626, the radar-trials Comet being used in development of the Nimrod early-warning AWACS.

(C.2) *Span:* 35.05 m (115 ft) *Length:* 29.26 m (96 ft) *Weight, loaded:* 54 431 kg (120 000 lb) *Cruising speed:* 772 km/h (480 mph)

Commandant Rivière

French sloop class, built 1957-1971. These handsome ships were designed as *avisos*, or colonials, with the dual role of escorts and patrol vessels for distant stations. For the latter role they have a modest speed with good endurance, but a reasonable antisubmarine armament is also included. All nine ships were built by Lorient arsenal (DCAN).

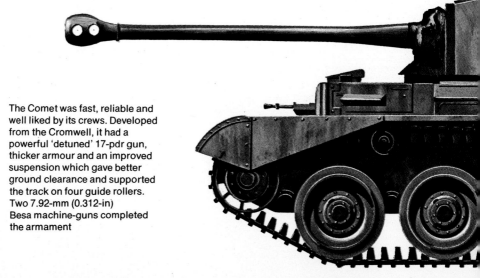

The Comet was fast, reliable and well liked by its crews. Developed from the Cromwell, it had a powerful 'detuned' 17-pdr gun, thicker armour and an improved suspension which gave better ground clearance and supported the track on four guide rollers. Two 7.92-mm (0.312-in) Besa machine-guns completed the armament

Creusot-Loire

The French sloop *Protet*, with her original armament. X 100-mm (3.9-in) gun was later replaced by a quadruple MM.38 Exocet launcher

For their colonial role the ships can embark troops and two 9-m (29 ft 6 in) landing craft (LCPs). The *Commandant Bory* has had her 100-mm (3.9-in) gun in X position replaced by four launchers for MM.38 Exocet surface-to-surface missiles, a powerful increase in armament. In 1973 the after 100-mm (3.9-in) gun was removed from the *Commandant Bourdais* and *Enseigne de Vausseau Henry* to make way for a helicopter platform, but is due to be resited on the quarterdeck (Y position) when the ships receive Exocet.

The ships have been used as test-beds for new machinery. In particular the *Balny* spent nine years between launch and final acceptance as she tried out a new Combined Diesel And Gas Turbine (CODAG) system. The *Commandant Bory* had Sigma free-piston generators and gas turbines, but in 1974-75 she was given the same SEMT-Pielstick diesels as her sisters.

Four more were built for Portugal by Chantiers de Bretagne at Nantes in 1964-69: *Commandant Joao Belo, C Hermengildo Capelo, C Roberto Ivens* and *C Sacadura Cabral,* with a slightly wider beam and 40-mm Bofors instead of 30-mm guns.

Displacement: 1750 tonnes (standard), 2250 tonnes (full load) *Length:* 103 m (338 ft) oa *Beam:* 11.5 m (37 ft 9 in) *Draught:* 4.3 m (14 ft 1 in) *Machinery:* 2-shaft diesels (except *Balny*), 16 000 bhp=25 knots *(Balny* 2 diesels, 1 gas turbine) *Armament:* (as completed) 3 100-mm (3.9-in) DP; 2 30-mm (1.18-in) AA; 1 quad 305-mm (12-in) DC mortar; 6 550-mm (21.6-in) A/S torpedo tubes *Crew:* 167

Name and no	launched
Commandant Rivière E.733	10/1958
Victor Schoelcher F.725	10/1958
Commandant Bory F.726	10/1958
Amiral Charner F.727	3/1960
Doudart de Lagrée F.728	4/1961
Balny F.729	3/1962
Commandant Bourdais F.740	4/1961
Protet F.748	12/1962
Enseigne de Vausseau Henry F.749	12/1963

Commandant Teste

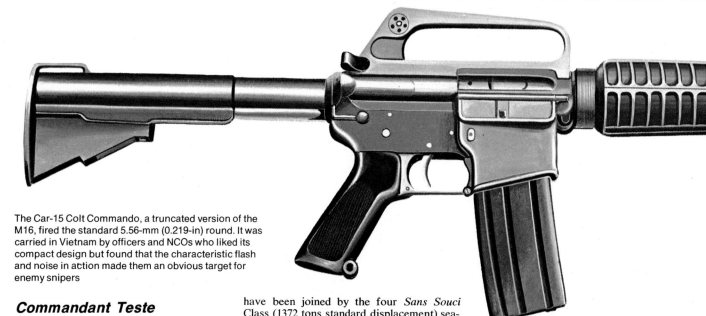

The Car-15 Colt Commando, a truncated version of the M16, fired the standard 5.56-mm (0.219-in) round. It was carried in Vietnam by officers and NCOs who liked its compact design but found that the characteristic flash and noise in action made them an obvious target for enemy snipers

Commandant Teste

French seaplane carrier. Seaplanes and flying boats played an important part in naval aviation up to the 1950s, and in the years between the two World Wars most major navies constructed a number of seaplane carriers to replace the vessels they had hastily converted during 1914-18. The single French interwar seaplane carrier, *Commandant Teste*, was one of the largest.

She was designed both to transport and operate seaplanes and flying boats, and had a large hangar 84 m (275 ft 7 in) long extending the full width of the ship. This had a head-room of 7 m (23 ft) and included repairs and maintenance shops. There were four three-ton Penhoët catapults, two on each side fore and aft of the funnel. The aircraft were recovered by five 512-ton cranes. She had two oil- and two coal-fired boilers, reflecting France's lack of an assured oil reserve.

Commandant Teste was built at Forges et Chantiers de la Gironde's shipyard at Bordeaux. Laid down in May 1927, she was launched on April 12, 1929, and completed in 1932. She saw extensive service in the years before the Second World War, and was to

have been joined by the four *Sans Souci* Class (1372 tons standard displacement) seaplane tenders that were authorized in 1937. However, these were completed as gunboats by the Germans during the war, and they never served in their designed role.

Like the aircraft carrier *Béarn*, *Commandant Teste* was not used operationally during the Second World War, but instead was used to transport new aircraft from the US to France She was scuttled at Toulon on November 27, 1942, and was salved in 1946. It was proposed to refit her either as a fast troop transport for French Indo-China or as a training carrier with a nearly full-length flight deck. In the event she was simply hulked and used to store the new equipment France had obtained from the US to refit her ships with. She was finally scrapped in 1950.

Displacement: 10 000 tons (standard), 11 000 tons (full load) *Length:* 167.03 m (548 ft) *Beam:* 27 m (88 ft 7 in) *Draught:* 6.9 m (22 ft 7½ in) *Machinery:* 2-shaft geared steam turbines, 21 000 shp=20.5 knots *Protection:* 50 mm (2 in) sides; 36 mm (1.4 in) deck *Armament:* 12 3.9 in (100-mm); 8 37-mm (1.46-in); 12 13.2-mm (0.52-in) *Aircraft:* 26 *Crew:* 686

The French seaplane carrier *Commandant Teste* photographed off Toulon during the 1920s

ECP Armées

Commandante Aguirre Peruvian cruiser
See *Dupuy de Lôme*

Commando

US armoured car. The Commando was produced for commercial sale by the Cadillac Gage Division of the Ex-Cell-O Corporation of America. The first production vehicle appeared in 1964, and various versions have since been adopted by the US Army and several other countries.

The basic model was the V-100 (known by the US Army as the XM706), a four-wheeled armoured amphibian hull which was either left open-topped or fitted with a fixed or rotating turret. Armament was generally two 0.30-in (7.62-mm) machine-guns or one 0.30-in and one 0.50-in (12.7-mm) in the turret, or three flexible machine-guns in the open-topped model. The latter can also be adapted as a mortar carrier.

In 1969 the V-200 was introduced, a larger vehicle of the same style but capable of mounting a 20-mm (0.79-in) automatic gun, or a 90-mm (3.5-in) cannon or carrying a 120-mm (4.7-in) mortar. This model was less widely adopted and led, in 1971, to an intermediate size, the V-150, which is still the standard production model.

The V-150, broadly speaking, combines the compactness and performance of the V-100 with the armament ability of the V-200, being able to carry 20-mm (0.79-in) or 90-mm (3.5-in) ordnance. It can also function as a troop carrier and a mortar carrier.

The four standard options are: twin machine-guns in turret, ten combat-equipped soldiers plus crew, one flexible machine-gun at the rear crew hatch; open topped with 81-mm (3.2-in) mortar, five mortar crew, five flexible machine-gun mounts; 20-mm Oerlikon 204GK gun in turret, eight passengers, one coaxial machine-gun and one AA machine-gun on turret roof; 90-mm (3.5-in) Mecar gun in turret, four-man gun crew, two machine-guns. It is noteworthy that the three turrets are interchangeable without any need for modifications to the basic armoured hull.

Length: 5.690 m (18 ft 8 in) Width: 2.260 m (7 ft 5 in) Height: 2.540 m (8 ft 4 in) Weight, combat loaded: 9185 kg (20 250 lb) Power unit: Chrysler 210 bhp petrol Speed: 87 km/h (54 mph) on land, 5 km/h (3 mph) in water Range: 780-965 km (485-600 miles) Crew: 2, plus passengers

Commando, Colt

US automatic rifle. The development of the Colt Commando can truly be said to be an outcome of the war in Vietnam. Under the close-quarter battle conditions of the jungle, the widely used M16A1—the military version of the 5.56-mm (0.219-in) Armalite—was at a disadvantage and continual demands were made for a lighter and handier version.

The Colt company responded to this demand by cutting down a standard M16A1 to make a very compact, though not particularly visually attractive, short weapon which weighed 0.36 kg (0.8 lb) less than the M16 and was substantially smaller in overall length. As many M16 components as possible were retained. The barrel was cut down to half the rifle length, but it was found that this gave a very large flash and muzzle blast, as might be expected, so a substantial flash hider had to be fitted which lost some of the advantage gained from the reduced length.

The butt was a telescoping tubular design, quite unlike any other Armalite component, and, apart from these obvious changes, there were scarcely any others. The body was identical with the M16, as was the method of operation, the magazine, sights and carrying handle.

This small rifle/submachine-gun was a limited success. It was tried as a survival rifle for the USAF, but was a little too heavy and large for that role. It had only limited use in Vietnam and has not been sold in any significant numbers.

Length: 787 mm (31 in) extended; 711 mm (28 in) telescoped Weight, loaded: 3.23 kg (7.1 lb) Operation: Gas Magazine: 20-round box Ammunition: 5.56-mm (0.219-in) M193 Muzzle velocity: 914 m/sec (3000 ft/sec) Rate of fire: 750 rds/min

Commando, Curtiss-Wright C-46/R5C

US transport aircraft. Second only to the C-47 Dakota (Douglas DC-3) as the leading US transport of the Second World War, the Commando will be remembered particularly for its invaluable service with US Army Air Force units in the Far East, including its round-the-clock supply and casualty evacuation flights across the Himalayas between China and India after the fall of Burma.

Designed in 1936, originally as a 36-passenger commercial transport, the CW-20 prototype (first flown on March 26, 1940) was later used by BOAC on wartime Mediterranean routes. Major USAAF production versions were the C-46A (1491 built), with 2000-hp Pratt & Whitney R-2800-51 Twin Wasp radial engines and a single large loading door on the port side; and the similarly powered C-46D (1410 built) with double side doors and a redesigned nose.

Also built for USAAF use were 25 C-46s (R-2800-43 engines), 17 single-door C-46Es and 234 double-door C-46Fs, the E and F models having R-2800-75 engines and the former a 'stepped' windscreen to the flight deck. The designations C-46B/C/G/H/K/L covered various experimental versions that did not go into production. The US Marine Corps received 160 counterparts to the C-46A, designated R5C1.

The Commando was used almost exclusively in the Pacific theatre during the Second World War, but appeared in Europe as a paratroop transport during the Rhine crossing in March 1945. Capacity was for 40 troops, 33 stretchers or 4536 kg (10 000 lb) of military cargo. Postwar, it continued in US service until the mid-1950s, long enough to see action in the Korean War. Several were brought out of reserve in 1962, during the early stages of the war in Vietnam, for counter-insurgency duties, their payload by then being increased to 7257 kg (16 000 lb) or 50 fully-equipped troops. Ex-US C-46s, mostly Ds and Fs, were also operated during the 1950s and 1960s by the air forces of Nationalist China, Dominica, Honduras, Japan, South Korea and Peru.

(C-46A) Span: 32.94 m (108 ft 1 in) Length: 23.27 m (76 ft 4 in) Gross weight: 25 401 kg (56 000 lb) Maximum speed: 433 km/h (269 mph)

Commencement Bay

US escort carrier class. The Commencement Bay Class were the last escort carriers to be built. Like the earlier Casablanca Class, they were specifically designed for their role and were not conversions from mercantile hulls. The Commencement Bay Class were longer than the Casablancas and had a cruiser stern rather than the usual transom. Their Allis Chalmers steam turbines were more complicated than reciprocating machinery, and could only be built by a limited number of firms. However, besides the usual benefits of turbine propulsion, they also gave the carriers one extra knot of speed.

In the light of battle experience the AA armament was increased and two instead of one 5-in (127-mm) guns were mounted aft. Two catapults instead of one were fitted and the increased hangar space permitted an extra six aircraft to be carried. All these improvements took time and each carrier took about 15 months to complete. The earlier Casablancas that had been designed primarily for ease of construction could be built in 3½ months and 50 were put into service in a year.

Nineteen Commencement Bay Class carriers were built during 1943-46 by Todd Pacific shipyards at Tacoma: Commencement Bay (CVE-105), Block Island (CVE-106), Gilbert Islands (CVE-107), Kula Gulf (CVE-108), Cape Gloucester (CVE-109), Salerno Bay (CVE-110), Vella Gulf (CVE-111), Siboney (CVE-112), Puget Sound (CVE-113), Rendova (CVE-114), Bairoko (CVE-115), Badoeng Strait (CVE-116), Saidor (CVE-117), Sicily (CVE-118), Point Cruz (CVE-119), Mindoro (CVE-120), Rabaul (CVE-121), Palau (CVE-122), and Tinian (CVE-123). A further 16 were cancelled on August 8, 1945.

The carriers were intended for service in the Pacific, but only a few were completed before the end of the war. In 1946 they were mothballed because they were too small and too slow for the new generation of US carrier aircraft. However, the rapid development of the helicopter in A/S and transport roles gave new life to these smaller carriers, and seven were brought back into service. The Commencement Bay, Cape Gloucester, Vella Gulf, Puget Sound, Saidor, Rabaul and Tinian were reclassified as escort helicopter aircraft carrier (CHVE) in 1955. In 1957 Block Island began conversion into a helicopter assault ship (CVHA later LPH). It was an elaborate process which involved removing the catapults, arrester gear and the aft end of the flight decks and adding extra quarters for the Marine complement. By 1958 escort carriers had become too small and slow to keep up with the new 20-knot amphibious assault ships and Essex Class fleet carriers were converted instead. The trial conversion of Thetis Bay—a Casablanca Class carrier —into a CVHA in 1955-56 had proved a slow and expensive business and so work was abandoned on the Block Island. Block Island, Salerno Bay, Puget Sound, Bairoko, Sicily, Mindoro, Rabaul and Palau were scrapped between 1960-62.

By 1959 the entire class had been reclassified as cargo and aircraft ferry ships (AKV) and some actually served in this role. During the Vietnam war some were reactivated as T-AKV and during 1962-64 Gilbert Islands was converted into a major communications relay ship (AGMR). All her aircraft handling equipment was removed and five large antenna towers, extensive electronics and a hurricane bow were fitted. Her guns were stripped out and replaced by eight 3-in (76-mm) guns in four twin mounts. Renamed Annapolis (AGMR-1) she was finally striken in 1975. The Vella Gulf was also to have been converted, but the larger, faster Saipan (CVL-48) was selected instead and she became the Arlington (AGMR-2).

Displacement: 11 373 tons (standard), 24 275 tons (full load) Length: 169.8 m (557 ft) Beam: 22.9 m (75 ft) Draught: 9.7 m (32 ft) Machinery: 2-shaft geared steam turbines, 16 000 shp=19 knots Armament: 2 5-in (127-mm), 36 40-mm (1.57-in), 30 20-mm (0.79-in) Aircraft: 34 Crew: 1066

Commodoro Py

Argentine torpedo boat class. In the last quarter of the nineteenth century many hundreds of torpedo boats were built for the navies of the world. However, only a handful of specialized shipbuilders possessed the technology and experience to build these craft. There was Normand in France, Schichau in Germany, and the rival firms of Thornycroft and Yarrow in Britain.

Condor

The first torpedo boats built by Yarrow were spar-carrying launches for the Argentine navy in the early 1870s. However, when the Argentine navy began looking for modern boats in 1888, it was Thornycroft who won the order, being temporarily in the lead in the continuous race to produce the fastest and most popular torpedo boat design of the day.

In 1887 the twin-screw *Ariete*, built for the Spanish navy, had become the fastest vessel in the world, and for some months Thornycrofts produced a series of improved versions of this two-funnelled design, and offered them to various navies. Several of these designs were offered to the Argentines, with reductions in price for a large order, but after a long series of negotiations the order placed in May 1889 was for only two vessels. Three months later, three of the same class were ordered by the Brazilian navy.

The combination of fixed bow tubes, one 18-in (46-cm) in the Argentine ships and twin 14-in (35.5-cm) in the Brazilian ships, and two rotating tubes aft was fairly typical of the larger torpedo boats of the day, as was the armament of two 3-pdr (47-mm) quick-firing guns. Reciprocating engines of Thornycroft design were provided with steam from the new, and still somewhat experimental, Thornycroft water-tube boilers, giving trial speeds of over 35 knots in carefully controlled conditions and with Thornycrofts' crack trial crew.

The three Brazilian boats, *Araguary*, *Iguatemi* and *Marcilio Diaz*, seem to have been delivered without any problems, but the Argentine order, *Commodoro Py* and her sister *Murature*, were not delivered by Thornycrofts until a year after completion, due to the Argentine government's lack of finance. Eventually a state-owned railway had to be sold in order to pay for the torpedo boats and other arms contracts.

Apart from the *Murature* taking a minor part in a revolution in 1894, these vessels saw little action during their service careers.

Displacement: 110 tons (normal), 150 tons (full load) *Length:* 46.75 m (153 ft) oa *Beam:* 4.42 m (14 ft 6 in) *Draught:* 1.6 m (5 ft 3 in) *Machinery:* 2-shaft reciprocating, 1500 ihp=24½ knots *Armament:* 2 3-pdr (47-mm) QF (2×1); (*Commodoro Py*) 3 17.7-in (45-cm) torpedo tubes (1 bow, 1 twin deck tube); (*Araguary*) 4 14-in (35.6-cm) TT (2 bow, 2 deck tubes) *Crew:* 27

Commonwealth Australian aircraft See **Boomerang CA-26, Mustang, Sabre**

CONBAT British recoilless anti-tank gun See **BAT**

Name	laid down	launched	builder
Condor	1898	12/1898	Sheerness
Mutine	1898	3/1900	Laird, Birkenhead
Rinaldo	1898	4/1900	Laird, Birkenhead
Rosario	1898	12/1898	Sheerness
Shearwater	1899	2/1900	Sheerness
Vestal	1899	2/1900	Sheerness

Condor

British sloop class. These sloops were practically identical to the earlier *Alert* Class, which were basically a larger steel-hulled version of the composite-hull gunboats built during the mid-nineteenth century. The design was on traditional lines, with yacht bow, a figurehead and a tall slim funnel.

They were among the last vessels to be built with sails for the Royal Navy. The three-masted sloop rig was initially adopted but in service it was found that the weight of canvas gave rise to problems of stability. As a result the Admiralty reduced the rig to that of a barquentine by removing the yards from the main masts.

The *Condor* was lost with all hands in a storm off Cape Flattery on December 3, 1901. As it was her first commission and she was the first of her class there was a thorough enquiry into the disaster, and it was decided that the scale of masting was too heavy.

The other five survived until the First World War, but *Mutine* became a survey ship in 1907; *Rosario* was converted into a submarine depot ship in 1910-11 and sent to Hong Kong, and *Shearwater* became the depot ship for the two Canadian submarines at Vancouver early in 1915. In 1914 the *Vestal* was a gunnery tender at Portsmouth, and in 1915 the *Rinaldo* was stationed off the Wash as a guardship before being sent to West Africa. Four were sold in 1921-22 but the *Mutine* returned to survey work. She had been paid off at Bermuda in 1914 but was recommissioned as a depot ship in December 1917. She paid off again in 1923, but became an RNVR drillship for another seven years.

Displacement: 980 tons (normal) *Length:* 54.86 m (180 ft) pp *Beam:* 10.06 m (33 ft); *Condor* and *Rosario* 10.13 m (33 ft 3 in) *Draught:* 3.5 m (11 ft 6 in) *Machinery:* 2-shaft vertical triple expansion, 1400 ihp=13¼ knots *Armament:* 6 4-in (102-mm) QF (6×1); 4 3-pdr (47-mm) *Crew:* 120

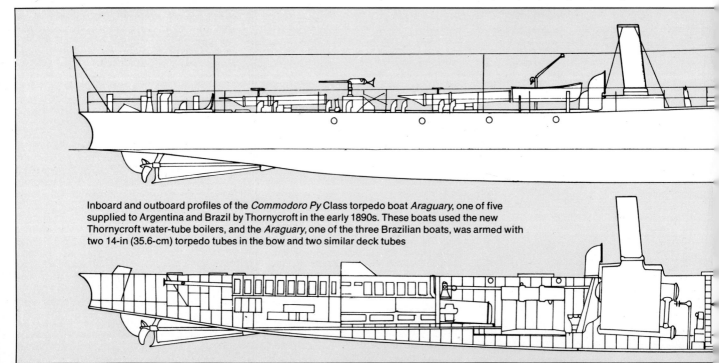

Inboard and outboard profiles of the *Commodoro Py* Class torpedo boat *Araguary*, one of five supplied to Argentina and Brazil by Thornycroft in the early 1890s. These boats used the new Thornycroft water-tube boilers, and the *Araguary*, one of the three Brazilian boats, was armed with two 14-in (35.6-cm) torpedo tubes in the bow and two similar deck tubes

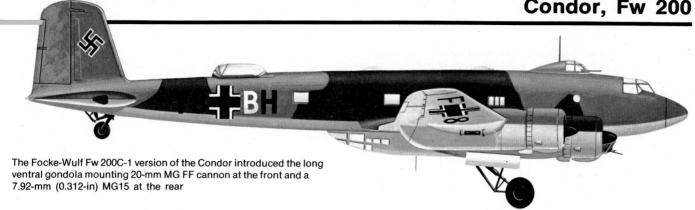

The Focke-Wulf Fw 200C-1 version of the Condor introduced the long ventral gondola mounting 20-mm MG FF cannon at the front and a 7.92-mm (0.312-in) MG15 at the rear

Condor, Curtiss BT-32/CT-32

US bomber. A rarity in the 1930s, the Condor was a large, twin-engined, fabric-covered biplane with a retractable main undercarriage. It was designed in 1932 primarily as a commercial transport, but a BT-32 bomber version was developed for sale to China in 1934. Powered by two 760-hp Wright SGR-1820F-52 Cyclone radial engines, this version carried an internal and external bombload of 658 kg (1450 lb) and was armed with five 0.30-in (7.62-mm) machine-guns: one in the nose, two at separate points on top of the fuselage, one underneath and one in the fuselage side.

Only the prototype was actually sold to China (as a personal transport for Chiang Kai Shek), but Colombia bought three BT-32s and one was sold to Peru. Three CT-32s, built as military freight transports, were sold to the Argentine navy, and China bought two T-32s and four AT-32s ex-commercial Condor transports. The US Army Air Corps evaluated two T-32s (as YC-30s), and two AT-32 floatplane versions were used by the US Navy as R4C-1s. The rapid development of the bomber and the availability of more modern monoplanes prevented further sales.

(BT-32) *Span:* 24.99 m (82 ft 0 in) *Length:* 14.81 m (48 ft 7 in) *Gross weight:* 8391 kg (18 500 lb) *Maximum speed:* 290 km/h (180 mph)

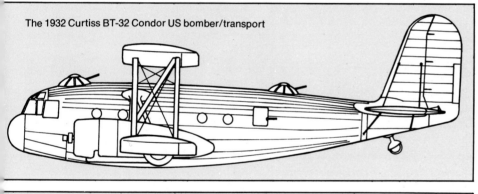

The 1932 Curtiss BT-32 Condor US bomber/transport

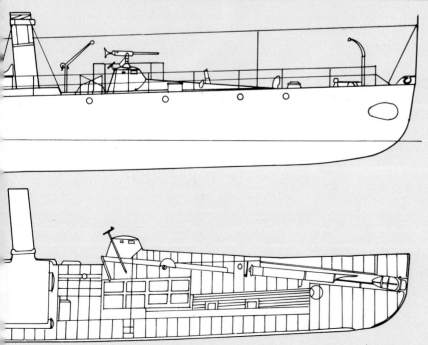

Condor, Focke-Wulf Fw 200

German transport, ocean patrol aircraft and missile platform. First flown in July 1937 as a long-range civil transport, the first prototype Fw 200 Condor demonstrated its range capability the following year with nonstop flights from Berlin to New York and back, and a flight from Berlin to Tokyo in under 48 hours. Various transport models were produced between 1937 and 1940 for airlines in five countries and for the Luftwaffe. The tenth prototype was secretly ordered by the Japanese navy as a maritime reconnaissance machine with a ventral gondola and mid-upper turret.

In the summer of 1939 the absence from the Luftwaffe of any long-range oceanic reconnaissance and antishipping aircraft (other than vulnerable and lightly-armed flying boats) resulted in urgent orders for a purpose-designed Condor, the Fw 200C series. The first Fw 200C-0 flew in January 1940, as an unarmed transport but powered by 830-hp BMW 132H engines in new long-chord cowlings, with three-blade variable-pitch propellers and twin mainwheels. With the next two it was used as a transport in the Norwegian campaign in April 1940.

The six remaining C-0 Condors were fitted with three 7.92-mm (0.312-in) MG 15 machine-guns and racks for four 250-kg (551-lb) bombs, and by the summer of 1940 I/KG 40 had begun a campaign that was to make the Condor, in Churchill's words, "The scourge of the Atlantic." One of its first victims was the liner *Empress of Britain*, which was finally despatched by a U-Boat after being wrecked by Condor bombs. For three years Condors served as the long-range eyes of the U-Boat packs, and also proved extremely dangerous to Allied merchant ships until 1941, when catapulted Hurricanes began to offer some defence.

The Fw 200C-1 introduced a long ventral gondola, different from the original arrangement designed for Japan, offset to the right and carrying a hand-aimed 20-mm (0.79-in) MG FF cannon at the front and an MG 15 at the rear. Fuel capacity was increased for the second time, but the basic airframe was inadequate for the task imposed by the military missions and catastrophic failures of the fuselage or rear spar greatly reduced serviceability (and popularity).

By March 1941, when KG 40 had been credited with 363 000 tonnes of shipping, the Fw 200C-2 introduced improved fuel and bomb provisions, but the C-3 of mid-1941 was a major improvement with a restressed structure and 1200-hp BMW-Bramo Fafnir engines. From then until the final delivery in February 1944 the assembly line at Cottbus

Condor, Rockwell AGN-53

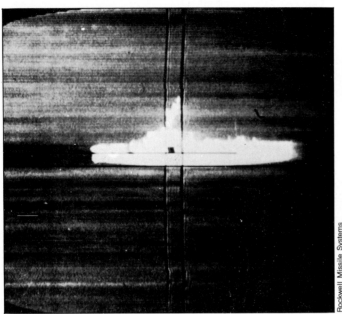

The Rockwell AGN-53 Condor television eye's view of a target ship   **Condor seconds before impact on the side of the target destroyer**

(which had taken over Fw 200 manufacture from the main Bremen plant) delivered a further 142 Condors of types basically differing from the C-3 only in armament and equipment.

The most numerous model was the C-4, in which FuG Rostock or FuG 200 Hohentwiel radars were fitted, the former giving an antiship search capability and FuG 200 adding blind level bombing. Defensive armament comprised a 20-mm (0.79-in) MG 151 in the front of the gondola, an MG 15 at the rear, two beam 13-mm (0.51-in) MG 131, and a third MG 131 in the aft dorsal cockpit and a forward dorsal turret with either an MG 15 or, with 30 km/h (19 mph) drag penalty, a large HDL 151 turret with an MG 151. Maximum bombload had risen to 2100 kg (4630 lb). The C-4/U1 was an 11-passenger transport with armament but a short gondola, which, together with at least 18 KG 40 aircraft hastily transferred from Bordeaux, ferried and later para-dropped supplies into the beleaguered 6th Army garrison at Stalingrad in early 1943.

In 1943 a number of C-3/U1 and /U2 Condors had been equipped to carry and direct the Hs 293 radio-guided missile. This 1045-kg (2304-lb) weapon was usually carried under the scalloped outer nacelles and after release steered into its target by signals from the FuG 203b Kehl III radio transmitter. In 1943 most Condor production was of the C-8 sub-type designed from the start for the Hs 293 missile and having deepened outer nacelles and an extended gondola.

The final sub-type was the C-8/U10, but though this was at last a refined and well proven aircraft (though still occasionally prone to structural failure), it seldom had the chance to display its considerable offensive potential.

By 1944 Allied command of European airspace made the Condor's life a matter of skulking from cloud to cloud, and most were being reassigned to transport duties. KG 40, the proud unit that had pioneered the long-range aerial commerce raider and collaboration with submarines far from land, was

disbanded in September 1944, all surviving aircraft being transferred to tactical Transportstaffeln or Luftwaffe HQ. In its day the Condor had been a menace, and achieved a remarkable amount considering that total production, including all civil airline versions and prototypes, was only 276.

(C-3) *Span:* 30.86 m (107 ft 9½ in) *Length:* 23.5 m (76 ft 11½ in) *Gross weight:* 22 700 kg (50 045 lb) *Maximum speed:* 333 km/h (207 mph)

Condor, Rockwell AGN-53

US air-to-surface missile. The Condor programme was abandoned in September 1976 to save money and avoid duplication of US antiship weapons, although testing had largely been completed and the project could still be resurrected. Condor is a long-range rocket-powered missile intended primarily to be launched from shipborne strike aircraft

such as the Grumman A-6E Intruder against ships, although land targets can also be attacked with the weapon.

Condor is guided to its target area automatically under the control of an on-board computer which exchanges information with the launch aircraft via a data link. The missile is tracked during flight by antennas mounted in the front and rear of a pod installed under the wing of the carrier aircraft; this allows the aircraft to fly away from the target once the missile has been launched. The normal sequence of missile operation is reversed, the weapon being fired first and aimed later via the data link.

When the Condor nears its target, the operator—normally the bombardier—navigator in a two-seat aircraft—acquires the objective with a television camera mounted in the missile's nose. Video signals from the camera are transmitted over the data link to a display in the operator's cockpit, and steering

The Condor showing the glazed nose which protects the TV camera used for in-flight guidance

The flash of the detonation as the Condor hits, ripping open the hull

The gap in the hull and damage to the superstructure of the target ship

commands generated by means of a joystick are returned to the round in flight. The normal method of operation is to position crosshairs manually over the target, with the missile then homing automatically to impact. If he wishes, however, the operator can steer the Condor throughout the attack.

A dual-mode radar/television seeker package was developed to allow attacks to be made at night and in all weathers, and a Garrett AiResearch J401 turbojet was installed in place of the solid rocket to show that extended ranges could be achieved. One such Turbo Condor hit a manoeuvring target at 195 km (120 miles).

Length: 4.21 m (13 ft 10 in) *Span:* 1.35 m (4 ft 5 in) *Diameter:* 43 cm (17 in) *Weight:* 958 kg (2100 lb) *Range:* 110 km (70 miles) *Speed:* Supersonic *Powerplant:* Rocketdyne Mk 70 solid rocket *Warhead:* 12-point linear shaped charge, 286 kg (630 lb)

Condore

Italian torpedo boat, built 1897-1900. This small coastal torpedo boat was one of a series of experimental craft built at the end of the nineteenth century, when new developments in machinery made higher speeds possible.

The ship was laid down at Sestri Ponente, near Genoa, by Ansaldo in 1897, launched on September 17, 1898, and completed on June 11, 1900. Her designed speed was 25.7 knots, on trials she reached 26.3 knots, but at normal load she made only 23.5 knots.

The *Condore* was not in commission at the outbreak of war in May 1915, but by 1917 she was serving with older torpedo boats in the Tyrrhenian Sea, on local patrol duties including convoy escort. In 1918 she was part of the 19th Torpedo Boat Division, in the so-called 'Traffic Defence Force', based on La Spezia. She was discarded in April 1920, with a number of other old torpedo boats.

Displacement: 136 tonnes (normal), 169 tonnes (full load) *Length:* 48 m (157 ft 6 in) oa, 47 m (154 ft 2 in) pp *Beam:* 5.56 m (18 ft 3 in) *Draught:* 1.36 m (4 ft 6 in) *Machinery:* 2-shaft vertical triple expansion, 2400 ihp=25.7 knots *Armament:* 2 37-mm (1.46-in)/20-cal (2×1); 2 35.6-cm (14-in) torpedo-tubes (2×1) *Crew:* 30

'Condottieri' Generic name for four Italian cruiser classes See **Alberico da Barbiano, Emanuele Filiberto, Luigi Cadorno, Muzio Attendolo**

Connecticut

US battleship class. The six ships of the *Connecticut* Class were improved versions of the preceding *Virginia* class battleships. They mark the final abandonment of the two-storey turret with twin 8-in (203-mm) guns above the main armament on US battleships, and they adopted a new 7-in (178-mm) QF gun in place of the 6-in (152-mm).

Although the 8-in (203-mm) and 7-in (178-mm) calibres appear to be very close together, the former fired a 113-kg (249-lb) shell and was intended to defeat all but the heaviest enemy armour, whereas the 7-in (178-mm) fired a 75-kg (165-lb) shell and was thought to be the largest gun capable of being easily hand loaded. In practice, 75-kg (165-lb) was too heavy for prolonged hand loading, and the US Dreadnoughts were to standardize on a 5-in (127-mm) gun.

The *Connecticut* Class were considerably longer than the *Virginia*s, which enabled them to make virtually the same speed on a considerably reduced horsepower. They were handy and basically seaworthy ships, but like many battleships of the period the QF guns were carried too low down in the hull, and were virtually unusable at sea. When the *Connecticut*s were employed in the Atlantic in the winter of 1917 the 7-in (178-mm) guns were removed and their casemates plated over.

USS *Connecticut* in her original form: battleworthy but outclassed by the *Dreadnought* era

Connecticut

The original Lockheed Model 049 Constellation as delivered to the USAAF in 1943 in its camouflaged finish. This aircraft later became the first Super Constellation and a flying test bed. The original aircraft could carry 65 passengers

Number and name	laid down	launched	completed
BB.18 *Connecticut*	2/1903	9/1904	9/1906
BB.19 *Louisiana*	2/1903	8/1904	6/1906
BB.20 *Vermont*	5/1903	8/1905	3/1907
BB.21 *Kansas*	2/1904	8/1905	4/1907
BB.22 *Minnesota*	10/1903	4/1905	9/1907
BB.25 *New Hampshire*	5/1905	6/1906	3/1908

The first two were authorized in 1902, and had 229-280 mm (9-11 in) main armour belt. The next three were authorized in 1903, and together with *New Hampshire,* authorized in 1904, they had a uniform 229 mm (9 in) main belt to compensate for having a thicker upper belt to defeat the larger secondary guns being mounted on foreign battleships. By 1917-18 they were mainly used for training, and in 1918-19 were employed to bring troops back from France. They were discarded in 1923.

Displacement: 16 000 tons (normal), 17 900 tons (full load) *Length:* 139.1 m (456 ft 6 in) *Beam:* 23.4 m (76 ft 9 in) *Machinery:* 2-shaft steam

USS *Connecticut* with the lattice masts fitted to the class in 1910-11 and the smaller bridge that resulted from the same refit

The Lockheed C-121C transport military version of the Super Constellation, can carry 75 passengers, 14 tons of cargo or 47 litter cases with their attendants. Magnesium alloy was used for the flooring, which besides being strong and light also gave a better footing

reciprocating, 16 500 ihp=18 knots *Protection:* 229-279 mm (9-11 in) sides; 203-305 mm (8-12 in) turrets *Armament:* 4 12-in (305-mm); 8 8-in (203-mm); 12 7-in (178-mm); 20 3-in (76-mm); 4 21-in (53-cm) torpedo tubes *Crew:* 880

Conqueror

British tank. Before the Second World War tanks had all carried small high-velocity guns, firing armour-piercing projectiles, and in order to give the tank units some ability to fire HE shell it became normal to fit a proportion with a large-calibre gun. This gun had to be of a lower muzzle velocity, and so was less use for antitank work, but the principle persisted in the British Army throughout and after the war. The postwar Centurions carried the 83-mm (3.3-in) 20-pdr gun, which was effective enough for most tasks, but the idea of the support tank and the heavier gun was still strong, and in 1948 the design of a large tank to carry a 120-mm (4.7-in) gun was started. This tank was to become the Conqueror.

Conqueror was the last of the large-gun support tanks, as it was soon realised that modern tanks can carry big enough guns to provide all the support and HE fire needed. For some reason however this was not clear in 1948. Technology was not sufficiently advanced in 1948 to permit an agile tank with such a large gun, and the resulting design was a triumph of firepower and protection over mobility. It would seem that the difficulties of moving such a large vehicle were not fully understood or appreciated at the time of building and as a result special transporters, bridges and servicing bays had to be provided. Transportation by rail was also tricky, due to the extra width.

Mobility was poor, due to the low power/weight ratio and general size and bulk, but the firepower was excellent, and the original concept of providing long-range protection against enemy heavy tanks was almost cer-

tainly met to the full. Many lessons were learned from Conqueror, not least in the layout of the turret and the mounting of a heavy gun, all of which was carried over into Chieftain. Another lesson that Conqueror taught was that it is important to balance the needs of protection against mobility. Because it was thought that Conqueror would fight it out with other heavy tanks the armour thickness was impressive, but the engine was insufficient to give the vehicle enough power. In order to maintain some sort of uniformity with Centurion the same engine was used, but boosted to give an extra 200hp, and fitted with fuel injection.

Conqueror was never particularly reliable, and servicing it was a nightmare. Speed and agility were indifferent, though at the time this was thought not to matter too much, since the tactics of the day used Conqueror as a heavy gun that could move itself around the battlefield, almost a self-propelled gun in fact. There is a story that in the early design stages there was a strong body of opinion in favour of making it an SP gun, but entrenched authority among tank generals insisted on it having an all-round turret, as failure to do so would make it an artillery vehicle.

The first Conquerors came into service in 1954, and stayed for seven troubled years until withdrawn on the arrival of the first Chieftains. Electrical unreliability had plagued them throughout their career and few units were sorry to see them go. The main responsibility for their unfortunate reputation lay with the sponsors who drew up the requirement, for Conqueror should definitely have been an SP gun.

Length: 7.85 m (25 ft 9 in) *Width:* 3.94 m (12 ft 11 in) *Height:* 3.50 m (11 ft 6 in) *Weight:* 65 957 kg (65 tons) *Armour:* 200 mm (7.87 in) *Crew:* 4

Consolidated US aircraft (later Convair) See Catalina, Coronado, Dominator, Liberator, P2Y, PB-2

Constellation, C-69/C-121 Lockheed

US transport, early-warning, reconnaissance and weather-research aircraft. Conceived as a civil transport, and ordered originally by Trans World Airlines and Pan American Airways, the first Constellations entered service in 1943 with the US Army Air Force as C-69s, the airlines having waived their rights to them on American entry into the war. After 22 had been built for the USAAF, the military contract was cancelled following VJ Day and Lockheed had to wait until 1948 before receiving another military order, this time from the newly-named US Air Force and covering ten of the longer-range Model 749 Constellations. These were designated C-121 and were all passenger transports.

The first stretched Model 1049 Super Constellations for military use were ordered by the USAF in 1951, these being designated C-121C, powered by Wright R-3350-34 Turbo Compound engines of 3500 hp and having a maximum takeoff weight of 61 416 kg (135 400 lb) compared with the 48 534 kg (107 000 lb) of the first C-121s. Meanwhile the US Navy had developed a version of the aircraft for radar early warning and intelligence gathering with large radomes both on top of and beneath the fuselage, and provision for a crew of up to 31 including spare pilots, engineers and radar operators. The USAF designated a similar version, packed with six tons of its own surveillance equipment, the RC-121, modifications to later models allowing an endurance of up to 24 hours. In the early 1960s computers and other new electronics were added to these aircraft which were then redesignated EC-121. Many were still in service in the mid-1970s, having in the main been used as the airborne component of the North American Air Defence network linked with the Sage ground radars.

In addition to being used by the US Navy

Constitucion

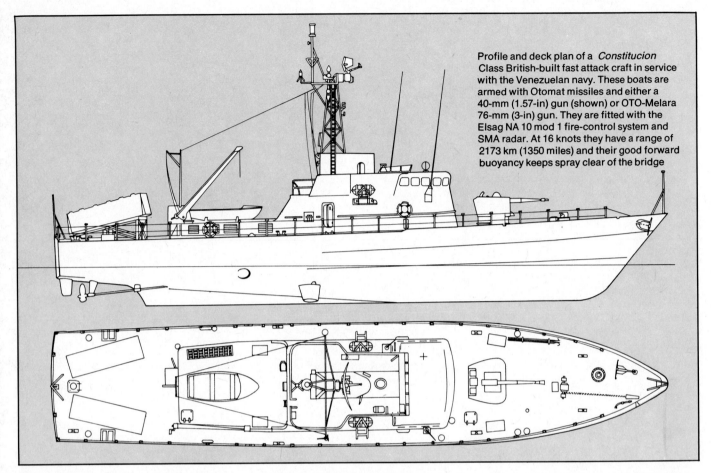

Profile and deck plan of a *Constitucion* Class British-built fast attack craft in service with the Venezuelan navy. These boats are armed with Otomat missiles and either a 40-mm (1.57-in) gun (shown) or OTO-Melara 76-mm (3-in) gun. They are fitted with the Elsag NA 10 mod 1 fire-control system and SMA radar. At 16 knots they have a range of 2173 km (1350 miles) and their good forward buoyancy keeps spray clear of the bridge

for transport, versions of the Super Constellation were used for weather reconnaissance and for testing out new turboprop engines, both the Pratt & Whitney T34 and the Allison 501, the latter as part of development work for the civil Lockheed Electra which later formed the basis of the antisubmarine warfare P-3 Orion.

(C-121C) *Span:* 37.49 m (123 ft 0 in) *Length:* 35.41 m (116 ft 2 in) *Maximum takeoff weight (C-121G):* 65771 kg (145000 lb) *Maximum speed (C-121G):* 592 km/h (368 mph) at 6096 m (20000 ft) *Maximum range (RC-121D):* 7403 km (4600 miles)

Constitucion

Venezuelan fast patrol boat class. The contract for these vessels was placed in April 1972. They were specifically designed for Venezuela and completed with either a fully-automatic gun capable of engaging missiles, aircraft or ships, or Otomat surface-to-surface missiles, the first FPBs to use this weapon system. All six ships in this class were built by Vosper Thornycroft.

The main feature of the hull design is that it maintains a good reserve of buoyancy forward, deflecting the spray well clear of the forecastle deck where it would interfere with

operation of the armament. This is achieved by use of modified round-bilge sections, a spray-deflecting knuckle forward just below the forecastle deck and a spray stake between this and the waterline. The all-welded steel hull is subdivided into seven watertight compartments while the aluminium alloy superstructure is partly welded and partly riveted. The ships are seaworthy both at high speed and in heavy following seas.

The diesel engines are remotely controlled, either from a noise-proof cubicle in the engine compartment, or from the enclosed bridge. The engine exhausts are sited at the ship's side, thus dispensing with the need for a funnel.

The vessels are equipped with a large operations room housing fire control, radar display, consoles etc, while a separate radio office is sited on the after part of the super-

The *Conte de Cavour* Class Italian battleship *Giulio Cesare* after the extensive alterations in 1933-37 which saw the midship turret deleted to allow more space for machinery, giving an increase in speed of 6 knots. The casemate guns were also removed, the upper decks and superstructure rebuilt and antiaircraft guns and modern fire-control equipment fitted

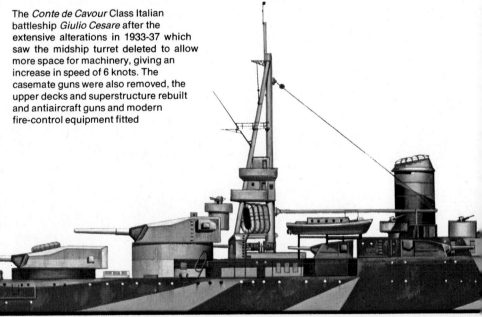

The *Constitucion* (right) with an OTO-Melara 76-mm (3-in) gun, and the missile-armed version, *Independencia* (below) armed with OTOMat missiles and Bofors 40-mm (1.57-in) gun on trials by Vospers before delivery

Constitution, Lockheed R6V

American transport aircraft. The Lockheed Model 89 was planned as the largest transport that could be flown on four 3500 hp Pratt & Whitney R-4360 Wasp Major engines. Two prototypes were ordered by the US Navy in 1943 as the R600-1, later changed to R6V-1, the first flying on November 9, 1946. Capable of seating 92 on the upper deck and 76 on the lower, in a pressurized double-bubble fuselage, the Constitution was also equipped for cargo and had two electric hoists. Though impressive, these two large machines were the only examples of their type.

Span: 57.8 m (189 ft 1 in) *Length:* 47.6 m (156 ft 1 in) *Gross weight:* 83 465 kg (184 000 lb) *Maximum speed:* 485 km/h (303 mph)

Conte di Cavour

Italian battleship class. The design was prepared in 1908, and differed from earlier Italian battleships in the layout of the main armament. Superfiring turrets were adopted for the first time, with a triple turret amidships capable of firing to port or starboard to maintain the heaviest possible broadside. Although completed during the First World War, the ships did not take part in any action. The *Leonardo da Vinci* was sunk in Taranto on August 2, 1916 when a magazine exploded. The hulk was salvaged on November 17, 1919 and subsequently scrapped.

During the mid-1920s the ships were refitted and the tripod mast moved to between the bridge and the forefunnel. They also had a catapult fitted in a fixed position on the forecastle to port, but the installation was not a success. A major modernization was undertaken between 1933 and 1937, when all the machinery was renewed, the new boilers and

Name	laid down	launched	completed
Constitucion	1/1973	6/1973	8/1974
Federacion	8/1973	2/1974	3/1975
Independencia	2/1973	7/1973	9/1974
Libertad	9/1973	3/1974	6/1975
Patria	3/1973	9/1973	1/1975
Victoria	3/1974	9/1974	9/1975

structure to starboard. A radar room is sited at the base of the mast. The ships are fully airconditioned throughout.

Displacement: 150 tons (standard) *Length:* 36.88 m (121 ft) oa *Beam:* 7.1 m (23 ft 3½ in) *Draught:* 1.7 m (5 ft 7¼ in) *Machinery:* 2-shaft MTU 16-cylinder diesels, 7080 bhp=27 knots *Armament:* 1 76-mm (3-in)/62-cal OTO-Melara DP gun; or 2 Otomat surface-to-surface missile launchers 1 40-mm (1.57-in) *Crew:* 18

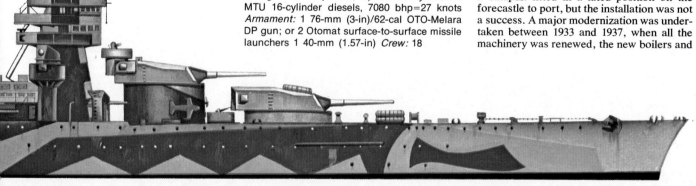

Name	laid down	launched	completed	builder
Conte di Cavour	8/1910	8/1911	4/1915	Navy Yard, La Spezia
Giulio Cesare	6/1910	10/1911	3/1914	Ansaldo, Genoa
Leonardo da Vinci	7/1910	10/1911	5/1915	Oderno-Terni, Genoa

engines being fitted *en echelon* to minimize the danger of bomb- or torpedo-damage putting both out of action.

With the machinery removed the opportunity was taken to improve the armour protection, which included the fitting of a new underwater protection system devised by the designer Pugliese. New bow and stern sections were also built on to the ships, which together with the greater horsepower developed resulted in an increase in speed. During modernization the upperworks and superstructure were rebuilt and modern fire control equipment fitted. The casemate guns were removed and a new secondary battery fitted together with new antiaircraft equipment. The main guns were also bored out from 12-in (305-mm) to 12.6-in (320-mm). The aircraft facilities were removed from *Giulio Cesare*. *Conte di Cavour* had two temporary catapults, one on either beam amidships, which were removed after trials.

During the Second World War, the ships took part in a number of actions in the Mediterranean, including the Battle of Punta Stilo on July 9, 1940. On November 11, 1940, the *Conti di Cavour* was struck by a torpedo during the raid on Taranto and sank in shallow water. She was raised for repairs in July 1941 but had to be scuttled in Trieste on Italy's surrender, before repairs were completed. She was raised by the Germans but sunk again in an air raid on February 15, 1945. The *Giulio Cesare* was relegated to use as a barrack ship after January 1942 and

after having had her name changed to *2.11* was handed over to Russia as war reparations in 1947, being renamed *Novorossiisk*. She was lost (probably after striking a mine) on October 29, 1955.

See also *Leonardo da Vinci*.

(As completed) *Displacement:* 21 751 tons (standard) *Length:* 176 m (577 ft 9 in) oa *Beam:* 27.97 m (91 ft 9¾ in) *Draught:* 9.37 m (30 ft 9½ in) *Machinery:* 4-shaft turbines 31 000 shp=21.5 knots *Protection:* 76-248 mm (3-9¾ in) belt; 25 mm (1 in) upper armoured deck; 38 mm (1½ in) lower armoured deck; 248 mm (9½ in) main barbettes; 280-84 mm (11-3⅓ in) turrets; 110-127 mm (4⅓-5 in) casemates; 280 mm (11 in) conning tower *Armament:* 13 12-in (305-mm)/46-cal (3×3, 2×2); 18 4.7-in (120-mm)/50-cal (18×1); 13 3-in (76-mm)/50-cal (13×1); 3 17.7-in (45-cm) torpedo tubes (fixed submerged, two abeam, one stern) *Crew:* 1197

(As modernized) *Displacement:* 23 619 tons (standard) *Length:* 186.38 m (611 ft 6 in) *Beam:* 27.97 m (91 ft 9¾ in) *Draught:* 10.39 m (34 ft 1 in) *Machinery:* 2-shaft geared turbines 93 000 shp=28 knots *Protection:* 76-248 mm (3-9¾ in) belt; 102 mm (4 in) upper armoured deck; 25 mm (1 in) lower armoured deck; 292 mm (11½ in) main barbettes; 280-84 mm (11-3⅓ in) turrets; 260 mm (10¼ in) conning tower *Armament:* 10 12.6-in (320-mm)/43.8-cal (2×3, 2×2); 12 4.7-in (120-mm)/50-cal (6×2); 8 3.9-in (100-mm)/47-cal (4×2); 16 37-mm (1.46-in) (8×2); 12 20-mm (0.79-in) (6×2) *Crew:* 1236

Conway

British experimental tank design. The single Conway built in 1955 represented an attempt to combine the firepower of the Conqueror with the mobility of the Centurion, and consisted of a Conqueror turret and 120-mm (4.7-in) gun mounted on a Centurion hull.

The idea was not a success. The axis of the gun was too high, leading to instability on firing, and the silhouette of the vehicle was likewise too high. In the words of one critic, it resembled 'a large turret without visible means of support'. It is now displayed at the RAC Tank Museum, Bovington.

Cookpot, Tupolev Tu-124

Soviet jet transport aircraft. A scaled-down, turbofan-powered development of the Tu-104 Camel, the Tu-124 was designed to replace the Il-14 Crate on Aeroflot's short-haul and medium-range routes. The type entered service in 1962 but the production run has been short by Russian standards, with fewer than 200 built. The airline models Tu-124 and Tu-134B carry 44 and 56 passengers respectively. Two VIP variants, the Tu-124K and Tu-124K2, are used to transport high-ranking Soviet officials; accommodation is provided for 36 and 22 passengers respectively. The Cookpot has also been supplied in small numbers to the air forces of East Germany and Iraq.

The powerplant of two 5400-kg (11 905-lb) thrust Soloviev D-20P turbofans give an economical cruising speed of 800 km/h (497 mph). Range with a 3500-kg (7715-lb) payload and maximum fuel is 2100 km (1305 miles); with the maximum payload of 6000 kg (13 320 lb) this is reduced to 1220 km (760 miles).

Span: 25.55 m (83 ft 9½ in) *Length:* 30.58 m (100 ft 4 in) *Gross weight:* 38 000 kg (83 775 lb) *Maximum speed:* 970 km/h (603 mph)

Giulio Cesare **battleship in her original form, with 3-in (76-mm) antitorpedo boat guns mounted on top of the main turrets**

USS *Macdonough,* a guided-missile frigate of the *Coontz* Class, escorting HMS *Ark Royal* during joint NATO naval exercises in the autumn of 1977

Coontz

US guided-missile frigate class. The design of the *Coontz* Class of guided-missile frigates was evolved from that of the *Mitscher* Class guided-missile destroyers. The design displays the traditional American flush-deck destroyer hull form with pronounced sheer sweeping gracefully aft for two thirds of the hull. To keep weight down and overcome problems of stability the class was built with an aluminium superstructure.

The vessels were designed as AA frigates for screening high-speed carrier task forces and for independent operations, and original plans provided for two single 5-in (127-mm) guns in A and B positions. With the need for increased A/S capabilities, however, B gun was replaced by an 8-tube A/S rocket launcher. The ships were also provided with a helicopter landing pad at the stern, but no hangar was fitted and the ships have only limited facilities for servicing helicopters.

Between 1968 and 1975 the ships were considerably modernized when the twin 3-in (76-mm) guns amidships were removed and the superstructure considerably enlarged to house extra electronic, command and guidance equipment. This modernization substantially improved their AA capability and they were equipped with improved Terrier/ Stan-

dard missiles and associated equipment.

The *Farragut* had been equipped with an improved Asroc reload capability which incorporates a forward sloping extension in front of the bridge.

Displacement: 4770 tons (standard) *Length:* 156.2 m (512 ft 6 in) oa *Beam:* 16 m (52 ft 6 in) *Draught:* 7.62 m (25 ft) *Machinery:* 2-shaft geared turbines, 85000 shp=34 knots *Armament:* 1 5-in (127-mm)/54 cal DP gun; 4 3-in (76-mm)/50 cal AA (2×2); 1 twin Terrier surface-to-air missile launcher; 6 21-in (53-cm) torpedo tubes (2×3); 1 8-tube Asroc launcher *Crew:* 370

Name	laid down	launched	completed	builder
Coontz	3/1957	12/1958	7/1960	Puget Sound navy yard
Dahlgren	3/1958	3/1960	4/1961	Philadelphia navy yard
Dewey	8/1957	11/1958	12/1959	Bath Ironworks
Farragut	6/1957	7/1958	12/1960	Bethlehem, Quincy
King	3/1957	12/1958	11/1960	Puget Sound navy yard
Luce	10/1957	12/1958	5/1961	Bethlehem, Quincy
Macdonough	4/1958	7/1959	11/1961	Bethlehem, Quincy
Mahan	7/1957	10/1959	8/1960	San Francisco navy yard
Preble	12/1957	5/1959	5/1960	Bath Ironworks
Wm V Pratt	3/1958	3/1960	11/1961	Philadelphia navy yard

Coot, Ilyushin Il-18

An Il-18 Coot lowers its undercarriage and flaps and throttles back as it comes in to land. The Il-18 is both a civilian and military transport

Coot, Ilyushin Il-18

Soviet turboprop transport aircraft. The Il-18 was designed from the outset as a civil airliner, entering service with Aeroflot in 1959. Passenger accommodation has been progressively increased from the original 75, reaching 122 in the Il-18D of 1965. More than 800 Il-18s have been built; none are thought to be operated in military roles within the USSR, although some of the 100-plus aircraft which have been exported are used for general military transport duties. Overseas air forces operating Coots include those of Afghanistan, Algeria, Bulgaria, China, Czechoslovakia, Poland and Yugoslavia. The Il-18 also served as the basis for the Il-38 May antisubmarine and maritime-patrol aircraft.

Span: 37.4 m (122 ft 8½ in) *Length:* 35.9 m (117 ft 9 in) *Height:* 10.17 m (33 ft 4 in) *Powerplant:* 4 Ivchenko AI-20M turboprops, 4250 ehp each *Cruise speed:* 625 km/h (388 mph) *Range:* 3700 km (2300 miles) with maximum payload and 1 hr reserve *Maximum takeoff weight:* 64 000 kg (141 095 lb)

Civil versions of the Il-18 Coot under production at the Znamya Truda plant in the USSR

Copperhead

US gun-launched guided projectile. Originally known as CLGP (cannon-launched guided projectile), Copperhead was developed by the Martin Marietta company for the US Army. Development began in 1972 and it is expected to be in service by 1980, the US Army having stated a requirement for some 200 000 of them.

CLGP is a cylindrical projectile weighing 63.5 kg (140 lb) which is loaded and fired from a 155-mm (6.1-in) howitzer using conventional artillery techniques. The nose carries a laser seeker, behind which is a shaped-charge warhead, and the rear of the projectile carries folding wings and tail fins and the electronic components of the guidance system. No modification to the howitzer is necessary and the CLGP can be fired interchangeably with normal shells. The sole special requirement is for a laser designator with the forward ground or airborne observer.

In operation the observer 'illuminates' the

A Copperhead missile nearing a target tank during range tests

Copperhead about to impact after being fired from a M109A SP gun

target with his laser designator. The CLGP, preset to the characteristics of the laser, is then fired into the general target area on a normal ballistic trajectory. On entering the target area a timer activates the laser seeker which then picks up the laser energy reflected from the target and commands the guidance mechanism to steer the CLGP so as to hit the target. The maximum range is said to be in excess of 20 km (12.5 miles).

Length: 137.5 cm (54 in) *Weight:* 63.5 kg (140 lb) *Warhead weight:* 6.4 kg (14 lb) *Maximum range:* 20 km (12.5 miles)

Cordoba

Argentine destroyer class. *Cordoba* and *La Plata* were built by the German firm of Schichau as part of a large programme of destroyers that the Argentine navy ordered in 1910. They were part of the modern navy that Argentina was constructing around the American-built battleships *Rividavia* and *Moreno* in reply to the expanding Brazilian fleet. All the destroyers that the Argentine navy ordered in 1910 were to be built abroad, four each in Germany, Britain and France.

In the event, the German four were the only ones to be delivered to Argentina. The British ships, built by Cammell Laird, were sold to Greece as the *Aetos* Class in October 1912. The French vessels, built by Chantiers de Bretagna, were still incomplete at the start of the First World War, and were incorporated into the French navy as the *Aventurier* Class. The other two German destroyers, *Catamarca* and *Jujuy*, were built by Krupp's Germania yard at Kiel and delivered to the Argentine navy in 1912.

Cordoba and *La Plata* were laid down in 1910. *Cordoba* was launched in November 1910 and *La Plata* in January 1911. They were completed and delivered in the following year. Their original armament was four 4-in (102-mm) guns and four 21-in (53-cm) torpedo tubes all in single mounts. The guns were made by the Bethlehem Steel company in the US. They had AEG built Curtiss turbines and Schultz-Thornycroft coal- and oil-fired boilers. Unlike the Cammell Laird boats the *Cordoba* Class easily made their contract speeds. *Cordoba* made 34.7 knots on trials and *La Plata* made 36.8 knots.

The *Cordoba* Class were fairly similar in appearance to the *Catamarca* Class but could

be recognised by their pronounced ram bow and by having all three funnels aft of the forecastle break. Like the *Catamarcas* they were converted to all-oil firing in the 1920s, and had one 4-in (102-mm) replaced by a 3-in (76-mm) AA gun, and a depth charge thrower was added. The 3-in (76-mm) was replaced by two 37-mm (1.46-in) AA guns in the 1930s. The vestigial bridge was also enlarged. They were relegated to harbour training by 1940, and were discarded in the 1950s.

Displacement: 1000 tons *Length:* 89.9 m (295 ft) *Beam:* 9 m (29 ft 6 in) *Draught:* 3 m (10 ft) *Machinery:* 2 shaft-steam turbines, 20 000 shp=34 knots *Armament:* 3 4-in (102-mm); 2 37-mm (1.46-in); 4 21-in (53-cm) torpedo tubes *Crew:* 99

Coronado, Consolidated PB2Y

US long-range maritime patrol flying-boat. Designed to meet a 1936 US Navy requirement, the XPB2Y-1 (Consolidated Model 29) made its first flight on December 17, 1937, powered by four 1050-hp Pratt & Whitney XR-1830-72 Twin Wasp radial engines and featuring a single fin and rudder. Like the

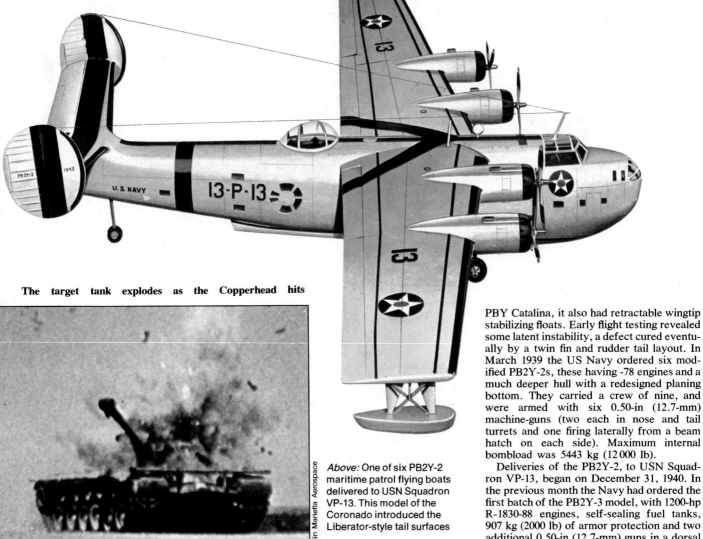

The target tank explodes as the Copperhead hits

Above: One of six PB2Y-2 maritime patrol flying boats delivered to USN Squadron VP-13. This model of the Coronado introduced the Liberator-style tail surfaces

PBY Catalina, it also had retractable wingtip stabilizing floats. Early flight testing revealed some latent instability, a defect cured eventually by a twin fin and rudder tail layout. In March 1939 the US Navy ordered six modified PB2Y-2s, these having -78 engines and a much deeper hull with a redesigned planing bottom. They carried a crew of nine, and were armed with six 0.50-in (12.7-mm) machine-guns (two each in nose and tail turrets and one firing laterally from a beam hatch on each side). Maximum internal bombload was 5443 kg (12 000 lb).

Deliveries of the PB2Y-2, to USN Squadron VP-13, began on December 31, 1940. In the previous month the Navy had ordered the first batch of the PB2Y-3 model, with 1200-hp R-1830-88 engines, self-sealing fuel tanks, 907 kg (2000 lb) of armor protection and two additional 0.50-in (12.7-mm) guns in a dorsal turret. Some aircraft had an ASV radar fairing on top of the fuselage aft of the flight deck. The PB2Y-3 remained in production (210 were built) until late 1943, the output included 10 PB2Y-3Bs supplied to the RAF under Lend-Lease (flown as freight transports by No 231 Squadron) and 31 unarmed PB2Y-3Rs with 'low altitude' -92 engines (still of 1200 hp) used as 44-passenger or cargo transports by the USN. In the maritime reconnaissance/bomber role, the Coronado began to give way in 1944 to the PB4Y-1, a USN variant of the Consolidated B-24 Liberator landplane bomber. A number of other PB2Y-3s were also refitted with R-1830-88 engines, combined with a substantial increase in fuel tankage and the addition of specialized equipment. In this form they became PB2Y-5 or -5R patrol bombers, able to carry a 3630 kg (8000 lb) bomb load over a distance of 2639 km (1640 miles), or PB2Y-5H 25-stretcher aeromedical transports. The XPB2Y-4 designation applied to a prototype conversion of a PB2Y-2 to a powerplant of Wright R-2600 Cyclone engines. This was intended as a backup version in case the wartime output of Twin Wasp engines proved inadequate, but the need for it failed to materialize. All Coronados were withdrawn from USN service by the end of 1945.

(PB2Y-3) *Span:* 35.05 m (115 ft 0 in) *Length:* 24.16 m (79 ft 3 in) *Gross weight:* 30 844 kg (68 000 lb) *Maximum speed:* 359 km/h (223 mph)

Coronel

German auxiliary cruiser. The *Coronel* was originally built as the *Togo* for the Woermann Line of Hamburg. She was requisitioned for naval use in August 1940 and renamed *Coronel* in December 1942. Work on converting her to an auxiliary cruiser began at Wilton-Fijenoord, Schiedam, Holland and was completed by Oder-Werke, Stettin, and the naval yard at Gotenhafen.

She sailed (as *Schiff 14*, British designation *Raider K*) on January 31, 1943, but the break-out was constantly frustrated by air and sea surveillance. A final attempt was made on February 10, 1943. In the Straits of Dover the ship came under fire from the British heavy

Togo (ex-*Coronel*) in her role as a fighter direction ship with an elaborate radar array

gun batteries and this was followed by an air attack by Whirlwind bombers of the RAF. The ship was damaged and put into Boulogne where further air attacks forced her back out to sea on February 14. The *Coronel* sailed east for Dunkerque, again coming under fire from the batteries at Dover. The next day she was ordered to return to Germany and arrived at Kiel on March 2. This was the last attempt by Germany to send an auxiliary raider to sea.

She was then converted into a fighter direction ship, renamed the *Togo*, and equipped with a Freya radar aerial forward and a Würzburg aft. The Freya FuMG A1 (Funkmessgerät Ausrüstung 1, or radar equipment 1) initially worked on a wavelength of 2.4 m, but this was subsequently reduced to 1.5 m. The range was between 40 and 75 km (25-47 miles) and the bearing accuracy ± 10°. The Würzburg (FuMG 65) worked on a wavelength of 53 cm with a range of 40-70 km (25-45 miles). The range accuracy was in the

region of ± 40 m (131 ft) and the bearing accuracy between ± 9° and 16°. The aerial was 3 m (9 ft 10 in) across and weighed 1500 kg (3307 lb).

The *Togo* fell into British hands in August 1945 and was towed back to an English port for a detailed examination of her radar and fighter-direction gear, before being handed over to the United States for a similar examination in January 1946. After two months in US hands the ship was stripped and handed over to the Norwegian navy on March 15, 1946, for use as an auxiliary, and renamed *Svalbard* in 1947. In 1954 she became the mercantile *Tilthorn*, then *Stella Marina* a year later, and was passed back to Germany in 1956 reverting to the original name *Togo*.

Displacement: 11 000 tons (standard) *Length:* 134 m (439 ft 7 in) oa *Beam:* 17.9 m (58 ft 9 in) *Draught:* 6.47 m (21 ft 3 in) *Machinery:* single-shaft 8-cylinder diesel 5450 bhp=16 knots

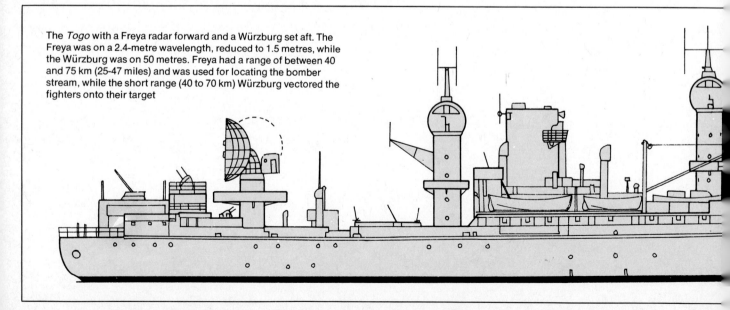

The *Togo* with a Freya radar forward and a Würzburg set aft. The Freya was on a 2.4-metre wavelength, reduced to 1.5 metres, while the Würzburg was on 50 metres. Freya had a range of between 40 and 75 km (25-47 miles) and was used for locating the bomber stream, while the short range (40 to 70 km) Würzburg vectored the fighters onto their target

Armament: 6 5.9-in (150 mm)/55-cal (6×1); 6 40-mm (1.57-in) (6×1); 8 20-mm (0.79-in) (2×4); 2 21-in (53-cm) torpedo tubes (fixed and submerged); 4 aircraft *Crew:* 350

Coronel Bolognesi

Peruvian scout cruiser class. The *Coronel Bolognesi* and her sister ship *Almirante Grau* were two scout type cruisers ordered from the British yard of Vickers in November 1905. For over fifty years these two small cruisers formed the backbone of the Peruvian navy. They were named after heroes in the war against Chile in 1879-1882.

The ships were refitted on a number of occasions during their life, the first being in the mid-1920s at Balboa in the Panama Canal Zone. During this refit the boilers were retubed and adapted for oil firing in place of the previous coal burning. During this refit six of the 6-pdr guns were removed. During the mid-1930s the ships returned to England for another refit at Yarrows. Here they were completely reboilered with only eight instead of the previous ten boilers. They were also rearmed and a new fire control system fitted. They were again rearmed in 1942-44 when the forward superstructure was rebuilt. During their later years the two vessels were used as depot and training ships and were removed from the fleet and scrapped in June 1958.

Name	launched	completed
Almirante Grau	3/1906	11/1906
Coronel Bolognesi	9/1906	3/1907

Displacement: 3180 tons (normal, *Coronel Bolognesi*), 3200 tons (normal, *Almirante Grau*) *Length:* 112.77 m (370 ft) pp *Beam:* 12.34 m (40 ft 6 in) *Draught:* 4.34 m (14 ft 3 in) max *Machinery:* 2-shaft vertical triple-expansion, 14 000 ihp=24 knots *Protection:* 38 mm (1½ in) deck; 76 mm (3 in) conning tower; 152 mm (6 in) gun shields *Armament:* (As built) 2 6-in (152-mm)/50-cal QF (2×1); 8 14-pdr (76.2-mm) QF (8×1); 8 6-pdr (37-mm) QF (8×1); 2 1-pdr QF (2×1); 2 18-in (46-cm) torpedo tubes (submerged, amidships): (After 1936) 2 6-in (152-mm)/50-cal QF (2×1); 6 14-pdr (76.2-mm) QF (8×1); 2 3-in (76-mm) AA (2×1); 4 20-mm AA (2×2); 5 mgs; 2 18-in (46-cm) torpedo tubes (submerged, amidships): (After 1944) 2 6-in (152-mm)/50-cal QF (2×1); 4 3-in (76-mm) (4×1); 2 3-in (76-mm) AA (2×1); 7 0.5-in (12.7-mm) Browning mgs; 1 Y gun; 2 depth charge racks *Crew:* 300

Corporal, Firestone Tire & Rubber

US short-range ballistic missile. Corporal, which carried the designations SSM-A-17, M2 and XM4E1 at various stages of development, was the United States' first ballistic missile. The weapon was developed by the Jet Propulsion Laboratory of the California Institute of Technology from early 1944 via the Private, WAC-Corporal, and Corporal E and F programmes.

Corporal was deployed by the US Army and the British Army in the mid-1950s, being intended to engage the enemy's rear areas in any weather. A missile battalion comprised 250 troops and technicians, a lightweight launch pedestal, erector, ground-based guidance equipment and support vehicles. Two batteries, each with five launchers, were assigned to a full battalion.

The missile was placed on its firing pedestal with the aid of a self-propelled hydraulic erector. Launch preparations took six or seven hours, and no more than two missiles could be fired in a day, so the choice of targets was limited. Corporal was tracked in flight by the ground-based radar, steering commands being transmitted by radio to correct minor deviations from the pre-set ballistic flightpath. The missile was replaced by Sergeant, which remains in service.

Length: 14 m (46 ft) *Span:* 1.9 m (6 ft 3 in) *Diameter:* 76 cm (30 in) *Weight:* 5443 kg (12 000 lb) *Range:* 120 km (75 miles) *Speed:* Mach 3 *Control:* graphite vanes in exhaust *Powerplant:* Ryan Aeronautical liquid rocket, monoethylaniline fuel and red fuming nitric acid oxidant, 9071 kg (20 000 lb) thrust, 60-second firing time *Guidance:* Ballistic with radio corrections *Warhead:* nuclear or high-explosive

Corrientes

Argentine destroyer class. The *Corrientes* was one of a class of seven destroyers built to the same design as the British 'G' Class for the Argentine navy. Like the British 'G' Class these destroyers were built with a single and double boiler room. The combining of the two boilers in a single space being necessitated by the reduced length—they were 1.8 m (6 ft) shorter than the earlier British 'C'-'F' Classes—which also entailed a slightly shorter engine room. The smaller boiler room was sited adjacent to the engine room to improve the sub-division of the hull.

The ships were named after territories in

Name	laid down	launched	completed
Buenos Aires	1936	9/1937	1938
Entre Rios	1936	9/1937	3/1938
Misiones	1936	9/1937	1938
Santa Cruz	1936	11/1937	10/1938
San Juan	1936	6/1937	3/1938
San Luis	1936	8/1937	1938

the Argentine Republic. The *Corrientes* was lost in a collision with the cruiser *Almirante Brown* on October 3, 1941. In 1956 the after set of torpedo tubes was removed from all ships in the class, and in 1971 the *Buenos Aires*, *Misiones* and *San Luis* were removed from the fleet. The rest of the class was withdrawn from service in 1973.

Displacement: 1375 tons (standard) *Length:* 98.45 m (323 ft) oa *Beam:* 10.59 m (34 ft 9 in) *Draught:* 3.25 m (10 ft 8 in) mean *Machinery:* 2-shaft Parsons SR geared turbines, 34 000 shp=35 knots *Armament:* 4 4.7-in (120-mm) (4×1); 8 0.5-in (12.7-mm) A/A (2×4), later replaced by 6 40-mm (1.57-in); 5 .303-in (7.7-mm) A/A (5×1); 8 21-in (53-cm) torpedo tubes (2×4) *Crew:* 130

Corsair, O2U series Vought

US scout and observation aircraft. In December 1925 Pratt & Whitney ran the first Wasp engine, an outstandingly modern air-cooled radial of 400 hp. The first aircraft

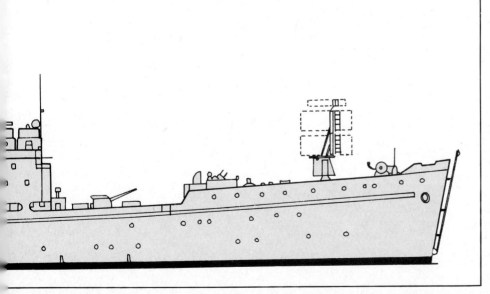

Corsair, F4U Vought

A Vought SU-2 Corsair US Navy scout and observation aircraft. Derived from the O2U Corsair, the new designation was adopted to indicate its role of scout fighter. The O2U Corsairs were used as fighter bombers during the American intervention in Nicaragua in 1927-28

Span: 10.97 m (36 ft 0 in) *Length:* (typical) 8.5 m (28 ft 0 in) *Gross weight:* 1700-1995 kg (3750-4400 lb) *Maximum speed:* 240-290 km/h (150-180 mph)

Corsair, F4U Vought

US Navy fighter. The XF4U-1 Corsair was ordered by the US Navy on June 30, 1938, and adopted the same name as two earlier Vought aircraft (the O2U-1 of 1926 and O3U of 1930). It was first flown on May 29, 1940, powered by an 18-cylinder 1850-hp Pratt & Whitney XR-2800-4 two-row radial engine. The original armament specification was for two 0.30-in (7.62-mm) machine-guns in the fuselage, one 0.50-in (12.7-mm) machine-gun in each wing. These were to be replaced by 23-mm (0.9-in) Madsen cannon if required and an internal bombload of 80 kg (176 lb) was to be carried in the wings. When the initial production contract for 584 F4U-1s was issued on June 30, 1941, this specification was changed first to two and later to three 0.50-in (12.7-mm) Browning machine-guns in each outer wing panel.

The production F4U-1, first flown on June 25, 1942, was of all-aluminium semi-monocoque construction, the fuselage comprising four sections. The engine section carried the 2000-hp Pratt & Whitney R-2800-8 Double Wasp powerplant. The forward fuselage section, with which the wing centre-section was integral, contained the self-sealing main fuel tank of 897 litres (237 US gal) capacity; the outer-wing leading-edge tanks could carry 238 litres (63 US gal) each,

designed for its use was an observation biplane ordered from Chance Vought by the US Navy as the O2U-1, two being bought in 1926. Notable for their efficient metal structure and fuselage of steel tubing with 'cheek' fuel tanks moulded to the skin profile, the O2U soon lost its pointed spinner and cross-axle landing gear, and a substantial proportion of the hundreds that followed were seaplanes or amphibians.

Most of the 1927 batch of 130 O2U-1 Corsairs had one fixed 0.30-in (7.62-mm) calibre gun and a second on a First World War Scarff ring in the rear cockpit. Many could carry up to 136 kg (300 lb) of bombs. In the Marine Corps action against Nicaraguan bandits in 1927-28 the new Wasp engine and Corsair proved the most reliable and satisfactory aircraft ever used by the Navy or Marines. A few also served successfully aboard the carrier *Langley*.

In 1928 there followed 159 O2U-2, -3 and -4 with detail changes, from which stemmed a vast range of O3U Corsairs. Many of these were powered by the larger 600-690-hp Hornet engine and were redesignated SU-1 to SU-4 to denote their role as scouts. From the O3U-2 the engine had a Townend ring cowl, the Scarff ring was eliminated and a dorsal fin was added, many sub-types having enclosed cockpits. Later models, such as the O3U-6 of 1934-35, had a fully cowled engine.

In December 1941 when the United States entered the Second World War, there were still 141 Corsairs on Navy/Marines strength, and a similar number of related Corsairs with Argentina, Brazil, China, Mexico, Peru and Siam. Several of the export variants, such as the Argentine V-80, were single-seat fighters. The V-80 had an enclosed cockpit and was equipped with interchangeable wheels and floats. It was powered by the R-1690 engine, while the V-99 and V-135 models had the 900-1000-hp Twin Wasp engine.

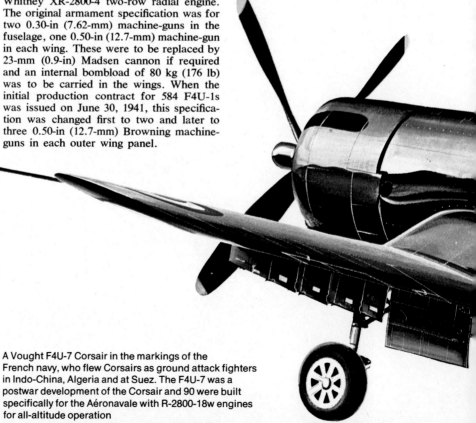

A Vought F4U-7 Corsair in the markings of the French navy, who flew Corsairs as ground attack fighters in Indo-China, Algeria and at Suez. The F4U-7 was a postwar development of the Corsair and 90 were built specifically for the Aéronavale with R-2800-18w engines for all-altitude operation

A US Navy Vought 02U-1 Corsair floatplane scout from the light cruiser USS *Raleigh* during a patrol on a naval exercise in the 1930s

and a drop-tank of 674 litres (178 US gal) could be carried under the fuselage. The mid-fuselage housed the cockpit, radio and navigation equipment, and the arrester gear attachments. The aft section carried the fin and stabilizer points, together with cutouts and fittings for the tailwheel and fairing doors.

Deliveries began on October 3, 1942. Most aircraft went to the Marine Corps and land-based Navy squadrons, as trouble with the landing gear, aggravated by the far-aft position of the cockpit, had been experienced

during test trials aboard the USS *Sangamon* in the preceding month. The unique inverted gull wing was designed to obviate the necessity for the ultra-long undercarriage legs which would otherwise have been required to provide deck clearance for the 4.01 m (13 ft 2 in) diameter propeller. The propeller was one of the biggest ever used up to that time, driven by the most powerful engine then to have been installed in a piston-engined fighter. The Corsair was the first production US warplane to exceed a speed of 644 km/h (400 mph) in level flight.

As the war in the Pacific advanced, two other companies were included in the production programme. Brewster built 735, designated F3A-1, before the factory was closed in 1944, and Goodyear completed 4007 as the FG-1/1A/1D. Total production of F4U-1 variants by Chance Vought amounted to 4699. A new raised cockpit hood design, to enhance pilot view while landing, was introduced on models being built by all three companies in August 1943.

F4U-1 133652

Corsair, F4U Vought

Vought

Vought's F4U-1C was introduced with four 20-mm (0.79-in) M2 wing cannon replacing the six machine-guns. The F4U-1D (Vought), F4A-1D (Brewster) and FG-1D (Goodyear) utilized the R-2800-8W water-injection engine and had provision for eight 5-in (127-mm) underwing rocket projectiles or a 907-kg (2000-lb) bombload. The Fleet Air Arm received 2012 aircraft (95 F4U-1s, 510 F4U-1As, 430 F3A1Ds and 977 FG-1Ds), designated Corsair I-IV respectively. Each wingtip was shortened by 20.3 cm (8 in) to facilitate stowage on British carriers. A further 370 F4U-1D Corsairs went to the Royal New Zealand Air Force.

Chance Vought became a separate division of United Aircraft Corporation in January 1943, and in that year 12 F4U-1s were modified by the Naval Aircraft Factory to become F4U-2s, bearing four wing-mounted 20-mm cannon and a radar scanner fitted into a fairing on the starboard wingtip. Another conversion was the F4U-1P, used for photo-reconnaissance missions.

On September 20, 1944, the first flight of the next (and final wartime) production model, the F4U-4 (Goodyear FG-4) took place. It was powered by an uprated Double Wasp R-2800-18W 'C' series engine of 2100 hp (2450 hp with water injection) and armed with six 0.50-in (12.7-mm) machine-guns in the wings and two 907-kg (2000-lb) bombs under the fuselage. Of the 6433 of these machines ordered, 2358 were built before production ended in 1947. Included in that number were 297 F4U-4Bs, with four 20-mm (0.79-in) cannon; nine photo-reconnaissance F4U-1Ps; and the F4U-4E and -4N Corsairs, fitted with APS-4 or APS-6 radar for night fighting. Goodyear produced five each of the F2G-1 and F2G-2 developed models with 3000-hp R-4360-4 Wasp Major engines.

The Corsairs in US service during the Second World War operated mainly from bases in the Pacific theatre. Given the nickname 'Whistling Death' by the Japanese, because of their highly individual engine note (caused by the air passing through the wing-root engine cooler inlets), the Corsairs lived up to this name by shooting down 11 enemy aircraft to every Corsair lost. Accounting for heavy enemy losses during Kamikaze attacks and the invasion of Iwo Jima and Okinawa, the Corsair was named 'The Sweetheart of Okinawa' by American pilots.

After the war, production continued with the F4U-5, powered by a 2300-hp R-2800-32W Double Wasp 'E' series engine and with a basic armament of four 20-mm (0.79-in) M3 cannon—two in each outer panel. Up to 726 kg (1600 lb) of bombs could be carried on each pylon and a further 907 kg (2000 lb) on the centreline rack, if this was not required for an additional fuel tank. The AU-1 (originally F4U-6) served with the US Marine Corps during the Korean War, and the F4U-7 with the naval air arms of France (94) and Argentina. The AU-1, of which 111 were built, was powered by a Chevrolet licence-built R-2800-83W engine and armed with four 20-mm (0.79-in) M3 cannon. The F4U-7 returned to the R-2800-18W powerplant, and

Corsair II, A-7 Vought

Left: A Vought A-7E Corsair II of the USS *Kitty Hawk* with six 227-kg (500-lb) bombs on each outer wing pylon. The Corsair II mounts a wide range of ordnance including one M61-A1 Vulcan 20-mm (0.79-in) cannon, air-to-air missiles, air-to-surface missiles, bombs, rockets, gun pods and drop tanks. *Background:* A-7Ds of the USAF, which has ordered 387 A-7Ds, while the Navy have 199 A-7As, 196 A-7Bs, 67 A-7Cs and 427 A-7Es. The similarity to the existing Vought F-8 Crusader is intentional: the US Navy wanted a replacement for the Skyhawk which could be produced cheaply and quickly, and this was done by adapting the Crusader design

all versions from the F4U-5 onwards were also fitted with rocket-firing equipment.

Total production of all Corsair variants by Chance Vought, which ended in December 1952, was 7829, making a grand total, with Brewster and Goodyear manufacture, of 12 571. The Corsair had thus the longest continuous production run of any US fighter of the Second World War, and it is generally conceded to have been the finest naval fighter used by any of the combatants during that period.

(F4U-4) *Span:* 12.49 m (40 ft 11¾ in) *Length:* 10.27 m (33 ft 8¼ in) *Gross weight:* 6654 kg (14 670 lb) *Maximum speed:* 718 km/h (446 mph)

Corsair II, A-7 Vought

US carrier-based light attack aircraft. Four companies—Douglas, Grumman, North American and Ling-Temco-Vought—responded to a set of US Navy operational requirements established in 1963 to find an

aircraft to replace the Douglas Skyhawk as a light attack machine. As it turned out, neither Douglas nor the eventual winner of the competition, Vought, could ever completely replace Heinemann's amazing little A-44, although the success of the A-7 Corsair II in the demanding conditions of the war in Vietnam has rightly earned it a place alongside the best known naval aircraft in history.

Vought won the initial contract in May 1964, and part of the reason for their success was the existence of the same company's F-8 Crusader. Because the US Navy wanted to keep costs to a minimum and needed the aircraft in a hurry they had stipulated that its new aircraft should be based on an existing design. Seven research and development A-7s were built, and they showed their lineage, although the design was smaller and, not being required to be supersonic, employed a non-afterburning version of the Pratt & Whitney TF30 engine which at that time produced 5148 kg (11 350 lb) of thrust.

In keeping with the subsonic speed, the

wing had somewhat reduced sweepback but mounted a total of six weapon pylons which, combined with two more hardpoints on the fuselage, allowed a maximum theoretical warload of 9072 kg (20 000 lb) to be carried, albeit with very considerably reduced internal fuel load. The wing also lacked the variable incidence of the F-8.

After a first flight on September 27, 1965, and a successful development programme, the first A-7As joined the squadrons in late 1966 and by about a year later were serving in Vietnam. Some 199 A-7As and 196 A-7Bs with higher-powered TF30 engines had been delivered to the USN by May 1969 and by this time the US Air Force had confirmed its interest in the type.

The USAF made two major modifications, substituting an Allison TF41 engine (in fact a slightly modified Rolls-Royce Spey built under licence) of 6464-kg (14 250-lb) thrust and installing very much more advanced electronics for navigation and weapon delivery. The system in the A-7D comprises a

Le Corse

Vought A-7D Corsairs of the USAF. The Corsair saw action in Vietnam where it was proved versatile and efficient and was popular with its pilots

forward-looking radar, digital computer, inertial navigation, moving map and, for the first time in a production combat aircraft, a head-up display with normal flight as well as weapon-delivery information. A laser search and tracking pod is planned for future installation on A-7Ds.

The change to the TF41 engine also made an impression on the US Navy, who decided to follow up the A-7B with the A-7E, equipped with virtually the same navigation and attack systems as the A-7D and powered by an even higher-rated engine producing 6804 kg (15 000 lb) of thrust. A land-based version of the A-7E, which nevertheless retains the naval type's folding wings, has been sold to the Greek air force, which operates 60 under the designation A-7H. These will not however be fitted with the forward-looking infrared pod being added to USN aircraft.

Although deliberately a single-seater from its inception, the Corsair II has also been developed into a tandem two-seat trainer, which can additionally be used for roles such as electronic countermeasures. Some 65 earlier model A-7s are being converted to TA-7C standard, with plugs in the fuselage both ahead of and behind the wing. All the equip-

ment and load-carrying capability of the operational aircraft can be retained. Although by the last quarter of the 1970s the production line was near to closing down, more than 1400 A-7s had been built and their combat record had endeared them to many pilots who discovered real precision weapon delivery with the help of the Corsair's systems.

Span: 11.8 m (38 ft 9 in) *Length:* 14.06 m (46 ft 1 in) *Maximum takeoff weight:* 19 050 kg (42 000 lb) *Maximum speed at sea level:* 1123 km/h (698 mph) *Maximum ferry range:* 4620 km (2870 miles)

Le Corse

French frigate class. Before the Second World War the French navy built many excellent destroyers and torpedo boats, but these all suffered badly from their lack of endurance. Experience gained in the war showed the excellence of the US destroyer escort type, examples of which served in the French navy. It was therefore logical that when the French started to rebuild their much-reduced navy after the war, their new

'escorteurs rapides' (frigates) should be influenced by the Dealey Class, the latest examples of destroyer escort building for the US Navy.

There were in fact to be two different French types, the E50 and E52, but as the only difference was in the arrangement of the armament they can be considered together. The first four built were of the E50 type, the *Le Corse* Class, in which the four sets of triple torpedo tubes for antisubmarine homing torpedoes were all forward, and the sextuple Bofors antisubmarine rocket projector aft.

The remaining ships, laid down somewhat later, were all of the E52 type, with the arrangement of torpedo tubes and projector reversed, and a different outfit of radar and sonar. The final three of this type were of the E52B variant with a new Strombos-Valensi funnel-cap, which had first been tried out in *Le Bordelais*.

Subsequent alterations included the fitting in the aftermost gun position of *Le Brestois* the new single 100-mm (3.9-in) gun mounting, developed jointly by France and Germany. This modification was retained but the twin Bofors 57-mm (2.24-in) mounting was never

ECP Armées

Le Bordelais, **French frigate of the** *Le Corse* **Class, also known as the** *Le Bordelais* **Class**

No and name	laid down	launched	completed	builders
E50 Group				
F761 *Le Corse*	10/1951	8/1952	4/1955	Lorient dockyard
F762 *Le Brestois*	11/1951	8/1953	1/1956	Lorient dockyard
F763 *Le Boulonnais*	3/1952	5/1953	8/1955	A & Ch de la Loire
F764 *Le Bordelais*	5/1952	7/1953	4/1955	Forges & Ch de la Mediterranée

No and name	laid down	launched	completed	builders
E52A Group				
F765 *Le Normand*	7/1953	2/1954	11/1956	Forges & Ch de la Mediterranée
F766 *Le Picard*	11/1953	5/1954	9/1956	A & Ch de la Loire
F767 *Le Gascon*	2/1954	10/1954	9/1956	A & Ch de la Loire
F768 *Le Lorrain*	2/1954	6/1954	1/1957	Forges & Ch de la Mediterranée
F769 *Le Bourguignon*	1/1954	1/1956	7/1957	Penhoët, St Nazaire
F770 *Le Champenois*	5/1954	3/1955	6/1957	A & Ch de la Loire
F771 *Le Savoyard*[3]	11/1953	5/1955	6/1956	Forges & Ch de la Mediterranée
F772 *Le Breton*[2,3]	6/1954	4/1955	8/1957	Lorient dockyard
F773 *Le Basque*[2,3]	12/1954	2/1956	10/1957	Lorient dockyard
F774 *L'Agenais*	8/1955	6/1956	5/1958	Lorient dockyard
F775 *Le Bearnais*[2]	12/1955	6/1956	10/1958	Lorient dockyard

No and name	laid down	launched	completed	builders
E52B Group				
F776 *L'Alsacien*[1,2]	7/1956	1/1957	8/1960	Lorient dockyard
F777 *Le Provencal*[1,2]	2/1957	10/1957	11/1959	Lorient dockyard
F778 *Le Vendeen*[1,2]	3/1957	7/1957	10/1960	Forges & Ch de la Mediterranée

[1]quadruple rocket launcher [2]different bridge arrangement [3]two gun mountings only

replaced. Some of the E52 Group also had one 57-mm (2.24-in) mounting removed and some were fitted with a four-barrelled rocket projector instead of the sextuple type.

Le Corse and *Le Bordelais* were removed from service in 1974 and *Le Brestois* in 1975. *Le Lorrain* was disarmed in 1975 and *Le Champenois* in 1976, and in the same year *Le Breton* and *Le Bourguignon* were placed in reserve. By early 1978 the *d'Estienne D'Orves* Class was entering service and it was thought that the remaining vessels in the *Le Corse* Class would be withdrawn.

Displacement: 1250 tons (standard), 1528 tons (normal), 1702 tons (full load) *Length:* 99.8 m (327 ft 5 in) oa *Beam:* 10.3 m (33 ft 9 in) *Draught:* 4.1 m (13 ft 5 in) maximum *Machinery:* 1-shaft geared turbine, 20 000 shp=28 knots *Armament:* 6 57-mm (2.24-in) (3×2); 1 6-barrelled 305-mm (12-in) A/S mortar, or 4-barrelled 375-mm (14.8-in); 12 53-cm (21-in) torpedo tubes (4×3), for K2 and L3 A/S torpedoes *Crew:* 171

Corvus

British chaff (Window) dispenser. The Knebworth Corvus 3-in (76-mm) chaff dispensing system was designed as a lightweight unit capable of providing immediate passive defence for surface vessels against surface-to-surface and air-to-surface radar-controlled missiles. The system originally comprised two 6-barrelled rocket-launchers (later versions are 8-barrelled) capable of dealing simultaneously with three missile attacks. These can be fitted in restricted upper deck areas, in all types of major warship down to destroyers and small frigates, as long as there is adequate space for training, loading and a clear arc of fire.

The system, which consists of a multi-barrelled rocket launcher, control and firing panel and chaff-dispensing rockets, is designed to deploy a number of chaff (antiradar) clouds around a ship threatened by missile attack. These clouds form a series of decoys to the radar homing device in the missile, and thus provide a variety of alternative 'targets' for the missile to home on. Different types of cloud pattern can be selected, depending on the form of threat posed.

The eight launching tubes are sited in two triple and twin sets, one above the other, the two lower sets being crossed at 90° in azimuth with the twin tubes aligned midway between the triple sets. The tubes are mounted on a cylindrical rotating structure which enables a training arc of 60° to 120° to be achieved, giving the angled triple tubes an effective arc of from 15° to 165°. The pedestal mounting is trainable through its 60° arc at fixed bearings of 15°.

The rockets holding the chaff are made of three sections comprising: 1) an electrically-fired solid-fuel motor; 2) a chaff head containing packs of chaff attached to the rocket motor by a tube, and 3) the nose with the fuze and head charge (a secondary rocket with two exhausts). At a predetermined moment the fuze ignites the head charge which with the nose and chaff head is ejected from the tube and main rocket motor. As the nose and chaff head emerge from the protective tube, pairs of packs of chaff are ejected into the atmosphere, where the exhaust from the

Cosmopolitan, Canadair

C & S Taylor

A Knebworth Corvus chaff dispensing system. The eight barrels can fire rocket rounds loaded with chaff or 'Window'. These strips of metallized foil are dispersed in the air around the ship and give a radar echo which confuses the guidance of enemy missiles

secondary rockets of the head charge breaks up the chaff packs and disperses it into the atmosphere.

The chaff or 'Window' has been designed for high-velocity dispensing from the rockets with a rapid cloud-forming capability, and is able to withstand high acceleration as it is ejected from the rocket. It thus provides rapid coverage over a wide area. There are a number of different chaff materials, such as silver metallized nylon filament, aluminium coated with lead-loaded paint and lacquer, or glass fibre coated with aluminium, fine copper etc. These are formed into different combinations of dipole size and shape to provide decoys against the various forms of missile homer which might be encountered.

Two new chaff-dispensing rounds were announced by Plessey Avionics in 1977. The first is a direct replacement for the existing 3-in (76-mm) RE Knebworth round used in the Corvus. Using the existing rocket-motor the new Plessey broad-band chaff (BBC) round has better resistance to corrosion, more efficient chaff-dispensing, greater payload and a broad-band ECM capability. Variable fuzing provides for dilution, dump and cen-

troid modes. The chaff-payload is supplied to meet wavelengths specified by the customer.

The second, shorter rocket is a broad-band chaff dispenser for use with the Vickers 105-mm (4.1-in) Seafan system, operating from fast patrol boats and other small warships. The Seafan system also uses infrared ammunition, and both rounds have a common motor and wrap-around fins to fit the smooth-bore launcher. Preselected fuzing on the chaff-rocket provides for dilution, dump and centroid modes, as with the bigger Corvus rocket.

The Corvus round can, only 2.5 seconds after bursting, and assuming a threat frequency of 25 mm (1 in), generate an estimated free-space echo-area of 1200 sq m (1435 sq yards), or 12 000 sq m (14 350 sq yards) with enhancement, resulting from a sea-surface multi-path echoing. The Seafan rocket will generate 250 sq m (300 sq yards), or 2500 sq m (3000 sq yards) with enhancement.

The quick-reaction Corvus launcher is manufactured by Vickers and is mounted in ships of the Royal Navy, French navy, Dutch navy and others.

Corvus launcher (Mk 2 version)
Calibre: 19.5 cm (7.68 in) *Length:* 160 cm (63 in) oa *Gross weight:* 584 kg (1288 lbs)

Corvus rocket (new BBC version)
Length: 158 cm (62.2 in) *Diameter of motor:* 76.2 mm (3in) *Diameter of chaff head:* 101.6 mm (4in) *Fin span:* 177.8 mm (7in) *Weight:* 22 kg (48.5 lbs)

Cosmopolitan, Canadair

Canadian military transport aircraft. Also called Canadair CL-66, Canadair 540 and (by the Canadian Armed Forces) CC-109, the Cosmopolitan was a turboprop development of the Convair 440 built at Montreal. The original engine was the 3500-ehp Napier Eland, and ten were bought by what was then the RCAF, the first flying on February 2, 1959. After Napier & Son was absorbed into Rolls-Royce the Eland was abandoned, and the RCAF replaced the British engines with Allison T56 installations similar to those of the C-130. In late 1978, seven Cosmopolitans were still serving as part of the equipment of CAF No 412 Sqn at Uplands, Ottawa.

HMS *Mohawk*, *Cossack* Class destroyer, on trials in the Solent. She has a turtleback forecastle, short fore funnel and no armament for her trials

Span: 32.2 m (105 ft 4 in) *Length:* 24.8 m (81 ft 6 in) *Gross weight:* 24 132 kg (53 200 lb) *Cruising speed:* 515 km/h (320 mph)

Cossack

British destroyer class. These ships, completed during 1907-10, were the first major destroyer class to be propelled by turbine machinery and to have completely oil fired boilers. They had a very high design speed of 33 knots, which most exceeded, but the specified gun armament of three 12-pdr, 3-in (76-mm) was completely inadequate. However, only the first group, the five ships of the 1905-06 Programme, were completed with this armament which was subsequently improved by the addition of two more 12-pdrs amidships.

The next two groups of the class (1906-07 and 1907-08 Programmes) were slightly larger than the first group, had more powerful machinery and were armed with two 4-in (102-mm) guns. Most of the class had four

funnels but the *Cossack*, *Afridi* and *Ghurka* had only three and the *Viking* was the only six funnelled ship ever built for the Royal Navy. Most had short square forecastles but *Mohawk*, *Tartar* and *Viking* were completed with turtleback forecastles.

Although intended as ocean-going destroyers, they had insufficient endurance for this function and were moreover bad sea-boats which rolled heavily and were very 'wet' forward. This latter problem was particularly bad in the *Mohawk* and prior to the First World War her turtleback was replaced by a standard square forecastle. They were reclassified as the 'F' Class in 1913 but were more commonly known as the 'Tribals'.

In 1914 the entire class was based at Dover as part of the 6th Destroyer Flotilla where all except *Mohawk*, which transferred to the Tees in 1918, remained until the end of the war. In 1916 concern about raids by enemy destroyers on the Dover Straits led to various proposals to improve the gun power of the Dover flotilla. The *Viking* was experimentally

fitted with a single 6-in (152-mm) gun but this proved to be unworkable in rough weather and was subsequently removed. The *Afridi* was fitted with two 4.7-in (120-mm) guns in place of her 12-pdrs and these were retained, but the other vessels of the class were not altered. Most of the class were fitted with a 6-pdr or 2-pdr AA gun and several were equipped with depth charge equipment during 1917-18.

Two of the class were lost during the war, both as a result of hitting mines; the *Maori* sank off the Belgian coast on May 7, 1915, and the *Ghurka* sank off Dungeness on February 8, 1917. In theory there was also a third vessel lost—on October 27, 1917. During an action with German destroyers off the Belgian coast, the *Nubian* had her bow blown off by a torpedo and her wreck drifted ashore on the South Foreland. Under normal circumstances she would have been a total loss but in November 1917 the *Zulu* had her stern blown off by a mine. As the two vessels were of the same general dimensions and design it was

HMS *Viking* after 1913, when the *Cossack* Class was redesignated the 'F' Class. *Viking* was the only six-funnelled ship built for the Royal Navy

decided to utilize the wrecks to build a new ship. The forward end of the *Zulu* was joined to the after end of the *Nubian* between the 3rd and 4th funnels, at Chatham dockyard. The new ship, now named *Zubian*, commissioned in June 1917 and on February 4, 1918, sank the submarine *UC50* in the Channel. The surviving units of the class were sold for scrap during 1919-21.

(1905-06 Programme: *Afridi, Cossack, Ghurka, Mohawk, Tartar*) *Displacement:* 850-880 tons *Length:* 76-82 m (250-270 ft) *Beam:* 7.5-7.9 m (24½-26 ft) *Draught:* 2.44 m (8 ft) *Machinery:* 3-shaft direct turbines, 14 500 ihp=33 knots *Armament:* 3 12-pdr, 3-in (76-mm) (3×1); 2 18-in (46-cm) torpedo tubes (2×1) *Crew:* 60

(1906-07 Programme: *Amazon, Saracen*) *Displacement:* 970 tons *Length:* 85.34 m (280 ft) *Amazon*, 82.9 m (272 ft) *Saracen Beam:* 7.92 m (26 ft) *Machinery:* 15 500 ihp=33 knots *Armament:* 2 4-in (102-mm) (2×1) *Crew:* 70 *Other details as 1905-06 Programme*

(1907-08 Programme: *Crusader, Maori, Nubian, Viking, Zulu*) *Displacement:* 998-1090 tons *Length:* 85.34 m (280 ft) *Beam:* 7.92-8.23 m (26-27 ft) *Other details as for 1906-07 Programme*

Cossack

British destroyer class. These ships were the 13th Flotilla of the Emergency War Programme and the 3rd group of the 'C' Classes. Ordered in July 1942 and laid down in 1943, they were of all-welded construction but in almost every other respect were repeats of the *Chequers* Class.

The *Contest* was the first all-welded destroyer built for the Royal Navy and her construction was carefully monitored in order to gain data and experience. Many parts of her hull were prefabricated beside the slip before being placed in position. The *Cockade, Contest, Cossack, Comet* and *Constance*, completed in late 1945, were fitted with a close-range armament of one twin 40-mm (1.57-in) Hazemeyer Bofors amidships, two 2-pdr singles abaft the funnel and a single 20-mm (0.79-in) in each of the bridge wings. The remaining three, completed in 1946, mounted a twin Mk V in place of the Hazemeyer and single 40-mm (1.57-in) Bofors in place of the 2-pdrs.

The *Constance* and *Comus* were sold for scrap in the mid-1950s but the remainder were taken in hand for modernization. Those vessels completed in 1945 had their close-range weapons altered to that of the vessels completed in 1946. All had the 20-mm (0.79-in) guns removed and two 'Squid' antisubmarine mortars fitted in place of X 4.5-in (114-mm) gun. The *Comet* and *Contest* were fitted for minelaying and also had Y 4.5-in (114-mm) gun and the torpedo tubes removed. The last six of the group were sold for scrap between 1961 and 1964.

Cockade, Comet—built by Yarrow
Comus, Concord—built by Thornycroft
Consort—built by Stephen
Constance, Cossack (hull only)—built by Vickers
Contest—built by White

Displacement: 1870 tons (standard) 2500 tons (full load) *Length:* 110.57 m (362 ft 9 in) *Beam:* 10.9 m (35 ft 9 in) *Draught:* 3.2 m (10 ft 6 in) *Machinery:* 2-shaft geared steam turbines, 40 000 shp=34 knots *Armament:* 4 4.5-in (114-mm) (4×1); 2 40-mm (1.57-in) (1×2); 2 2-pdr (2×1); 2 20-mm (0.79-in) (2×1); 4 21-in (53-cm) torpedo tubes (1×4) *Crew:* 186

Cougar, F9F6-8 Grumman

US carrier-based fighter-bomber and photographic reconnaissance aircraft. Grumman's first jet fighter, the straight-winged F9F Panther, gave rise to the Cougar, the first swept-wing fighter to serve aboard US Navy carriers. The last Panther variant was the F9F-5, and three XF9F-6 Cougar prototypes (first flight September 20, 1951) were produced by the relatively simple expedient of adding a 35° swept wing to the fuselage, powerplant and a tail unit of the Panther. Thus evolved a fighter of which 1985 were built for the US Navy and Marine Corps, some later variants continuing in service until the mid-1970s. The Navy's 'Blue Angels' acrobatic team flew Cougars from 1955-58. Cougars still in service in 1962 received new F-9 series designations, which are given in parentheses following the F9F designations.

Deliveries to the US Navy Squadron VF-32 began in November 1952 with the F9F-6 (F-9J), most of which were powered by a 3288-kg (7250-lb) static thrust Pratt & Whitney J48-P-8 turbojet engine, 3855-kg (8500-lb) static thrust with water injection. The fighter version was armed with four 20-mm (0.79-in) cannon in the nose, and could carry a 907-kg (2000-lb) bombload beneath the wings; also produced was an F9F-6P unarmed photographic reconnaissance version with an enlarged nose containing a battery of semi-automatic cameras. Total F9F-6/6P production was 706 aircraft. These were followed by 168 examples of the F9F-6 except for an Allison J33-A-16A engine of 2880-kg (6350-lb) static thrust or 3175-kg (7000-lb) static thrust with water injection.

In 1954, the F9F-7 was superseded in production by the improved F9F-8 (F-9J), first flown in prototype form on December 18, 1953. This reverted to the J48-P-8 engine, but introduced a 0.20 m (8 in) longer fuselage, with an under-nose radome and redesigned canopy, and larger-area wings with extended-chord outer panels—instead of leading-edge slats—and extended trailing edges.

A total of 712 F9F-8s were built, including 110 photographic F9F-8Ps (RF-9J; first flight August 21, 1955); a number of F9F-8Bs (AF-9J). The final Cougar production model (399 built, ending in December 1959) was the tandem two-seat F9F-8T (TF-9J) combat trainer, first flown on April 4, 1956, having an 86 cm (34 in) longer fuselage and only two 20-mm (0.79-in) nose guns. Although used principally by US Navy training squadrons, this version also saw combat service in Vietnam, carrying four Sidewinder missiles or six HVAR rockets on its underwing pylons. Cougars were phased out of first-line units by the end of 1960, but continued to serve with reserve units until the early 1970s.

(F9F-8) *Span:* 10.52 m (34 ft 6 in) *Length:* 12.88 m (42 ft 3 in) *Gross weight:* 9072 kg (20 000 lb) approx. *Maximum speed:* 1149 km/h (714 mph)

'County' British cruiser class (1903) See *Monmouth*

'County' British cruiser class (1904) See *Devonshire*

'County' British destroyer class See *Devonshire*

The Grumman F9F-6 was the first swept-wing jet fighter to serve aboard an American carrier. It first flew in 1951, saw action in Vietnam and remained in service with reserve units into the 1970s

Flight International

The former cruiser HMS *Courageous* after her conversion to an aircraft carrier, which was completed in 1928. This stern view gives an indication of the height of the new superstructure added to the original cruiser hull

Courageous

British aircraft carrier. During 1914-15 Admiral Sir John Fisher, the First Sea Lord, ordered over 600 warships under the Emergency War Programme for his 'Baltic Project'. This plan, which was abandoned when Fisher left the Admiralty, involved landing a large army on the Pomeranian coast of Germany for a direct assault on Berlin. Although its feasibility was open to considerable question, it was a most original plan and the precursor of the massive seaborne assaults of the Second World War.

Among the specialized ships constructed for this ambitious project were the 'large light cruisers' *Courageous*, *Glorious* and *Furious* which were intended, if Fisher is to be believed, as high speed shore-support vessels. They were large ships, later reclassified as battle-cruisers, and the sole reason for their original classification was to circumvent a ruling that no further capital ships should be constructed during the war. The requirements for these ships were that they should have high speed, to allow rapid deployment of their guns along the coast and escape from more heavily-armed but slower capital ships; shallow draught, enabling them to work in the inshore waters of the Baltic; the heaviest possible main armament; and the protection of a light cruiser.

In order to save time in design and construction, all three ships employed the same machinery design as that of the light cruiser *Champion* but with double the number of turbines, having four shafts instead of two, and 18 boilers instead of eight which increased the power from 40 000 to 90 000 shp. The boilers were of the small-tube type not previously employed in a large ship in spite of advocacy by the design department. Compared to the large-tube boiler they provided a substantial saving in weight and improved efficiency, but were more difficult to maintain and required more frequent atten-

tion. Minimal hull protection was provided by protective plating rather than armour, while underwater defence was provided by an integral bulge similar to those of the *Renown* and *Repulse*.

The *Courageous* and *Glorious* were armed with two twin 15-in (381-mm) turrets, one forward and one aft, while *Furious* was modified to carry two 18-in (457-mm) guns in single turrets. These armaments were reasonably adequate for shore bombardments, but were almost useless for all other purposes as the number of guns was insufficient for accurate salvo firing. In general, the class could best be described as costly errors of judgement. In their original role, they would certainly not have been as effective as Fisher thought, as he always greatly overestimated the destructive power of the big gun, while once the Baltic project was abandoned they no longer had a role to fulfil.

The *Courageous* was laid down by Armstrong Whitworth in March 1915, launched on February 5, 1916, and completed in January, 1917. She served initially with the 3rd Light Cruiser Squadron and then, with *Glorious*, joined the 1st Cruiser Squadron which acted as a spearhead to the fleet's scouting forces. She took part in the inconclusive action off Heligoland on November 17, 1917, but otherwise her war service was comparatively quiet.

During 1917 she was fitted with six pairs of 21-in (53-cm) torpedo tubes on the upperdeck, four abreast the after turret and two abreast the mainmast, which gave her a total torpedo armament of 14 21-in (53-cm) tubes, including the two submerged tubes with which she was built. In the same year she was fitted out to serve as a minelayer, having four sets of mine rails aft which earned her quarterdeck the nickname of 'Clapham Junction'. Other war modifications included the fitting of searchlight towers on the funnel and the erection of aircraft platforms on the roofs of both turrets.

After the war, the *Courageous* was attached for a short period to the gunnery school at Portsmouth and then became flagship of the Reserve Fleet. For a while her fate was open to question, but eventually it was decided that she, and *Glorious*, should be converted into aircraft carriers along similar lines to work already being carried out on *Furious*. For this purpose the two ships were, surprisingly, ideal, having the speed, protection and dimensions required for medium-sized carriers. Within a few years they were transformed from white elephants into valuable additions to the fleet.

The *Courageous* was converted at Devonport dockyard at a fairly leisurely pace between June 1924 and February 1928 at a cost of £2 025 800. The original superstructure and armament were removed and a new structure added over the full width of the ship and to a height of four decks. This structure was surmounted by a flight deck 180 m (591 ft) long and 30 m (100 ft) wide which, unlike that in *Furious*, carried an island superstructure on the starboard side through which the boiler uptakes passed.

The main hangar was immediately below the flight deck and opened out, at the forward end, onto a short flying-off deck known as the slip deck from which aircraft could be launched while others were landing on the main flight deck, above. The use of the slip deck was discontinued in about 1932 because it was too short for the new heavier aircraft types with which she was being equipped. Below the main hangar was a second, shorter, hangar which gave her a total capacity of 48 aircraft (six flights). For some years she and her sister had the largest aircraft capacity of any carrier in the British fleet.

She was the first carrier to be equipped with a system of multiple athwartship arrester wires which, although giving some teething trouble, proved to be very successful and subsequently became standard in all British carriers. Her new gun armament consisted

Courbet

entirely of 4.7-in (120-mm) AA weapons. It was considered that surface defence should be provided by her escort. The only modification made to the ship's hull protection was additional bulges on each side to improve underwater defence.

On completion of her reconstruction, the *Courageous* joined the Mediterranean Fleet. In 1930 she transferred to the Atlantic Fleet and in 1932 to the Home Fleet. During 1935-36 she was taken in hand for a major refit, including the fitting of two aircraft catapults at the forward end of the flight deck, compensating for the loss of use of the slip deck. She was also fitted with three eight-barrelled pom-pom mountings, one on each side of the slip deck and one abaft the island superstructure, two four-barrel 0.5-in (12.7-mm) machine-gun mountings, abreast the after end of the flight deck, and four AA directors, one at each corner of the flight deck, to control the 4.7-in (120-mm) armament. At the same time, her pole mast was converted into a tripod and the opening at the forward end of the main hangar, for access to the slip deck, was blanked off.

After her refit she served in the Home Fleet, but occasionally visited the Mediterranean. On the outbreak of war in September 1939, antisubmarine patrol groups were formed around each British carrier to search for U-Boats in the Western Approaches and the North Sea; the remaining vessels in each group being destroyers. On September 17, while returning from one of these patrols, she was torpedoed and sunk about 563 km (350 miles) west of Land's End by the German submarine *U 29*. She was hit by two torpedoes on the port side amidships and sank in about 20 minutes, taking about 500 of her crew with her. This disastrous event brought an abrupt end to the special antisubmarine groups which, apart from endangering Britain's valuable carriers, had achieved little against enemy submarines.

Displacement: 19 320 tons (normal load) 22 690 tons (full load) *Length:* 240 m (786 ft 3 in) *Beam:* 25 m (81 ft) *Draught:* 7 m (23 ft 4 in) *Machinery:* 4-shaft geared steam turbines, 90 000 shp=32 knots *Protection:* 76 mm (3 in) sides, 178-330 mm (7-13 in) gun positions, 25.4-44 mm (1-1¾ in) decks *Armament:* 4 15-in (381-mm) (2×2); 18 4-in (102-mm) (6×3); 2 3-in (76-mm) AA (2×1); 2 21-in (53-cm) torpedo tubes (submerged) *Crew:* 840

Displacement: (As an aircraft carrier 1928) 22 500 tons (standard) 26 500 tons (full load) *Beam:* 27 m (90 ft 6 in) *Draught:* 7 m (24 ft) *Machinery:* As before except speed 29.5 knots *Protection:* As before except no armour to gun positions. *Armament:* 16 4.7-in (120-mm) AA (16×1) *Aircraft:* 48 *Crew:* 1200 (including 460 Fleet Air Arm personnel)

Courbet

French battleship. The *Courbet* was one of a class of four Dreadnoughts, the first of this type to be designed for the French Navy in 1909-10. The standardized calibre chosen for the main armament was 12-in (305-mm), and 12 guns in twin turrets were mounted in A, B, X and Y positions with the other two turrets sited amidships to port and starboard. These ships mounted a much larger battery of secondary guns than some foreign contemporaries, but of smaller calibre. The French chose the smaller calibre because of the role of the guns as anti-torpedo boat weapons. This necessitated a high rate of fire for them to be effective, in this case 5-6 rounds per minute as against the 3½ rounds per minute of the heavier 6-in (152-mm) guns of the British Dreadnoughts.

By the end of the First World War the ships had become obsolete owing to lack of modernization during the war. In 1920, the *Paris* was experimentally fitted with an air-craft flying-off platform on B turret, similar to the platforms fitted in British battleships. Between 1926 and 29, the vessels were refitted when the two forward funnels were trunked into a single unit and the pole foremast replaced by a tripod. The bridge was also enlarged and extra AA guns added and the ships reboilered. However, this was insufficient to bring the ships up to the standard of the modernized battleships of Britain, Japan and the US, and the French

Name	laid down	launched	completed
Courbet	9/1910	9/1911	9/1913
France	11/1911	11/1912	7/1914
Jean Bart	11/1910	9/1911	6/1913
Paris	11/1911	9/1912	8/1914

The *Courbet* Class were the first French Dreadnoughts. The *Courbet* (below) was launched in 1911 and ended her career as a breakwater for the Mulberry harbour

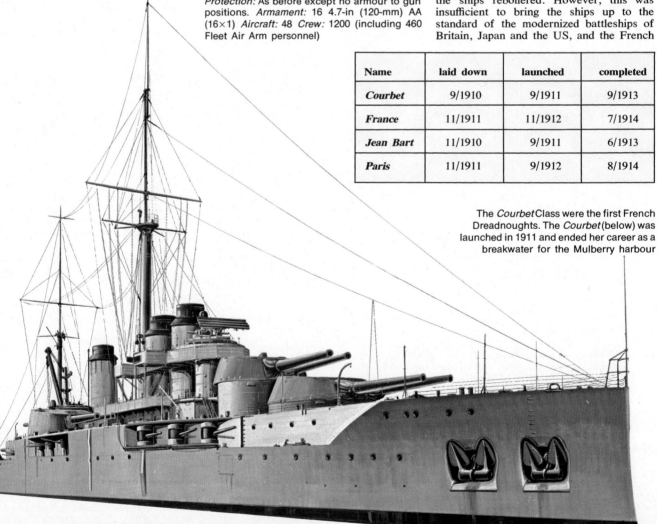

The British Convenanter light cruiser tank—Cruiser Mark V or A13 Mark III—saw almost no action during the Second World War, but was used as a training tank by British and Commonwealth troops

ships were withdrawn from operational service. They were then used as harbour training ships. The *France* had already been lost when she ran aground in Quiberon Bay on August 26, 1922. When the *Jean Bart* paid off in 1936 she was renamed *Ocean* so that her original name could be used for a new battleship under construction. *Courbet* and *Paris* escaped to Britain when Germany invaded France and were later used as harbour ships. The Germans captured the *Ocean* and used her as a target ship. *Courbet* was scuttled as a breakwater during the Normandy landings on June 10, 1944, while *Paris* was scrapped at the end of 1955.

Displacement: 22 189 tons (standard) *Length:* 167 m (548 ft) (oa) *Beam:* 27 m (88 ft 6 in) *Protection:* 273-mm (10¾-in) belt (amid), 184-mm (7¼-in) belt (ends), 50-mm (2-in) upper deck, 95-mm (3¾-in) main deck, 292-mm (11½-in) turrets, 279-mm (11-in) barbettes, 177-mm (7-in) casemates, 304-mm (12-in) conning tower. *Armament:* 12 12-in (305-mm)/45 cal. (6×2); 22 5.5-in (139-mm)/55 cal. (22×1); 4 47-mm (1.8-in) (4×1); 4 18-in (45-cm) torpedo tubes (underwater) *Crew:* 1108

Covenanter

British light cruiser tank, one of the series of 'Cruiser' designs of the early 1940s. Officially known as the Cruiser Mark V or A13 Mark III.

Covenanter was a development of the cruiser series and intended to be a 'heavy' cruiser by adding more armour to the earlier A13 design. Important innovations were the use of a Meadows flat-12 horizontally-opposed engine and a Wilson epicyclic steering gearbox. In the haste of early 1939, the Covenanter was ordered 'off the drawing board' without a pilot model being built and tested, and when the production models appeared in the summer of 1940, they were found to be defective in several respects. The engine cooling system was the principal problem and the vehicles had to be restricted to operation in temperate climates. Another defect lay in the complicated compressed-air control system for steering and transmission.

As a result, it was retained solely as a training tank and never used in combat. However, a bridgelaying version was built later and a few of these were used by

Australian troops in Bougainville, Solomon Islands, in 1945.

Length: 5.79 m (19 ft) *Width:* 2.62 m (8 ft 7 in) *Height:* 2.23 m (7 ft 4 in) *Weight:* 18 288 kg (18 tons) *Crew:* 4 *Engine:* Meadows flat-12 300-hp *Speed:* 50 km/h (31 mph) *Armour:* 7 to 40 mm (.27 to 1.57 in) *Armament:* 2-pdr gun and 7.92-mm MG. Some later converted to close support tanks and armed with 3-in (76-mm) howitzer

COW

British aircraft gun. Many of the most famous aircraft cannon—automatic guns firing explosive shells—used in both World Wars originated in the period 1909–14. One such was the COW gun, named after Coventry Ordnance Works where it was designed. From the start the most common calibre was 37-mm (1.46-in), but there were variations giving projectiles weighing from just over 454 kg (1 lb) to twice this mass. Most COW guns were fully automatic but firing at low cyclic rates around 100 rds/min, usually fed by a clip of five rounds directly above the breech.

The first installation was almost certainly in the Royal Aircraft Factory F.E.3 in 1913, and though the gun was almost certainly not fired in the air, it was tested satisfactorily while the pusher aircraft was suspended from a Farnborough hangar. By 1918 hundreds of COW guns had been flown, most being more powerful than the 1913 model. One of the drawbacks of the COW was its length, typically 1.8 m (6 ft 1 in). A normal bare gun weighed 90–100 kg (198–220 lb) and the recoil force in a fixed ground mount was often as great as 1000 kg (2200 lb) though this was said to be reduced in the air. Blast from the muzzle was extreme, and the axial pumping of the sprung barrel made it difficult to hold the aim while a whole clip was fired.

Notable COW fighters of the 1920s were the Westland Westbury, which had two guns in bow and dorsal cockpits, and the Vickers and Westland COW gun fighters built to the same F.29/27 specification with a gun fixed at an angle of some 55°. By this time, Vickers was promoting the gun as the Vickers-Armstrongs 37-mm (1.46-in) cannon, and designed special mountings and a 50-round

Courbet in December 1938. In 1940 she escaped to Britain and was used for harbour defence

Marius Bar

C.R.1, Fiat

Fiat C.R.1: extensive bracing was needed to support the greater weight of the lower wing

along with the final version, the C.R.20 A.Q. which replaced the A.20 used on previous production machines with a Fiat A25 engine. The C.R.20 saw combat in Libya and Ethiopia, while a number supplied to Austria in 1936 were taken over by the Luftwaffe in 1938 when Austria was occupied by Germany.

Span: 9.785 m (32 ft 1¼ in) *Length:* 6.58 m (21 ft 7 in) *Gross weight:* 1397 kg (3080 lb) *Maximum speed:* 280 km/h (174 mph)

C.R.25, Fiat

Italian fighter and reconnaissance aircraft. The C.R.25 was a large three-seat monoplane first flown in 1939 and powered by an 840-hp Fiat A.74 RC.38 14-cylinder radial engine. Two prototypes were produced and a single C.R.25D was used as personal transport by the Italian air attaché in Berlin, and nine C.R.25 bis were delivered to 173 maritime reconnaissance squadron. The armament of two 12.7-mm (0.5-in) Breda-SAFAT machine-guns in the nose and a single 12.7-

feed (the Westland F.29/27 had a 39-round drum). Probably the last installation was in the bow cockpit of the Blackburn Perth patrol flying boat.

CP-140 Canadian Armed Forces designation for Lockheed P-3 maritime patrol aircraft
See **Orion**

C.R.1, Fiat

Italian biplane fighter. The first of a series of Italian fighter designs by Ing Rosatelli, also responsible for the B.R. series of bombers, the C.R. (Caccia Rosatelli, or Rosatelli Fighter), was built by Fiat in 1923. An unequal-span biplane, with the lower wing considerably longer than the upper, the C.R.1 was powered by a 300-hp Hispano engine. The following year the fighter was ordered by the newly-formed Regia Aeronautica as the C.R.1, incorporating slight modifications and powered by a 450-hp Isotta-Fraschini Asso engine. Twin synchronized .303-in (7.7-mm) machine-guns were mounted in the engine cowling. The C.R.1 was delivered to the 1° Stormo Caccia (Fighter Group), and it remained in service for several years.

Span: 8.95 m (29 ft 4¼ in) *Length:* 6.24 m (20 ft 5¾ in) *Gross weight:* 5613 kg (12 374 lb) *Maximum speed:* 270 km/h (168 mph)

C.R.20, Fiat

Italian biplane fighter. First flown in 1926, the Fiat C.R.20 formed the bulk of Italian fighter strength during the late 1920s and early 1930s. Like the C.R.1 it was an unequal-span biplane, though this time the upper wing was the longer, with two synchronized .303-in (7.7-mm) Vickers machine-guns mounted in the engine cowling; power was provided by a 400-hp Fiat A.1. The C.R.20 entered production in 1926, and the following year was joined by the C.R.20B trainer and the C.R.20-I fighter seaplane built by C.M.A.S.A. The C.R.20 bis, with minor improvements, a slightly reduced wing area and lower top speed, entered production in 1929,

The Fiat C.R.20 (above) was the first aircraft adopted by the Regia Aeronautica's official display team. *Below:* **The C.R.30B two-seater which won the Coppa Principe Bibescu air race in 1932**

mm in a power-operated dorsal turret was considered too light, however, and the type was relegated to transport duties.

Span: 15.8 m (51 ft 10 in) *Length:* 13.56 m (44 ft 5¾ in) *Gross weight:* (C.R.25 bis) 6525 kg (14 385 lb) *Maximum speed:* 460 km/h (286 mph)

C.R.30, Fiat

Italian biplane fighter. The C.R.30 combined a 600-hp Fiat A.30 engine with a much cleaner fuselage and a great deal of streamlining to give much improved performance. It entered production in 1932 and became a standard Regia Aeronautica fighter, serving with the 2° Stormo Caccia as fighter and photo-reconnaissance aircraft in Libya as well as at home and with display teams. Numbers of the C.R.30B two-seat trainer were produced in 1932, and in 1934 a few C.R.30 Idro seaplanes were also built. Small numbers of C.R.30s were supplied to Austria, China and Paraguay in 1934-36, and a few of those in Italian service survived until 1943.

Span: 10.49 m (34 ft 5 in) *Length:* 6.68 m (21 ft 11 in) *Gross weight:* 1891 kg (4169 lb) *Maximum speed:* 349 km/h (217 mph)

C.R.32, Fiat

Italian fighter aircraft. Designed by Celestino Rosatelli and flown for the first time in 1933, the C.R.32 was virtually outdated as a fighter by the outbreak of the Second World War. However, 292 of these machines, together with 143 of the later C.R.42s, comprised more than 80% of the fighters available to the Regia Aeronautica at that time.

A robust and highly manoeuvrable biplane of sesquiplane construction, the C.R.32 retained the basic features of its earlier stable companions the C.R.20 and C.R.30. It was powered by a 600-hp Fiat A30 RA engine and carried an armament of two fixed, synchronized Vickers 0.303-in (7.7-mm) or Breda-SAFAT 12.7-mm (0.5-in) machine-guns firing through the propeller.

Three hundred and fifty C.R.32s were built and put into service from 1936 by the Italian Aviacion del Tercio and the Spanish Nationalists during the Civil War. Those in service with the Spanish were named Chirri.

This version was followed by 283 production models of the C.R.32 *bis* for the Regia Aeronautica, powered by the 600-hp Fiat A30, mounting 7.7-mm (0.303-in) Breda machine-guns in the lower wings and capable of a 100-kg (220-lb) bombload. From late 1936, the C.R.32 *ter* and the most numerous version, the C.R.32 *quater*, entered production for the Regia Aeronautica, 150 and 337 respectively being built for that service. These had improved gunsights and instrumentation, but reverted to the original armament because of the reduced performance caused by the extra guns on the heavier 32 *bis*.

On Italy's entry into the Second World War in June 1940, units of C.R.32 variants were operational on night fighter, close support and ground strafing missions, but they were gradually replaced by the C.R.42 Falco.

A total Italian production figure of 1212, of all models, included some 90-100 aircraft

Fiat C.R.32. Note the auxiliary fuel tank mounted on the centreline of the top wing

purchased by Austria, China, Hungary, Paraguay and Venezuela, and ended in the autumn of 1939. In Spain the Hispano-Suiza company built 1000 C.R.32 *quaters* in 1938-39 as HS-132Ls, 40 of which were eventually converted to two-seat C1 fighter trainers.

Span (C.R.32 *ter*): Upper 9.50 m (31 ft 2 in), Lower 6.14 m (20 ft 1¾ in) *Length:* 7.405 m (24 ft 3½ in) *Gross weight:* 1910 kg (4211 lb) *Maximum speed:* 355 km/h (220 mph)

C.R. 42 Italian (Fiat) fighter   See **Falco**

Crab

British mine-clearing vehicle. Based on the Sherman tank, this was probably the best such device employed during the Second World War.

Various methods of exploding mines by pressure were tested in Britain before the Normandy landings, and the most effective system was a rotating flail in front of a tank which thrashed the ground by lengths of chain attached to a rotating drum. This idea originated with a South African officer, Major A S du Toit, and flails were fitted to tanks in time for the Battle of Alamein.

In 1943, a Sherman flail, driven by the tank's engine instead of by auxiliary engines, was developed by the AEC company. The drive shaft came through the right-hand side of the hull, and the flail unit could be lifted and lowered hydraulically for use or for transport. The tank used was the M4A4 Sherman and some 600 vehicles were built. They were used in the Normandy landings and subsequently in northwest Europe.

In addition to the flail unit, the tanks were fitted with 'lane markers', hoppers on each

Sherman Crab I flail tank demonstrates its extremely effective mine-clearing technique

rear quarter which contained powdered chalk. This was dribbled out as the tank moved forward, so as to mark the extremities of the cleared path. Lights were also fitted at the rear for use when troops were following the tank in a night attack.

The only defect of the Crab was a tendency for the flails to miss a section of ground if the tank happened to rear up over an obstacle or undulation. To remedy this, the Crab II had an automatic contouring mechanism which held the flail at the correct height above the ground irrespective of the tank's attitude.

Crane/Bobcat Cessna

US trainer and utility transport. Cessna brought out the prototype T-50 five-seat cabin tourer (two 245-hp Jacobs L-4MB radials) in 1939 and built 40 before the Second World War. The first military order came in September 1940, from the Royal Canadian Air Force, for 640 to use as trainers in the Commonwealth Joint Air Training Plan. Their RCAF name was Crane 1.

In 1941, the USAAF had 33 At-8s (240 hp Lycoming R-680 radials) to train pilots of bombers and other multi-engined aircraft. The improved AT-17 Bobcat, a year later, had 245 hp Jacobs R-755-9 engines, which remained standard on all subsequent variants. Canada ordered 550 similar Crane 1As, but received only 182, the rest going to the USAAF as AT-17A/C/Ds (232) and UC-78Cs (136), differing only in internal equipment and military use. The AT trainer series was completed by 466 AT-17Bs. Extensive use was made of the Bobcat as a utility or staff transport, the latter known briefly—and unofficially—as Brasshats.

Cessna delivered 3313 UC-78/78A/78B/78Cs (including 67 US Navy JRC-1s and 17 impressed AT-50s), plus another 131 converted from AT-17s, bringing the total production to 5339 by 1944. Many Bobcats suffered from a weak main spar, and were limited to 2404 kg (5300 lb) gross weight.

Span (UC78): 12.78 m (41 ft 11 in) *Length:* 9.98 m (32 ft 9 in) *Gross Weight:* 2585 kg (5700 lb) *Maximum speed:* 314 km/h (195 mph)

Crate, Ilyushin Il-14

Russian piston-engined transport aircraft. The Il-14 was developed from the Il-12 Coach for service with Aeroflot and the Soviet Air Force, entering service in 1954. Compared with the Il-12, the Il-14 has uprated engines (ASh82Ts), a new wing and redesigned tail surfaces: some Coaches are thought to have been converted to Crates.

The military Il-14 has a strengthened floor and double doors on the port side of the rear fuselage, allowing freight to be carried, and is

fitted with observation blisters aft of the flight deck for use during paratroop operations. The An12 Cub began to replace Crates in 1959, but the Il-14 remained in service with the Soviet air force in comparatively large numbers for many more years. Production of the Coach/Crate series totalled at least 1200, with some sources giving a figure as high as 3500. The Il-14 was also built in East Germany and Czechoslovakia. Production in the Soviet Union ended in 1958, but the type still serves with a number of overseas air forces.

Span: 31.69 m (104 ft) *Length:* 22.3 m (73 ft 2 in) *Height:* 7.9 m (25 ft 11 in) *Powerplant:* two Shvetsov ASh82T 14-cylinder air-cooled radial engines, 1900 hp each *Cruise speed:* 310 km/h (192 mph) *Range:* 1300 km (808 miles) minimum *Max takeoff weight:* 18 000 kg (39 683 lb)

Grayford British aircraft rocket gun
See **Vickers**

CRDA Cant Italian aircraft See **Airone, Alcione, Cabbiano, Leone**

Crescent

British destroyer class. These ships were the last of the 'C' group and the final destroyer class of the Emergency War Programme, completing the 96 vessels (12 flotillas) whose design originated in the *Quilliam* Class ordered in 1940. They were laid down during 1943-44 and completed during 1945-47, none being finished in time to take part in the war. On completion the *Cromwell, Crown, Croziers* and *Crystal* were sold to Norway, and renamed *Bergen, Oslo, Trondheim* and *Stavanger* respectively. They were virtually unaltered until scrapped during the 1960s.

The *Crescent* and *Crusader* were transferred to the Royal Canadian Navy in 1945. In 1956, the *Crescent* was converted into a fast anti-submarine frigate at Esquimalt dockyard. This entailed rebuilding the superstructure, extending the forecastle deck and removing the original armament. A Limbo antisubmarine mortar was fitted aft, 2 3-in

(76-mm) AA guns (1×2) added and 2 4-in guns (102-mm) (1×2) mounted on the forecastle. In 1960, the *Crusader* was fitted with an experimental variable depth sonar aft, Y gun being removed. Shortly afterwards this gear was transferred to the *Crescent*, which also had her Limbo removed and three homing torpedo launchers fitted. Both the Canadian vessels were scrapped in the early 1960s.

The only two to join the Royal Navy, *Creole* and *Crispin*, were converted to antisubmarine training ships during 1948-49, both having B gun replaced by a W/T cabin. In 1956, they were sold to Pakistan, but were refitted by Thornycroft before transfer in 1958; B gun was reinstated and X gun was replaced by two 'Squid' antisubmarine mortars.

Crispin, Creole—built by White
Cromwell, Crown—built by Scotts
Crescent, Crusader—built by J Brown
Croziers, Crystal—built by Yarrow

HMS *Hogue* in 1902. Twelve years later she was one of three *Cressy* Class cruisers to be sunk in the North Sea by a single German submarine. *Hogue* was sunk by two torpedoes fired from a range of only 275 m (300 yards), so close that the submarine had to execute swift manoeuvres to avoid collision with the target ship

Displacement: 1870 tons (standard) 2500 tons (full load) *Length:* 110 m (362 ft 9 in) *Beam:* 10.9 m (35 ft 9 in) *Draught:* 3.2 m (10 ft 6 in) *Machinery:* 2-shaft geared steam turbines, 40 000 shp=34 knots *Armament:* 4 4.5-in (114-mm) (4×1); 6 1.57-in (40-mm) (1×2+2×1); 4 21-in (533-mm) torpedo tubes (1×4) *Crew:* 186

Cressy

British cruiser class. During the late 19th century all the cruisers constructed for the Royal Navy were 'protected cruisers', as their vitals were protected by a thick arched steel deck. The alternative was the 'armoured cruiser', in which the principal protection was vertical side armour, additionally giving security to the ship's hull.

Unfortunately, the weight required for the latter was much greater and would have resulted in ships of excessive cost and size. However, the development in the 1890s of face-hardened steel armour, which could provide adequate protection with thinner and therefore lighter plates, made the construction of armoured cruisers a feasible proposition.

The *Cressy* Class were the first British cruisers constructed for the Royal Navy since the *Orlando* class of 1886. They were fitted with a 152-mm (6-in) thick belt of Harvey armour, 70 m (230 ft) long and 3.5 m (11 ft 6 in) deep enclosed at the ends by 127 mm (5 in) thick bulkheads. A 25.4 mm (1 in) thick deck was fitted across the top of this 'citadel' while across the bottom the arched deck of the protected cruiser was retained but with the thickness reduced to 38 mm (1½ in). The total weight of the armour was 1100 tons.

In most other respects they were generally similar to the 1st class protected cruisers of the period. They were primarily intended for trade protection at a time when France was looked upon as Britain's most likely adversary. Rapid developments in naval technology and the shift of emphasis to warfare in the North Sea quickly rendered the design obsolete.

The six ships of the class were laid down in 1898-99, launched in 1899-1901 and, except for *Euryalus*, completed during 1901-02. This latter ship was beset by accidents—first her launch was delayed by damage to the dock at Barrow, she was then damaged by fire while fitting out and when docked for repairs, slipped off the blocks and received severe underwater damage. She finally commissioned in 1904, after needing further repairs following a collision at Devonport in 1903.

In August 1914 all except *Sutlej* were commissioned for service with the 7th Cruiser Squadron, with the principal duty of patrolling the southern North Sea and eastern entrance to the Channel. It was soon realized that they were very vulnerable in this area. Steps taken to modify the situation were too slow and too late to prevent one of the worst naval disasters of the war.

On September 22, while patrolling the Broad Fourteens off the Dutch coast, the *Aboukir* was torpedoed by the submarine *U9*. The two vessels in company, the *Hogue* and *Cressy*, were ordered to close their sinking sister ship to pick up survivors. As they stopped, they too were torpedoed by *U9*. All three ships went to the bottom, taking 1459 men of the 2200 on board with them. The event was made even more tragic by the fact that the majority of the crews were naval reservists.

For the remaining three the war was fairly uneventful. The *Bacchante* and *Euryalus* went to the Mediterranean in 1915 and took part in the Dardanelles operation. In 1916, the *Euryalus* became flagship of the East Indies station and in 1917 *Bacchante* joined the 9th Cruiser Squadron off West Africa, where both remained until 1918. The *Sutlej* served in home waters until 1916 when she transferred to the 9th Cruiser Squadron until relieved by *Bacchante*. During 1917-19 she was employed as an accommodation ship and then a depot ship (renamed *Crescent*) at Rosyth. All three were sold for scrap during 1920-21.

Aboukir, Cressy—built by Fairfield
Bacchante, Sutlej—built by J Brown
Euryalus, Hogue—built by Vickers

Displacement: 12 000 tons (navy list) *Length:* 144 m (472 ft) *Beam:* 21 m (69 ft 6 in) *Draught:* 7.6 m (25 ft) (mean) *Machinery:* 2-shaft triple expansion steam engines, 21 000 ihp=21 knots *Protection:* 152 mm (6 in) sides, 76 mm (3 in) deck, 152 mm (6 in) guns *Armament:* 2 9.2-in (233-mm) (2×1); 12 152-mm (6-in) (12×1); 14 12-pdr (14×1); 2 45-cm (17.7-in) submerged torpedo tubes (2×1) *Crew:* 615

Cristobal

Dominican submachine-gun. The Cristobal SMG was produced for a short time in the Dominican Republic in a state-owned arms factory set up by the President in an attempt to bring work to his impoverished country. The prospect foundered in the internal revolution and destruction of the early 1960s and only small numbers of this interesting weapon were completed. There are accounts

Cristobal Colon

that some were sold to countries in South America, but hardly any have been located.

The Cristobal owed much to the Beretta designs, several of whose workmen went to the Republic to set up the factory. Although firing from an open bolt, as with almost all blowback guns, the Cristobal had a form of delayed blowback, using a two-part bolt and an accelerating lever to move the heavier part. This particular device is a prewar Hungarian invention and it was necessary since the Cristobal fired the 0.30-in (7.62-mm) US carbine cartridge, which is more powerful than the usual pistol ammunition used in smgs. This round was probably used in the hope of obtaining a longer effective range, but is too light to make it much better than a 9-mm (0.35-in) Parabellum pistol round.

The first guns had a long wooden stock much like the Beretta model 1938, and the same two triggers for single shot and automatic. A later model in 1962 had a cut down stock and metal forehand guard, and occasionally a folding butt. It was a gallant attempt to make a different type of smg, but it was an almost total failure.

Length: 945 mm (37.2 in) *Weight:* 3.51 kg (7 lb 11 oz) *Operation:* Blowback with delay *Magazine:* 30-round box *Ammunition:* .30 in (7.62 mm) M1 US Carbine *Muzzle Velocity:* 563 m (1847 ft) sec *Rate of fire:* 575 rpm

Cristobal Colon

Italian armoured cruiser class, built in Italy by Ansaldo as one of the *Garibaldi* Class. Of the ten ships of this type built between 1894–1904, only three served in the Italian navy. Four, including the original *Giuseppi Garibaldi*, went to Argentina; two, also originally intended for Argentina, went to Japan; and *Cristobal Colon*, which was laid down for the Italian navy as the first replacement *Giuseppi Garibaldi*, was bought by Spain.

Cristobal Colon, which was laid down in 1895 and launched on September 16, 1896, was urgently needed by Spain because of the threat of war with the US over Cuba.

Spain was desperately short of large modern warships, and *Cristobal Colon*, had she been completed, would have been the equal of any American cruiser. The *Garibaldi*s were the first cruisers to use the new Krupp armour which gave protection to large areas of their side against any but the largest shells, while carrying an armament little smaller than that of some battleships. They were well-designed ships, instantly recognizable because they had a single mast midway between the two funnels. Most were armed with a single 10-in (254-mm) gun forward and a twin 8-in (203-mm) turret aft, but some, including *Cristobal Colon*, had a single 10-in (254-mm) turret fore and aft.

Unfortunately, the Spanish needed *Colon* so soon that they could not finish the 10-in (254-mm) guns in time. Although she carried the turrets, the guns were never mounted. She was commissioned on May 16, 1897, and sailed almost immediately for Cuba. With the rest of the Cuba squadron, she was blockaded in Santiago harbour by the Americans. On July 7, 1896, she took part with *Teresa, Vizcaya* and *Oquendo* in the final ill-fated sortie. Armed only with her medium and light guns, she could do no serious damage to the American squadron, and was shot to pieces by the *Brooklyn*. She sank in shallow water with heavy loss of life.

Displacement: 6840 tons (normal) *Length:* 100 m (328 ft) *Beam:* 18.2 m (59 ft 8 in) *Draught:* 7.6 m (25 ft) *Machinery:* 2-shaft steam triple expansion, 13 000 ihp=20 knots *Protection:* 150 mm (5.9 in) side and main turrets *Armament:* 2 10-in (254-mm); 10 6-in (152-mm); 6 4.7-in (120-mm); 10 2.24-in (57-mm); 10 1.46-in (37-mm); 5 45-cm (17.7-in) torpedo tubes (submerged) *Crew:* 543

Crocodile

British flame-throwing tank modification applied to Churchill and Sherman tanks. Flame-throwing equipment was principally developed in Britain by the Petroleum War-fare Department, and their first vehicle-mounted device was the 'Cockatrice'. After demonstrations of the PWD pressure-operated equipment, the General Staff outlined a requirement for a flame-thrower mounted on a Churchill tank, to have a range of 73 m (80 yards) and a flame duration of not less than one minute. Twelve pilot models were ordered in July 1942.

In the following month a change of policy led the War Office to cancel the requirement, but PWD continued their work, convinced that there was a need for a flame tank. In April 1943, their persistence was vindicated with an official recognition of the need, recognition which was largely due to the success which PWD had had with their design. In August an order for 250 Crocodiles was placed, later increased to 1000, of which some 800 were built before the war ended. The equipment remained in service for several years after the war.

Crocodile consisted of a Churchill M7 tank fitted with a flame projector in place of the hull machine-gun. A 6½-ton armoured trailer carried 1818 litres (400 gal) of flame-thrower fluid, five pressure bottles of nitrogen, and the necessary valves, connection and controls. The trailer was connected to the tank by a link unit which acted both as a towing connection and as a flexible pipeline for the flame fluid. If the trailer was hit by enemy fire or otherwise damaged, the link could be severed by a quick-release device and the trailer dropped, after which the tank could continue in action as a normal combat tank.

The flame projector could achieve a range of about 109 m (120 yards) with a favourable wind, though 73-91 m (80-100 yds) was the more usual figure. There was sufficient fuel to allow 80 seconds of fire, either as one continuous burst or in several smaller shots.

Seeing the success of the Churchill Crocodile, the US Army requested a similar design for the Sherman tank. PWD developed one, but there were several difficulties, notably the refusal of the Americans to give

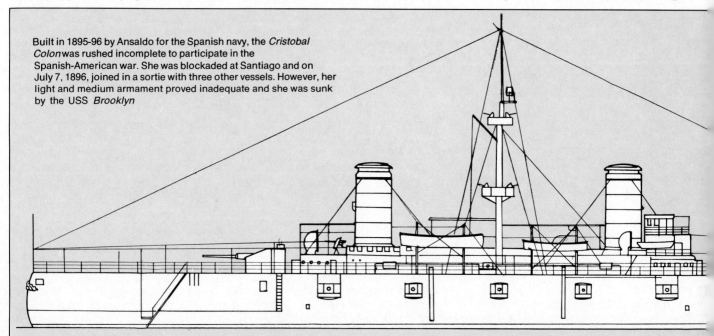

Built in 1895-96 by Ansaldo for the Spanish navy, the *Cristobal Colon* was rushed incomplete to participate in the Spanish-American war. She was blockaded at Santiago and on July 7, 1896, joined in a sortie with three other vessels. However, her light and medium armament proved inadequate and she was sunk by the USS *Brooklyn*

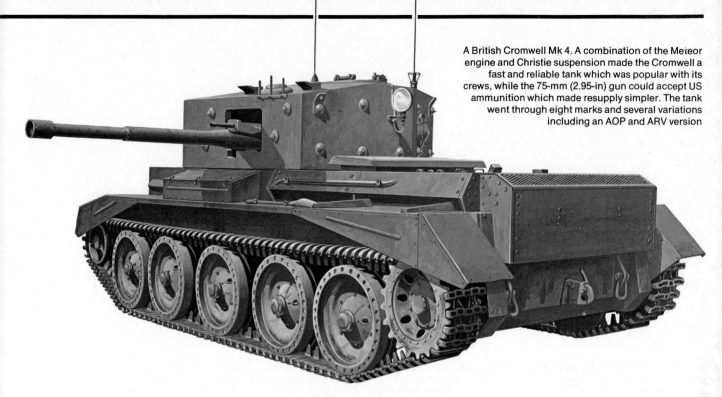

A British Cromwell Mk 4. A combination of the Meteor engine and Christie suspension made the Cromwell a fast and reliable tank which was popular with its crews, while the 75-mm (2.95-in) gun could accept US ammunition which made resupply simpler. The tank went through eight marks and several variations including an AOP and ARV version

up the hull machine-gun to allow the flame gun to be mounted, as in the Churchill. Eventually the projector was externally mounted on a platform, and protected by an armoured housing. Six were built, but the project lapsed in late 1944 due to lack of interest in the US. Four were issued to the US Army and operated in Germany, but most of America's flame requirements were met by loaning them Churchill Crocodiles.

Cromwell

British cruiser tank. Introduced in 1944, this was also known as the A27 or Cruiser Mk VIII. In 1941, Leyland Motors suggested a tank design using an adapted Rolls-Royce Merlin aero-engine. The idea was accepted but, since there was a shortage of the Rolls-Royce engines (called 'Meteor' in this application), they were asked to go ahead with two designs. One used a Liberty engine until Meteors were available, and one had the Meteor engine as the 'long-term' object. The Liberty-engined project became the Centaur and the Meteor-engined model the Cromwell.

In fact, the two were identical, since the early Centaurs were designed for the Meteor engine and then modified to take the Liberty as a temporary measure; once Meteors were available, the engines were changed and they became Cromwells. Production of Cromwells began in January 1943.

Cromwell used the Christie suspension and, with the Meteor engine, had an impressive turn of speed and good manoeuvrability. Moreover, the new engine proved to be much more reliable than some of the engines used in earlier tanks, which gave the Cromwell a good reputation. Armament was the standard 6-pdr gun at first, but this was later replaced by a new 75-mm (2.95-in) gun of British design which could use American ammunition, a compromise which simplified ammunition supply in the European theatre.

Several variant models of Cromwell appeared: **Mk 1** Original early 1943 production with 6-pdr gun and 2×mgs; **Mk 2** Mk 1 with wider tracks and the hull front machine gun removed; **Mk 3** Centaur Mk 1 refitted with Meteor engine; **Mk 4** Centaur Mk 3 with Meteor engine; **Mk 5** Welded hull instead of riveted, and fitted with 75-mm (2.95-in) gun; **Mk 6** Close support tank, fitted with 95-mm (3.7-in) howitzer in turret; **Mk 7** Mk 4 with added armour and wider tracks; **Mk 7W** Mk 4 modified as for Mk 7; **Mk 8** Mk 6 modified as above; **Cromwell AOP** Armoured observation tank for artillery forward observers. Fitted with a dummy gun and extra radio equipment, externally indistinguishable from the fighting tank; **Cromwell ARV** Armoured recovery vehicle. Turret removed, fitted with crane, winch, etc, for recovering damaged gun tanks under fire.

Length overall: 6.400 m (21 ft) *Width:* 3.048 m (10 ft) *Height:* 2.514 m (8 ft 3 in) *Weight:* 27 941 kg (27.5 tons) *Crew:* 5 *Power unit:* Rolls-Royce V-12, 600 bhp *Speed:* 61 km/h (38 mph) *Range:* 130-278 km (81-173 miles) *Armour:* Hull 25-63 mm (1-2½ in); Turret 63-76 mm (2½-3 in) *Armament:* 6-pdr gun or 75-mm (2.95-in) gun; one or two 7.92-mm (0.312-in) machine-guns

Crotale, Thomson-CSF/Matra R440

French low-level surface-to-air missile. Development of Crotale was partially sponsored by South Africa, by which the system is known as Cactus. The weapon has since been adopted by France's *Armée de l'Air* and by additional export customers. By mid-1977 some 35 of the 50 or so systems on order had been delivered.

A typical target for a Crotale battery would be a fighter-bomber with a fluctuating radar cross-section of 1.2 m² (13 ft²) flying at Mach 1.2 at a height between 50 m (165 ft) and 3000 m (9842 ft) in any weather. The aircraft may be manoeuvring at up to 2g while diving at 20° to attack a target 1.6 km (1 mile) behind the missile battery.

A typical battery comprises four electrically propelled 12-tonne Hotchkiss-Brandt wheeled vehicles. One carries a Thomson-CSF S-band pulse-Doppler surveillance and target-designation radar and the other three each mount four missile launcher/containers. The search-radar antenna rotates at 60 rpm and transmits two stacked beams, allowing the target's height to be measured in addition to range, bearing and speed. Typical targets flying at speeds between 135 m/sec (300 mph) and 1440 m/sec (3200 mph) can be detected at ranges of up to 18.5 km (11.5 miles). A digital track-extraction and target-evaluation unit detects up to 30 targets and can track and evaluate 12 of them simultaneously. Target information is supplied to the firing units by land line or over a radio link.

The launcher vehicles are surmounted by a

Cruiser Tanks

A Thomson-CSF/Matra R440 Crotale (Rattlesnake) streaks from its mobile launcher. The booster has just burned out but the flame is still visible

turret which carries a target-tracking radar antenna with two container/launchers on either side. The J-band radar acquires and tracks its target, and a missile can be launched six seconds after the initial detection by the surveillance radar.

The round is accelerated out of the container by a single-stage solid-propellant rocket motor which burns for 2.3 sec and boosts the missile to its top speed of Mach 2.3. An infrared sensor mounted on the turret detects radiation from flares on the missile, allowing its off-boresight angle to be measured so that the round can be gathered on to the radar sightline. Steering commands are transmitted over a microwave link to bring the missile into the radar's 1.1° beam. The remainder of the engagement is carried out by radar command-to-line-of-sight guidance: the radar can track two missiles simultaneously in addition to the target by means of transponders mounted in the round. Television tracking is available as a back-up.

A development of Crotale known as Shahine (Hunting Falcon) has been ordered by Saudi Arabia for delivery from 1980. The wheeled vehicles are replaced by AMX30 tank chassis, the number of launchers carried by each fire unit is increased to six to lengthen the interval between reloadings, and the surveillance radar is fitted with a broader antenna. Beamwidth is reduced from 3.5° to 1.4° in azimuth to improve target discrimination. Minor improvements to the missile extend its range to 10 km (6 miles), the new round being designated R460.

The French *Marine Navale* has ordered more than 20 units of Crotale to defend its new warships. The number of launchers on each turret is again increased, this time to eight, and some minor alterations are incorporated. The weapon system is planned to enter service in mid-1978 aboard the *Georges Leygues,* which is acting as trials ship.

Length: 2.93 m (9 ft 7 in) *Span:* 54 cm (21 in) *Diameter:* 15.6 cm (6.1 in) *Weight:* 85 kg (187 lb) *Min/max range:* 0.5/8.5 km (0.3/5 miles) *Min/max altitude:* 50/3600 m (164/11 811 ft) *Speed:* Mach 2.3 *Powerplant:* SNPE "Lens" single-stage solid rocket, 2.3 sec burn time, 4850 kg (10 692 lb) (thrust) *Warhead:* 15 kg (33 lb) fragmentation with infrared proximity fuze

Cruiser Tanks

Series of British tanks developed 1936-39. In 1936, General Wavell, on a military mission, visited the Soviet army manoeuvres and saw the performance of the BS series of tanks, based on the American designs of Walter Christie. In October of that year a Christie experimental tank, the M1932, was purchased, christened the A13E1, and placed on test.

It should be understood that prewar British policy was based on experience in the First World War and envisaged large, well-protected, slow-moving 'infantry' tanks to accompany the foot soldiers in the assault. The Tank Corps, however, were insistent that such tanks should be supported by lighter, fast-moving tanks which could strike into the enemy's rear area; these received the name 'cruiser tanks' from the naval analogy. With the growing threat of war in the middle 1930s, this point of view was finally accepted and a design sought, which led to the purchase of the Christie tank.

However, work had started before that with the A9 series, designed by Carden and made by Vickers-Armstrong. This used a small-wheel suspension and was the first British tank to mount the new 2-pdr gun. Although unsatisfactory in many respects, there was nothing better on the market and 125 were ordered in 1937, to become the Cruiser Mk I.

A similar design was put forward at the same time, but with more armour. The object was a better-protected tank to act in close support of infantry. After trials, it was realized that the slight amount of added armour did not make it sufficiently well protected for this role, and so it became a 'heavy cruiser'. Some 170 were ordered as the Cruiser Mk II.

During this time the A13 Christie had been evaluated and Nuffield Mechanization were given the task of developing a service tank around the Christie suspension. While Christie's tanks were fast and lively, they had insufficient room in them to be practical fighting vehicles, hence the need to redesign. The first model used 14 mm (0.5 in) of armour and mounted a 2-pdr gun in the turret. This added weight, plus early problems with the

engines and transmissions, led to a great deal of trouble in development. Nevertheless, a production order was given in January 1938, for the Cruiser Mark III and 665 were eventually made. An improved model, the Cruiser Mk IV had 30 mm (1.18 in) of armour without detracting greatly from the performance.

The next step in the progression was Cruiser Mk V, which became known as the Covenanter. The Cruiser Mk VI was Crusader.

The next major design was the Cromwell, but as an interim measure while this was being developed, the Cruiser Mk VII or Cavalier was designed. This was based on the Crusader design but had thicker armour and a new turret which carried a 6-pdr gun. Although accepted for service, it was only used as a training vehicle.

The Cromwell was the last combat tank in the cruiser series, but there were other developments. Challenger was a lengthened Cromwell mounting a 17-pdr gun in an unwieldy turret; Charioteer was a Cromwell hull with a Centurion's gun; and the abortive A33 design was a heavy cruiser using Cromwell components but with 152 mm (6 in) of frontal armour and a 75-mm (2.95-in) gun; three were built in 1944, but the idea never went further.

The final cruisers, Cromwell and Centaur, were successful and reliable vehicles, though in truth they were obsolescent before they reached the battlefield. The earlier models had a long and dismal history of mechanical troubles, partly due to bad design and partly to the unfamiliarity of the crews with the complex degree of maintenance demanded. Most of the trouble stemmed from the fact that design and manufacture were not separated by a period in which pilot models could be made and the mechanical problems thoroughly explored. Because of the worsening political situation, the project was ordered off the drawing board, in the hope that during the production period the worst of the defects could be remedied. In some cases, this happened. However, no action was taken to correct many minor points, until the tanks had been in service for some time, and the crews lost confidence in their vehicles. In the eyes of many critics the war in the desert was won in spite of the Cruiser tank.

Crusader

British cruiser tank. This was the last of the prewar designs and the original version was employed entirely in North Africa. Crusader was developed by Nuffield Mechanization as a 'heavy cruiser', to the same broad specification which had produced the Covenanter.

The Nuffield design retained the Christie suspension of its forerunners and incorporated several features of the Covenanter. The hull, however, was lengthened and an extra pair of road wheels fitted. An auxiliary turret was fitted in the hull, alongside the driver, to mount a 7.92-mm (0.312-in) BESA machine-gun; alongside this turret was a similar structure, non-rotating, which was the driver's vision hood, and this also carried a BESA machine-gun. The turret, as with the Covenanter, was of diamond section, the sides being acutely angled to deflect shot. The main armament was the 2-pdr gun, but later marks were fitted with the 6-pdr.

The whole cruiser series had a history of mechanical troubles stemming from poor design and insufficient development, and the Crusader inherited many of these, notably the compressed air control of steering and transmission, poor turret ventilation, and cooling problems. The auxiliary turret was discovered to be a danger to its occupant because of lack of ventilation and was removed with the driver's machine-gun.

The first Crusaders were sent to Egypt in 1941 and went into action in the abortive Operation Battleaxe in June. With the 2-pdr gun it was outclassed by the German tanks and suffered accordingly. Later versions with the 6-pdr gun appeared late in 1942, in time for action at Alamein. It was also used in Tunisia, and was withdrawn at the end of the North African campaign.

The following variant models existed: **Mk 1** Original version with auxiliary turret. Basic 40 mm (1.57 in) of armour; **Mk 2** Armour improved to basic 50 mm (1.9 in); **Mk 3** 6 pdr gun, no auxiliary turret; **Crusader Command** Normal tank with gun replaced by a dummy and additional radio equipment; for brigade and divisional headquarters; **Crusader OP** Similar to the command tank, mounting a dummy gun and extra radio, and used by artillery forward observers; **Crusader AA** Three versions existed: the AA Mk 1 mounted a single 40-mm (1.57-in) Bofors gun in place of the turret; Mks 2 and 3 had twin 20-mm (0.79-in) Oerlikon in' the modified turret; **Crusader ARV** Turret removed, crane and winch fitted; **Crusader Gun Tower** Turret removed and hull modified to an open-topped form so as to carry eight men and 40 rounds of 17-pdr gun ammunition, the gun being towed behind. Less stressed and less hard worked than the tank, this modification served well and remained in service almost until the end of the war; **Crusader CS** Close support version, mounting a 3-in (76-mm) howitzer in place of the 2-pdr gun.

Length: 5.98 m (19 ft 7½ in) *Width:* 2.64 m (8 ft 8 in) *Height:* 2.23 m (7 ft 4 in) *Weight:* 19 300 kg (19 tons) *Crew:* 5 *Power unit:* Liberty V-12 petrol, 340 bhp *Speed:* 44 km/h (27.5 mph) *Range:* 235-320 km (146-200 miles) *Armour:* Hull 14-30 mm (0.55-1.18-in); Turret 24-50 mm (1-2 in) *Armament:* 2-pdr gun, replaced by 6-pdr; Coaxial 7.92-mm (0.312-in) mg; Auxiliary turret 7.92-mm (0.312-in) mg, later removed.

Crusader

British destroyer class. The four ships of the *Crusader* or C Class were ordered under the 1929 programme, laid down in 1930, launched in 1931 and completed in 1932. Originally there were to have been eight, following the standard practice of the time, but the number was reduced to four by the Labour Government as an economy measure following the Wall Street crash of 1929.

Their design was much the same as that of the preceding *Beagle* Class except that oil fuel stowage was increased from 390 tons to 470 tons which increased their endurance from 7724 to 8834 km (4800 to 5500 miles) at 15 knots. They also carried a new main armament director and a somewhat unusual split bridge. The forward section of this bridge consisted of a wheelhouse with the compass platform on its roof and the after section of a charthouse surmounted by the director and rangefinder. Later in their careers, the gap between the two was bridged by joining the compass platform to the director platform. As completed, they carried a 3-in (76-mm) AA gun between the funnels, but in 1936 this was replaced by 2 single 2-pdr pom-poms.

On completion, all were commissioned for service in the 2nd Destroyer Flotilla. In 1937-38, they were transferred to the Royal Canadian Navy, the *Crescent, Cygnet, Crusader* and *Comet* being renamed *Fraser, St Laurent, Ottawa* and *Restigouche* respectively.

In 1940, the after bank of torpedo tubes was replaced by a 12-pdr AA gun and the mainmast was removed. Later quadruple 0.5-in (12.7-mm) gun mountings replaced the 2-pdr guns, 2 20-mm (0.79-in) guns were added and Y gun removed to increase the space available for depth charge equipment. By the end of war, the surviving units were armed with 2 4.7-in (120-mm) (2×1) guns in A and X positions, 2 6-pdr (1×2) and a 'hedgehog' antisubmarine weapon in B position, and 6 20-mm (0.79-in) (6×1) AA guns, the 12-pdr and 0.5-in (12.7-mm) guns having been removed. They were also fitted with radar and HF/DF equipment, the aerials for the latter being mounted on a stump mainmast.

The majority of the ships' wartime service was on Atlantic escort duties. Two of the class were lost, the *Fraser* was sunk in an accidental collision with the cruiser *Calcutta* off Bayonne on June 28, 1940, and the *Ottawa* was torpedoed by the *U 91* while escorting a convoy in the Gulf of St Lawrence on September 9, 1942. The *St Laurent* assisted in the sinking of two submarines, the *U 356* on December 27, 1942, and the *U 845* on March 10, 1944. The *St Laurent* and *Restigouche* were sold for scrap in 1945.

Fraser, St Laurent—built by Vickers Armstrong
Ottawa, Restigouche—built by Portsmouth dockyard

Displacement: 1375 tons (standard) 1880 tons (full load) *Length:* 100.2 m (329 ft) *Beam:* 10 m (33 ft) *Draught:* 2.6 m (8 ft 6 in) *Machinery:* 2-shaft geared steam turbines, 36 000 shp=35½ knots *Armament:* 4 4.7-in (120-mm) (4×1); 1 3-in (76-mm) AA; 8 53.3-cm (21-in) torpedo tubes (2×4) *Crew:* 145

Crusader, F-8 Vought

US carrier-based fighter/interceptor. The F-8 Crusader was in many ways to the US Navy what the North American F-100 was to the US Air Force, although it surprised many people when it demonstrated that, in spite of being a carrier-based aircraft with all that entails in terms of complexity and weight, it could out-perform the land-based type using the same Pratt & Whitney J57 afterburning engine. The Crusader was remarkable, too, for its variable-incidence wing which hinged upwards around the rear spar, at the same time automatically drooping the ailerons, one section of the flaps and all of the leading edge.

The wing characteristics were developed in the pursuit of slower, and thus safer, carrier-

A Crusader AA Mk 2, with twin 20-mm Oerlikon cannon, which was deployed in Normandy

Crusader, F-8 Vought

A rebuilt Vought F-8J Crusader banks above its parent carrier USS *Enterprise.* The Crusader went through a wide range of variations, sub-types and some 446 were cycled through a conversion and updating programme between 1967 and 1970. Total production, including both the F-8 fighter and the RF-8 reconnaissance aircraft was 1261. A versatile aircraft, the Crusader mounted four 20-mm (0.79-in) Colt Cannon in the fuselage nose, and four Sidewinders externally on the fuselage. Late production F-8Es have underwing pylons for attack weapons including two 454-kg (1000-lb) or 907-kg (2000-lb) bombs, four 225-kg (500-lb) bombs, twelve 113-kg (250-lb) bombs or 24 Zuni rockets with eight more replacing the Sidewinders

Crusty, Tupolev Tu-134

A Vought F-8U-3 Crusader III comes in to land, with a Sidewinder missile visible in its position on the forward underside of the fuselage

approach speeds while still giving the pilot a good view over the nose—something he would have lost if the fuselage angle of attack had risen with that of the wing. Yet the F-8 was the first shipboard aircraft capable of exceeding Mach 1 in level flight, a speed it reached on its maiden sortie on March 25, 1955.

Exactly two years later the first day interceptor F-8A entered squadron service, powered, after delivery of the first few aircraft, by a J57 producing 7348 kg (16 200 lb) of afterburning thrust and capable of a maximum speed of Mach 1.67. Some 318 were built, in addition to 144 RF-8A photo-reconnaissance versions in which cameras replaced the four Colt-Browning cannon and fire-control equipment, before production switched to the F-8B which had limited all-weather capability by virtue of a small radar scanner in the nose. Production of F-8Bs ran to 130 before the higher-powered F-8C was substituted on the line, in 1958. This version ran to 187 by 1960 when it was replaced by the F-8D, which embodied a number of improvements.

Standard armament for the A, B and C model Crusaders had been two Sidewinder missiles, four cannon and folding-fin rockets. The F-8D had provision for two more Sidewinders in place of the rockets and a push-button autopilot as well as more fuel. Thrust from the J57 was by now up to 8164 kg (18 000 lb) with afterburning, which allowed carrier-based gross weight to be increased from a normal 12 500 kg (27 558 lb) to about 14 500 kg (32 000 lb). Deliveries of 152 took until January 1962.

The final production version for the US Navy proved to be the most numerous, 286 F-8Es being delivered by mid-1964. All-weather performance was again upgraded, this time by the installation of an APQ-94 radar, larger and more powerful than its predecessor. Furthermore, underwing pylons were added allowing the carriage of bombs or Bullpup air-to-surface missiles in addition to

the air-to-air armament. A substantial number of F-8Bs, Cs, Ds and Es were refurbished and updated during the 1960s to become, respectively, F-8Ls, Ks, Hs and Js. Among the modifications was the addition of boundary-layer control for even better low-speed performance and handling.

The only export customer for the Crusader was France, which ordered 42 for use aboard her two aircraft carriers. Because of the small size of these ships, the F-8E(FN)s of the French Navy embodied several modifications to the wing, including two-part leading-edge flaps, trailing-edge flap-blowing, doubled aileron and flap deflection and a 2° reduction in the angle, by which wing incidence can be changed. The overall result is a 27 km/h (17 mph) reduction in approach speed. Like the USN's F-8E, the French navy aircraft have multiple missions although they are primarily still retained for interception duties.

Span: 10.72 m (35 ft 2 in) *Length:* 16.61 m (54 ft 6 in) *Maximum takeoff weight (from land):* 15 422 kg (34 000 lb) *Maximum speed:* Mach 1.7 *Maximum range:* 2253 km (1400 miles)

Crusty, Tupolev Tu-134

Russian turbofan transport aircraft. The Tu-134 was originally planned as a derivative of the Tu-124, and was designated Tu-124A, but in the event the type emerged as virtually a new design. The rear-engined, T-tail layout popular with Western designers at the time was adopted for the Tu-134, which has replaced 118 Coots on many services.

The basic Tu-134 entered service with Aeroflot in 1967 and was followed in 1970 by the stretched Tu134A, with maximum accommodation increased from 72 passengers to 80. A 37-seat VIP version is used to transport high-ranking Russian civilian government and military personnel, and the type is used by the air forces of Czechoslovakia, Hungary and Poland.

Span: 29 m (95 ft 2 in) *Length:* 34.35 m (112 ft 8 in) *Height:* 9.02 m (29 ft 7 in) *Powerplant:* 2 Soloviev D-30 turbofans, 6800 kg (15 000 lb) thrust each *Cruise speed:* 750 km/h (466 mph) *Range:* 2400 km (1500 miles) *Max takeoff weight:* 44 500 kg (98 105 lb)

CS2F Canadian armed forces' designation for De Havilland Canada-built Grumman S-2 ASW aircraft   See **Tracker**

CSS-1

Chinese medium-range ballistic missile. The CSS-1 (Chinese surface-to-surface missile No 1), thought to resemble the Russian SS-4 Sandal, is reported by the United States Department of Defense to have been in service since 1966. The liquid-fuelled missile is not emplaced in siloes, but its launch pad is thought to be partially protected against blast. The weapon can also be transported from one launch site to another to reduce the likelihood of it being destroyed in a pre-emptive attack.

Estimates of the number of CSS-1s in service vary between 30-40 to more than 90; the weapon may be replaced by the CSS-2 IRBM.

Range: 1000-1800 km (621-1118 miles) *Warhead:* nuclear, possibly 1 MT

CSS-2

Chinese intermediate-range ballistic missile. CSS-2 (Chinese surface-to-surface missile No 2) has been operational with the Second Artillery of the Chinese People's Liberation Army since 1971, according to the United States Department of Defense.

The single-stage, liquid-propellant missile is deployed in western China on semi-hardened above-ground launch pads and is transportable. Up to 30-40 may be in service, with the most recent rounds possibly replacing interim-standard CSS-1 mrbms. The CSS-2, which resembles the Russian SS-5 Skean, is thought to have formed the first stage of China's original satellite booster.

Range: 2400-2800 km (1500-1740 miles) *Warhead:* nuclear, 1 MT

CSS-3

Chinese limited-range intercontinental ballistic missile. This first-generation liquid-fuelled ICBM is thought to have been operational in north-west Sinkiang since late 1975. The weapon, which is silo-launched, probably uses the CSS-2 IRBM as its first stage with the addition of one or more likely two further stages. The CSS-3 (Chinese surface-to-surface missile No 3) is thought to be capable of reaching the European Soviet Union with a relatively small payload, but probably not with the three-megaton thermonuclear warhead designed for China's extended-range ICBM.

Range: about 6500 km (4000 miles) *Warhead:* thermonuclear, probably 3 MT over reduced ranges

CSSX-4

Chinese intercontinental ballistic missile. CSSX-4 (Chinese experimental surface-to-surface missile No 4) is a full-range ICBM which began flight trials at the end of 1976. Development from first flight trial to operational deployment is likely to take three years. Chinese ICBM development has been slow and painful. A launch facility was built at Shuang-ch'eng-tzu as early as 1965, and since then the United States Department of Defense has regularly predicted imminent testing of an ICBM. However, the facility was dismantled in 1968-69 and not rebuilt until February 1970.

US reports indicate that CSSX-4 has two or three stages and uses liquid propellants. Other sources postulate that the weapon may comprise the limited-range CSS-3 ICBM with an additional stage to extend its range and raise maximum payload. China is also known to have built a plant to produce solid propellants.

Range: 11 000 km (6845 miles) *Warhead:* thermonuclear, 3 megaton

Cub, Antonov An-12

Russian transport aircraft. The An-12 was developed from the civil An-10A as the Soviet air force's standard paratroop and logistics aircraft, entering service in 1959. Cub differs from its predecessor in having a redesigned rear fuselage fitted with an integral loading ramp which can be lowered for delivery of loads while in flight. The hold measures 13.5 m (44 ft 4 in) by 3 m (9 ft 10 in) by 2.4 m (7 ft 10 in) and the floor is stressed for loads of 1500 kg/m² (307 lb/ft²). The built-in gantry can lift 2300 kg (5070 lb).

Typical loads include the ZSU-23-4 Shilka self-propelled 23-mm (0.9-in) quadruple antiaircraft cannon, PT-76 amphibious light tank, ASU-57 or ASU-85 self-propelled assault guns, the BRDM-1 reconnaissance vehicle and BTR-60 or BTR-152 armoured personnel carriers. A compartment aft of the flight deck can accommodate up to 14 crew members for these vehicles. Alternatively up to 100 paratroops may be carried.

The normal flight crew comprises five members, and a sixth may be carried to operate the rear turret containing twin NR-23 23-mm (0.9-in) cannon. A Gamma-A tail-warning radar is fitted and the I-band Toad Stool is used for navigation.

More than 900 An-12s have been built, and some two-thirds of these serve with the Soviet air force. Cubs make up nearly half the Russian military air transport fleet and can carry two army divisions, comprising 14 000 troops and their equipment, over a radius of 1200 km (750 miles). The Cub C variant is used by the Soviet air force and Navy on ECM (electronic countermeasures) duties. Tail-mounted electronic equipment housed in a fairing replaces the gun turret and additional pods are faired into the forward fuselage and belly.

An-12s have been supplied to a number of overseas air arms, one of those acquired by Egypt being used to flight-test the Helwan E-300 turbojet.

Span: 38.0 m (124 ft 8 in) *Length:* 33.1 m (108 ft 7 in) *Height:* 10.53 m (34 ft 6 in) *Ceiling:* 10 200 m (33 464 ft) *Max takeoff weight:* 61 000 kg (134 500 lb) *Powerplant:* four Ivchenko AI-20K turbo-props, 4000 ehp each *Cruise speed:* 550 km/h (340 mph) *Range:* 3600 km (2237 miles) with max payload of 20 000 kg (44 000 lb)

An Antonov An-12 Cub unloads plant for an atomic power station under construction in eastern Siberia. The twin 23-mm (0.9-in) cannon are not mounted in this Aeroflot Cub, but the tail cockpit position for the gunner is retained

Cuckoo, Sopwith T.1.

A Sopwith T.1 Cuckoo drops a 454-kg (1000-lb) Whitehead torpedo during a training exercise. It was a stable, sturdy aircraft with good slow-flying handling qualities

Cutaway illustration of a Sopwith Cuckoo. The Cuckoo resulted from a request by Commodore Murray Sueter for a deck-launched torpedo bomber in a land-plane configuration. The Cuckoo served with the RAF and the Fleet Air Arm on *Argus, Eagle* and *Furious*. The naval version had folding wings to facilitate stowage

Cuckoo, Sopwith T.1

British torpedo bomber. Stemming from a variety of torpedo-dropping aircraft tested and used from 1914, the 'Sopwith T.1 Torpedo Aeroplane'—its official title—resulted directly from an explicit request by Commodore Murray Sueter in October 1916, who asked designers for a deck-launched torpedo bomber in land-plane configuration. The prototype Sopwith T.1 was completed in mid-1917 and given the serial N74, but production of the Cuckoo (as it was dubbed in 1918) was slow, due mainly to the inexperience of the design's subcontracted manufacturers.

The Sopwith-built prototype was powered by a 200-hp Hispano-Suiza engine, but production versions were mainly fitted with the 200-hp Sunbeam Arab. Later, experimental versions used a 200-hp Wolseley Viper or 275-hp Rolls-Royce Falcon III powerplant. Production Cuckoos were initially delivered to the Navy in early 1918. By October 31, 1918, 69 Cuckoos were in service and by the Armistice, of the 350 machines contracted for production slightly more than 150 had been brought on service charge.

In performance, carrying a single 454-kg (1000-lb) Whitehead torpedo, the Cuckoo proved to be a stable, sturdy design, with excellent slow-flying handling qualities. For stowage aboard ships the wings incorporated a folding mechanism. In service use, the type was eventually issued to RAF Squadrons Nos 185, 186 and 210, while others served aboard the aircraft carriers *Argus*, *Eagle* and *Furious*.

In 1921 a British Air Mission was despatched to Japan (Britain's ally in 1914-18) to set up the Imperial Japanese naval air service, and took with it six examples of the Cuckoo. Subsequently Mitsubishi produced the Mitsubishi 10 ship-borne torpedo bomber—a virtual carbon copy of the Cuckoo, attributable to the fact that the head of the Japanese firm's design team was Herbert Smith, ex-chief designer for Sopwith.

Span: 14.25 m (46 ft 9 in) *Length:* 8.68 m (28 ft 6 in) *Height:* 3.25 m (10 ft 8 in) *Maximum speed:* 165 km/h (102.5 mph) at 1980 m (6500 ft) *Gross weight:* 1761 kg (3882 lb)

Calatafimi, Italian destroyer of the *Curtatone* Class, sunk by the Greek submarine *Pipinos*

Curl, Antonov An-26

Russian transport aircraft. Curl was developed from the An-24RT in the 1960s as a replacement for the Il-14 Crate and entered service in 1969. The rear fuselage has been redesigned to incorporate a two-position door which can be lowered to form a loading ramp or swung forward under the fuselage for loading from trucks.

Curl can accommodate vehicles such as the GAZ-69 or UAZ-469 and may be fitted with tip-up seats along the walls to cater for 40 paratroops. The aircraft can be converted in the field for the paratroop role, or to accommodate 24 stretcher patients. This conversion takes from 20-30 minutes. The An-26 can use rough fields and has been exported to a number of air forces, including several in the Warsaw Pact.

Span: 29.2 m (95 ft 9½ in) *Length:* 23.8 m (78 ft 1 in) *Height:* 8.575 m (28 ft 1½ in) *Ceiling:* 8100 m (26 500 ft) *Max takeoff weight:* 24 000 kg (53 000 lb) *Powerplant:* 2 Ivchenko AI-24T turboprops, 2820 ehp each *Cruise speed:* 435 km/h (270 mph) *Range:* 900 km (560 miles) with 4500 kg (9900 lb) payload

Curtatone

Italian destroyer class, built 1920-24. Four improved *Palestro* Class were ordered on December 31, 1916, at the same time as the other group. The design was modified by the navy and Orlando, with a longer and slightly narrower hull, the same machinery, and a better layout of armament. In place of the four single 4-in (102-mm) guns of the earlier design they were given two twin 4-in (102-mm)/45-cal mountings, the first destroyers in the world with this feature. Another improvement was triple 17.7-in (45-cm) torpedo tubes on the centreline in place of twin mountings on the beam.

The machinery was identical to the *Palestro* Class, two-shaft French Zoelly turbines with steam supplied by four Thornycroft boilers. In spite of the slightly heavier weight

of armament, the longer and finer hull-form gave one extra knot of speed; the *Curtatone* reached 33.6 knots on trials in light condition, but the class were good for 28 knots at sea under normal conditions. All four were built by Orlando at Livorno (Leghorn), and were reclassified as torpedo-boats in 1938.

The class comprised *Curtatone*, launched in March 1922; *Castelfidardo*, launched in June 1922; *Calatafimi*, launched in March 1923; *Monzambano*, launched in August 1923.

During the Second World War the 3-in (76-mm) AA guns were replaced by 20-mm (0.79-in) Breda guns, and 8-mm (0.315-in) machine-guns were added. The two German units, *TA.16* and *TA.19* (see below) were partially rearmed with two sets of twin 21-in (53-cm) torpedo tubes and six single 20-mm (0.79-in) AA guns. The *Monzambano* was rearmed in 1946-47 with single 4-in (102-mm) guns, one forward and one aft, and five single 20-mm (0.79-in)/65-cal AA guns, and also received a twin 21-in (53-cm) torpedo tube in place of the two triple 17.7-in (45-cm). She also received two single Menon depth-charge mortars, mounted on deck aft.

Three of the ships suffered the usual disasters of the Regia Navale. The *Curtatone* was mined in the Aegean on May 20, 1941, during the attack on Greece. The *Calatafimi* and *Castelfidardo* were both captured in the Piraeus on September 9, 1943, at the time of the Italian surrender, and became the German *TA.19* and *TA.16* respectively. The former was torpedoed on August 9, 1944, by the Greek submarine *Pipinos*, while her sister was sunk by rockets from British aircraft at Heraklion, Crete, on June 2, 1944. The *Monzambano* survived the debâcle of September 1943, and served as an escort with the Allies, running between North Africa and Sicily. After 1945 she was attached as a seagoing tender to the Naval Academy, until stricken in April 1951.

See also *Palestro* Class.

Displacement: 876.3 tonnes (standard), 1210 tonnes (normal) *Length:* 84.72 m (277 ft 11½ in) oa *Beam:* 8 m (26 ft 3 in) *Draught:* 2.46 m (8 ft 1

Cutlass

in) *Machinery:* 2-shaft steam turbines, 22 000 shp=32 knots *Armament:* (Original) 4 4-in (102-mm)/45-cal (2×2); 2 3-in (76-mm)/30-cal (2×1); 17.7-in (45-cm) torpedo tubes (2×3); Rails for 16 mines; (As rearmed) 4 4-in (102-mm)/45-cal; 2 20-mm (0.79-in) AA (increased to 6 in 1943); 6 17.7-in (45-cm) torpedo tubes; 2 depth-charge throwers *Crew:* 117

Curtiss US aircraft See **B-2, Condor BT-32, CS/SC, F2C/F3C/F4C, F7C, F8C, Goshawk, H-4, H-12, H-16, Hawk, Helldiver SBC, Helldiver SB2C, Kittyhawk, NC-4, Orenco D, Shrike, Sparrowhawk, Tomahawk, Warhawk**

Curtiss-Wright US aircraft See **CW-21, Commando**

Cutlass, Chance Vought F7U

American naval fighter. Winner of a 1945 US Navy design competition for a carrier-based fighter powered by the Westinghouse 24C axial turbojet, the Chance Vought XF7U-1 flew on September 29, 1948. It was one of the most unconventional combat aircraft ever to lead to an operational type, with a stubby fuselage and twin tails mounted on a broad swept wing. It was the first Navy aircraft designed to have afterburning engines, or a swept wing or steerable nosewheel. It was also the first to be cleared to drop stores beyond Mach 1 in a dive.

Flight development showed great potential, despite the poor engines, later designated J34-WE-23. After extensive and sometimes fatal problems the aircraft was totally redesigned, and testing of the new F7U-3 began on December 12, 1951.

It missed the Korean war, but eventually 288 production Cutlasses were delivered, the last in August 1955. The first 16 had the Allison J35-A-29, but the standard engine was the Westinghouse J46-WE-8 rated at 2722 kg (6000 lb) each with afterburner. Features included full-span slats, extremely long twin-wheel nose gear, four 20-mm (0.79-in) cannon above the engine inlets, and fully powered controls with artificial feel. Variants included the F7U-3M with four Sparrow I air-to-air guided missiles, and the -3P with a lengthened camera-filled nose.

Between June 1954 and December 1956 these odd fighters equipped 13 Navy squadrons at shore bases and on carriers, while the Marines experimented with high-speed minelaying. Six squadrons later used the -3M, the first missile-armed fighter in service. Though unserviceability and accidents were problems, the Cutlass was tough, manoeuvrable and popular. Today one survives at NAS New Orleans and one at Fort Lauderdale.

Span: 12.09 m (39 ft 8 in) *Length:* (-3M) 13.1 m (43 ft 1 in) *Gross weight:* (-3M) 14 948 kg (32 954 lb) *Max speed:* (-3 level) 1130 km/h (702 mph)

CV/3,CV/29 Italian tanks   See **Fiat**

CV/33 Italian tank   See **Ansaldo**

Cyclone

French torpedo boat class. In the 1890s, France, rather than follow the British exam-

ple in building destroyers, concentrated on refining still further the smaller torpedo boats of which she already had a large force. In 1896, influenced by the success of *Forban* and *Aquilon*, two fast examples of *torpilleurs de haute mer* built by the best French torpedo boat builder, Le Normand of le Havre, the French decided to order an 'improved *Forban*' from the same builder. This vessel, the *Cyclone*, was also a success on her trials in 1898, making 30.38 knots. Normand's success in eliminating vibration by careful balancing of the triple-expansion engines, and the use of nickel-steel permitted the thickness of plating and frames to be reduced, thereby saving weight with no loss of strength.

In 1898 six more boats were ordered to be built to Normand's design, modified to fit a lightly-armoured citadel to protect the machinery spaces. This consisted of 24-mm (0.94-in) sides and bulkheads, with a 9-mm (0.35-in) deck. It was Normand's idea to protect the vitals of the boat against the fire from 12- and 6-pdr guns fitted to British destroyers. Another modification was the installation of a third rotating torpedo tube on the forecastle, but this was not a success, and was soon discarded. Despite the extra weight of the protection which, it was thought, would reduce the speed to 26 knots, three of these boats made over 28 knots on trials.

Finally, in 1899, another four boats were ordered, this time reverting virtually to the original *Cyclone* design. The two Normand-built boats both made over 31 knots on trial. They were, however, already obsolete. Even before the previous armoured class were ordered the French navy had finally begun to build destroyers.

The *Cyclone* and the others of the class all served on local patrols during the First World War, some in the North Sea, some in the Mediterranean. Though all survived the war to be removed from service between 1921 and 1927, there had been several serious accidents. *Trombe* ran ashore early in her programme of trials, and the entire bows had to be rebuilt. *Bourrasque* and *Boreo* were damaged in collisions, and *Trombe* was again damaged in a boiler explosion in 1915. *Rafale* was sunk in 1917 when her depth charges exploded, but was subsequently raised and restored to service.

Cyclone was launched in 1898. Of the armoured group, *Trombe* and *Audacieux* were launched in 1900 and *Mistral, Sirocco, Simoun* and *Typhon* in 1901. The final group, *Bourrasque, Rafale, Boreo* and *Tramontane* were all launched in 1901.

Length: 46.5 m (152 ft 7 in) oa, 45 m (147 ft 8 in) pp *Beam:* 4.9 m (16 ft); Armoured group 5.15 m (16 ft 10¾ in); Final group 5.06 m (16 ft 7 in) *Draught:* 2.51 m (8 ft 3 in) *Displacement:* 114.5 tonnes (normal), 152.39 tonnes (full load); Armoured group 114.92 tonnes (normal), 185.8 tonnes (full load); Final group 120.88 tonnes (normal), 167.7 tonnes (full load) *Machinery:* 2-shaft triple-expansion *Armament:* 2 47-mm (1.85-in) guns; 2 38-cm (15-in) torpedo tubes (3 in Armoured group) *Crew:* 26

CZ (Ceska Zbrojovka)

Czech small arms manufacturer. This company was founded in 1919 in Pilsen as the

Jihoceska Zbrojovka, with the intention of building up a firearms industry in the new country of Czechoslovakia. Alois Tomiska, gunsmith and designer, became the manager, and production began with the 'Fox' pocket pistol. In 1921 the factory was moved to Strakonitz, and in 1922 it amalgamated with the Hubertus engineering firm to become Ceska Zbrojovka.

Their first military connection was a contract to produce pistols for the Czech army, after which they expanded to cover pistols, rifles, machine- and submachine-guns, bicycles, artillery, machine tools and motorcycles. By 1955 the changing nature of their production was confirmed by a change of name to the Cesky Zavody Motocyklove (Czech Motorcycle corporation).

Confusion arose, however, since there was another firearms company in Czechoslovakia with the same initals: Ceskoslovenska Zbrojovka of Brno. The difference lies in the wording; 'Ceska' really means 'Bohemian', while 'Ceskoslovenska' means 'Czecho-slovakian'. This second company was formed in Brno in 1919 by the Czech government, using the services of numerous Czech firearms experts who had previously been working in Austrian and Hungarian factories. This state-owned enterprise found that there were political obstacles in the way of trading and it was reorganized as a limited company in 1924, becoming the Zbrojovka Brno or ZB.

While operating under the CZ initials, this company produced the Czech Army Mauser Rifle Model 1924, working under licence from Mauser, and it also produced the 9-mm (0.354-in) Pistol 'N' or CZ22 to a design by Josef Nickl of Mauserwerke. As ZB the company retained the manufacture of the rifle and went on to produce some famous machine-guns, but it passed the pistol design across to CZ in Strakonitz in 1923. Thereafter the ZB company ignored pistols until after the Second World War, and its post-1923 products will be considered under ZB.

To revert to Ceska Zbrojovka, their first product, the 'Fox', was a cheap 6.35-mm (0.25-in) blowback automatic pistol of little merit. In original form it was unusual in having a folding trigger without a guard, but it was revised to become the CZ22 by adding a conventional trigger and guard in 1922, though the Fox continued to be made until 1926. In 1924, as related above, they took over production of the Czech army's pistol, the 9-mm 'N' or CZ22 (one can see what confusion can arise—two pistols with the same designation but totally different).

The 'Nickl Pistol' was a 9-mm (0.354-in) using the 9-mm (0.354-in) Short cartridge and employing barrel rotation to hold the breech closed during firing. There was absolutely no need for such complications with a cartridge as low-powered as the 9-mm Short, and Frantisek Myska, the CZ chief designer, made radical alterations, changing the design to a simple blowback in 7.65-mm (0.301-in) calibre. This was easier and cheaper to make and just as effective. This became the CZ27 and remained in production until the end of the Second World War.

Other important pistol designs from CZ include the CZ38, an unusual double-action-only weapon and not a particularly good design; the CZ50, a 7.65-mm (0.301-in) which

CZ (Ceska Zbrojovka)

appeared to have been inspired by the Walther PP; and CZ52, a remarkable pressed-metal design with a roller-locked breech, firing a 'hotted-up' version of the Soviet 7.62-mm (0.30-in) pistol cartridge.

The first submachine-gun design to come from the CZ factory was the CZ1938, designed by Myska. It was an unusual weapon in that it was chambered for the 9-mm Short cartridge, and it was intended for the Czech Army. But Germany occupied the country and the weapon was abandoned. It used either a double-row box magazine of 24 rounds or a 94-round drum magazine, and later versions were modified to accept the 9-mm (0.354-in) Parabellum cartridge. It was widely demonstrated; no overseas sales were made.

After the war the design was modified and appeared as the CZ47. This was chambered for the 9-mm (0.354-in) Parabellum cartridge and used only a box magazine, but was remarkable in that the magazine could be used in two positions, either below the weapon or extending to the left side. The theory behind this was that the firer could adopt whichever position was more convenient to him, having regard to his position. Small numbers of these were sold to South America but it was not adopted by the Czech army.

The most important design was the CZ23, which was actually designed by Vaclav Holek of Zrojovka Brno but placed in production by the CZ subsidiary factory at Uhersky Brod. This weapon introduced the

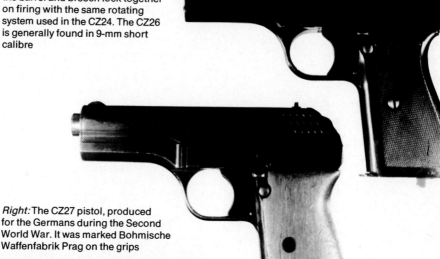

Right: The Czechoslovakian CZ26, an experimental design in which the barrel and breech lock together on firing with the same rotating system used in the CZ24. The CZ26 is generally found in 9-mm short calibre

Right: The CZ27 pistol, produced for the Germans during the Second World War. It was marked Bohmische Waffenfabrik Prag on the grips

Left: The CZ38, though well finished and easy to strip, was clumsy to hold and difficult to fire. The double-action lockwork makes accurate shooting difficult and the CZ38 has been called a 'terrible weapon'

overhung bolt, or telescoping bolt, concept into production submachine-guns. In the design of blowback weapons it is vital to have a specific mass for the bolt so that there is sufficient inertia to hold the bolt closed against the rearward pressure on the cartridge case when the shot is fired. This demands a certain length of metal, as the bolt is merely a solid block behind the breech, and this, in turn, demands a certain length of weapon in order to allow the bolt to reciprocate on recoil. But by hollowing out the face of the bolt so that it fits around the rear of the barrel it is possible to retain the weight while reducing the length behind the breech, since much of the weight now overhangs the barrel. Slots in the bolt allow for feeding and extraction, and the result is that the weapon can be made much more compact.

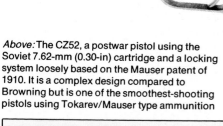

Above: The CZ52, a postwar pistol using the Soviet 7.62-mm (0.30-in) cartridge and a locking system loosely based on the Mauser patent of 1910. It is a complex design compared to Browning but is one of the smoothest-shooting pistols using Tokarev/Mauser type ammunition

COMPARATIVE DATA—PISTOLS

Model	Calibre (mm/in)	Weight (kg/lb)	Length (cm/in)	Barrel length (cm/in)	Magazine (rounds)	Muzzle velocity (m/sec/ft/sec)
CZ22, CZ24	9/.354	0.7/1.5	15.2/6	9.1/3.55	8	295/970
CZ26, CZ27	7.65/.301	0.71/1.56	15.8/6.25	10/3.9	8	280/920
CZ38	9/.354	0.94/2.06	20.6/8.11	11.8/4.65	8	300/980
CZ50	7.65/.301	0.67/1.47	16.8/6.6	9.7/3.75	8	280/920
CZ52	7.62/.30	0.88/1.94	20.9/8.25	12/4.71	8	396/1300

CZ

Above: The CZ23 submachine-gun with a 40-round magazine and wooden stock. Designed in the late 1940s it included novel features like a wrap round bolt and pistol grip magazine housing

The CZ23 design used this system. The bolt was 11 in (280 mm) long but in fact some 6.5 in (165 mm) of it were wrapped around the barrel. As a result it was possible to mount the magazine inside the pistol grip and produce a weapon no more than 27 in (68.6 cm) long, including the wooden stock. Over 100 000 of these were produced between 1948 and 1952, and it was widely sold abroad. A variant model, the CZ25, used a folding metal stock instead of a wooden one.

The CZ23 and CZ25 were chambered for the 9-mm Parabellum cartridge, but when the Czech army came under Soviet control the 7.62-mm (0.30-in) Soviet pistol cartridge became standard. Two fresh models were therefore produced, the CZ24 and CZ26; the sole difference being that these were chambered for the 7.62-mm (0.30-in) round.

The most recent production is the Vz/61 (Vz=Vzor=model) or 'Skorpion', a very small weapon chambered for the 7.65-mm (0.301-in) pistol cartridge. This was intended to be used either as a holster pistol or submachine-gun, being small enough to be

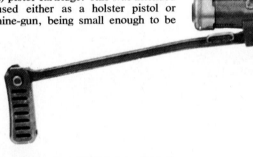

Above: The CZ25, similar to the CZ23 but with a folding metal strip stock. A handy and compact design the CZ25 is popular with terrorists and saw wide use during the Nigerian civil war. It is no longer in service with the Czech armed forces

carried in a (rather large) belt holster by tank crews and other personnel requiring light-weight firepower in emergency. With the wire stock folded it is just over 10 in (254 mm) long and can be fired one-handed like a pistol. Due to the lightness of the reciprocating parts it has been necessary to fit a retarding mechanism into the pistol grip so as to slow down the return of the bolt and thus keep the rate of fire down to manageable proportions. The Skorpion can also be fitted with a silencer to make an effective weapon for raiding troops, but the small bullet makes it a marginally effective combat weapon. Nevertheless it has been adopted by the Czech army and has sold widely in various African states.

The larger products of the CZ factory have principally been contracted manufacture of other people's designs. For example, during the Second World War the company made components of the German MG42, assembled self-propelled guns, built artillery to Skoda designs and so forth. So far as original designs are concerned, only pistols and submachine-guns are of significance.

Above: The CZ61 Skorpion can fire automatic or single shot but its light round and compact design make it difficult to classify as either a pistol or a submachine-gun

COMPARATIVE DATA—SUBMACHINE-GUNS

Model	Calibre (mm/in)	Weight (kg/lb)	Length (cm/in)	Barrel length (cm/in)	Magazine (rounds)	Cyclic rate (rds/min)	Muzzle velocity (m/sec/ft/sec)
CZ23, CZ25	9/.354	3.09/6.75	68.6/27	28.2/11.1	24 or 40	600	380/1250
CZ24, CZ26	7.62/.30	3.29/7.25	44.5/17.5 (stock folded)	28.4/11.2	32	600	548/1800
CZ61 Skorpion	7.65/.301	1.31/2.875	27.1/10.65 (stock folded)	11.4/4.5	10 or 20	700	296/975

In 1937 the US Army belatedly realized that it owned nothing specifically designed as an antitank gun. The matter appeared urgent, and to give the designers some guidance two German 3.7-cm (1.46-in) PAK 36 guns were purchased. After exploring various byways, the designers produced what amounted to a copy of the PAK 36, and in October 1938 this was standardized as the 37-mm Gun M3. It was produced in large numbers and was widely distributed but, in truth, it was obsolete before America entered the Second World War in December 1940. Nevertheless, it could still deal with light armour, and consequently saw much use in the Pacific theatre, though in Europe it was less useful.

57-mm M1

In 1940 the army realized the deficiencies of the 37-mm gun and began looking for a replacement. The quickest solution was to adapt an already proven design, and the British 6-pdr was selected. Drawings were obtained from Britain, and on May 15, 1941, the design was standardized as the 57-mm (2.24-in) Gun M1. The only significant change was in the barrel length. The original British design had been for a 50-calibre barrel, but due to production problems in Britain in 1940, the production guns were only 43 calibres long. The Americans, having ample long gun lathes, adopted the original 50-calibre length. The 57-mm was popular and served widely.

3-in M5

At the same time as the 57-mm (2.24-in) was suggested, the Ordnance Department were asked to design the next generation, a gun capable of stopping any tank in the world. Their quick answer was to put together a gun by marrying-up the barrel of the 3-in (76-mm) AA gun T9, the breech ring and block of the 104-mm (4.1-in) Howitzer M2 and the carriage of the 105-mm Howitzer. This was approved as the 3-in Gun M5 in December 1941.

Surprisingly, it turned out better than might have been expected, and might have gone on to become one of the great guns, but

The US 37-mm antitank gun M3 was based on the German 3.7-cm Rheinmetall gun, however by 1941 it had become obsolescent. It saw action in North Africa and the Pacific

it was bedevilled by two things. Firstly, the ammunition design was poor, particularly in the matter of the fuzes for the AP shells; and secondly, the Tank Destroyer Board, who were responsible for all antitank equipments, were obsessed with the idea of having self-propelled guns which would get out and chase tanks. After the M5 had been standardized, production was held up while the TD Board developed and tested a self-propelled carriage which, eventually, proved to be useless. When this had run its course, M5 production was reluctantly allowed to begin, after which the ammunition problems began to show up. By 1944 the gun was acceptable, but by then most people had lost faith in it.

A 37-mm M3A1 is towed ashore by a Mk 3 LVT (3) during American landings in the Pacific, it was used against bunkers and hardened positions

Antitank

COMPARATIVE DATA

Gun	Weight in action (kg/lb)	Length of bore (calibres)	Weight of shell (kg/lb	Muzzle velocity (m/sec/ft/sec)	Maximum range (m/yards)	Penetration at 0° and 914 m (1000 yards) (mm/in)
37-mm M3	413.7/912	53	0.87/1.92	884/2900	11 750/12 850	61/2.4*
57-mm M1	1225/2700	50	2.85/6.28	853/2800	9380/10 260	73/2.9†
3-in M5	2211/4875	50	6.985/15.4	792/2600	14 720/16 100	100/3.9
76-mm T3	1733/3820	52	5.9/13.0	823/2700	9145/10 000	100/3.9
90-mm T8	3084/6800	51	11.1/24.5	853/2800	19 570/21 400	122/4.8
105-mm T5	7257/16000	65	15.9/35	945/3100	24 690/27 000	210/8.27

* 0° at 457 m (500 yards) †20° at 914 m (1000 yards)

90-mm T8

Having now equipped the US Army with two foreign equipments and a home-brewed lash-up, the Ordnance Department decided that it was time to develop an American gun from the ground up, and in 1943 they began work on two projects, a 90-mm (3.5-in) gun and a 76-mm (3-in) gun. The 90-mm (3.5-in) model was based on the existing 90-mm AA gun, and by the end of 1943 two prototypes had been built. One was an orthodox split-trail carriage weapon, but this turned out to be too heavy and had to be sent back for redesign to get the weight down. The other was an unorthodox carriage in which the shield formed the basic member and the trail legs were hinged to the top corners; the legs stretched rearwards for firing and could be folded forward to lie alongside the barrel for towing. This design was worked on through 1944 and 1945 but without reaching a service-able result, and late in 1944 the orthodox design was revived and procurement of 600 was authorized. Production was slow in start-ing and in August 1945 the number was cut to 200. They appeared in 1947 but were never standardized and it remained the 90-mm Gun T8 on Carriage T5E2 throughout its service.

3-in T3

The 76-mm (3-in) design fared equally badly. The 76-mm calibre had begun as a tank gun, the object being to produce something more powerful than the standard 75-mm tank gun but still small enough to go inside a Sherman turret. To solve this, the 3-in Gun T16—a combination of 3-in barrel and 75-mm (2.95-in) breech, firing 3-in shells by way of a new design of cartridge, was devised.

In July 1942 this was renamed the 76-mm Gun T1 and in the following month it was standardized, to become the armament of several tanks and Gun Motor Carriages. It was now appropriated and put on to a towed carriage to become the Gun T3 on Carriage T4, more or less a scaled-up version of the 57-mm (2.24-in) M1 carriage design, fol-lowed by the T5 carriage, similar to the unorthodox 90-mm (3.5-in) T9 model, the shield being the basic structure. Both these proved to be unsatisfactory and another design was put up, the T7 carriage, which was more or less the carriage of the 3-in M5 gun. In the end, none of them met the requirements of service and apart from a handful issued after the war on a trials basis, the 76-mm antitank gun was a non-starter.

105-mm T5

The final American antitank venture was the 105-mm (4.1-in) Gun T5. Like the 76-mm (3-in) and 90-mm (3.5-in) projects, this began as a projected tank gun. By mid-1944 it had grown to 65-calibre length and somebody suggested mounting it on a towed carriage as an antitank gun with a dual role as a long-range field gun. Work on the gun continued after the Second World War in spite of the fact that the Field Artillery had said they could see no use for it. Two pilot models were built and test-fired in 1946, after which the project was closed down.

The 105-mm (4.1-in) gun had shown—along with the German 12.8-cm (5-in) and the British 32-pdr, that the conventional antitank gun firing kinetic-energy projectiles had now grown too big for the battlefield. Other methods of attacking tanks were being devel-oped, and the heavyweight gun had had its day. One must be honest and say that in the American service, it never had much of a day at all.

The crew of a 57-mm (2.24-in) antitank gun M1 take cover from sniper fire during heavy fighting in western Normandy in July 1944

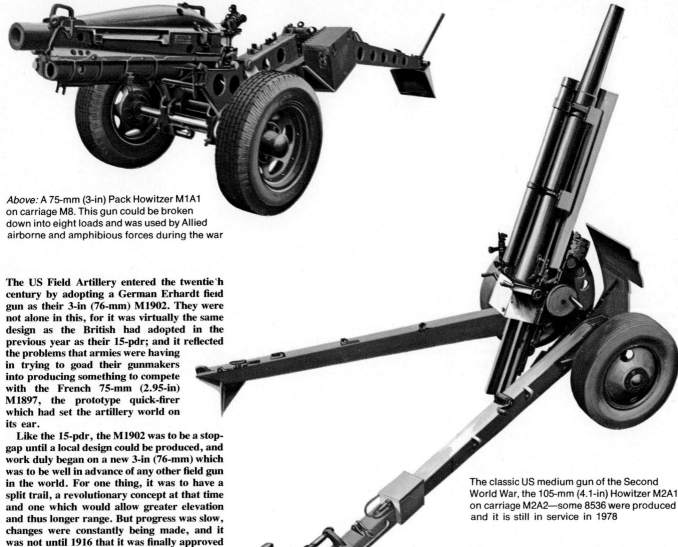

Above: A 75-mm (3-in) Pack Howitzer M1A1 on carriage M8. This gun could be broken down into eight loads and was used by Allied airborne and amphibious forces during the war

The classic US medium gun of the Second World War, the 105-mm (4.1-in) Howitzer M2A1 on carriage M2A2—some 8536 were produced and it is still in service in 1978

The US Field Artillery entered the twentie'h century by adopting a German Erhardt field gun as their 3-in (76-mm) M1902. They were not alone in this, for it was virtually the same design as the British had adopted in the previous year as their 15-pdr; and it reflected the problems that armies were having in trying to goad their gunmakers into producing something to compete with the French 75-mm (2.95-in) M1897, the prototype quick-firer which had set the artillery world on its ear.

Like the 15-pdr, the M1902 was to be a stop-gap until a local design could be produced, and work duly began on a new 3-in (76-mm) which was to be well in advance of any other field gun in the world. For one thing, it was to have a split trail, a revolutionary concept at that time and one which would allow greater elevation and thus longer range. But progress was slow, changes were constantly being made, and it was not until 1916 that it was finally approved as the 3-in M1916. But before production could begin, America entered the First World War and found that it needed field guns quickly.

The full story of the American field gun programme in 1917-18 is a chapter of disasters too long to be covered in detail here; readers are recommended to the book *Signposts of Experience* by General William Snow, published in 1940, which tells the whole sorry story.

In summary: for the sake of standardization the US Army were persuaded to adopt the French 75-mm M1897 for their troops in France. From this it was a logical step to rebarrel the M1916 to take 75-mm ammunition, but the M1916 turned out to be an extremely difficult manufacturing proposition during wartime conditions.

As a stop-gap, the British 18-pdr, rebarrelled to 75-mm, was adopted as the 75-mm M1917. Of all these, only the M1917 achieved any significant production during the war. After the war numbers of all three were produced and became the standard field guns—the M1897 as a first-line weapon, the M1916 and M1917 as reserve guns. The M1897 was periodically improved, by better ammunition, pneumatic tyres and better sights, eventually becoming the 75-mm M2A2 in 1939.

75-mm Howitzer M1

In the 1920s a 75-mm (2.95-in) howitzer was developed to replace the handful of mountain howitzers remaining from prewar days. The 75-mm Howitzer M1 used a similar shell to the gun but had a multi-charge cartridge, and the whole equipment could be quickly dismantled into six pack loads for mule carriage. It was introduced in 1928 and was later followed by the 75-mm Howitzer on Carriage M3, a split-trail carriage with shield. This was intended to be the horse artillery weapon for batteries accompanying cavalry.

105-mm Howitzer M1, M2A1

After the First World War a board of review was convened by the War Department in order to study the wartime use of artillery and make recommendations for the future. The unspoken aim was to ensure that the

1917-18 fiasco was never to be repeated in the future. The Westervelt Board, named after the presiding officer, made far-reaching recommendations which were to be the basic guidelines for US artillery development for many years. A basic factor in the recommendations was the acknowledgement that the 75-mm (2.95-in) gun was no longer an effective weapon and should be replaced by a 105-mm (4.1-in) howitzer.

Design work began in 1920 but, as with every military project of the time, lack of money held up progress and it was not until 1928 that it was standardized as the 105-mm Howitzer M1 on Carriage M1. Only 14 were made before funds dried up, but for once the shortage of money was a blessing in disguise. The M1 had been designed for horse draught, but during the early 1930s the mechanization of the army got under way. The 105-mm carriage was redesigned for mechanical draught, so that when the financial brake was finally released in 1939 there was a modern design ready, and no expensive stocks of obsolete weapons to be used up. Some minor changes in the ordnance had also taken place in the light of practical experience, and in March 1940 the 105-mm Howitzer M2A1 on Carriage M2 went into production. During the war years 8536 were built, and it became the standard divisional artillery piece.

COMPARATIVE DATA

Gun	Weight in action (kg/lb)	Length of bore (calibres)	Shell weight (kg/lb)	Muzzle velocity (m/sec/ft/sec)	Elevation limits (degrees)	Maximum range (m/yards)
3-in M1902	1133/2497	29.2	6.8/15.0	518/1700	−5 to +26	6858/7500
75-mm M1916	1456/3210	28.4	6.1/13.5	579/1900	−7 to +53	11 420/12 490
75-mm M1917	1356/2990	29.8	6.76/14.9	579/1900	−5 to +16	11 430/12 500
75-mm M2A2	1560/3440	40	6.76/14.9	663/1250	−10 to +46	13 695/14 975
75-mm How M1	576/1269	15.9	6.76/14.9	381/1250	−5 to +45	8925/9760
75-mm How M1A1	980/2160	15.9	6.76/14.9	381/1250	−9 to +50	8925/9760
105-mm How M2A1	2259/4980	22.5	15/33.0	472/1550	$-4\frac{3}{4}$ to +66	11 160/12 205
105-mm How M3	1132/2495	16.5	15/33.0	311/1020	−99 to +69	7585/8295
105-mm How M102	1150/3196	29.6	15/33.0	610/2000	−5 to +75	12 800/14 000

105-mm Howitzer M3

In 1941, with the emergence of airborne troops, the US Army asked for a 105-mm howitzer suitable for carriage by air. In response the M2A1 was shortened by 68.6 cm (27-in) and fitted to a modified 75-mm (2.95-in) Howitzer M3A1 carriage, with the recoil system of the 75-mm Pack howitzer grafted to it, the whole thing becoming the 105-mm Howitzer M3, standardized in February 1943. Although originally intended for airborne troops, it was employed in 1942 as an infantry weapon, being issued to infantry cannon companies in North Africa. The idea was not a success and the guns reverted to airborne use. It was an effective weapon but, due to the short barrel and light recoil system, its maximum range was severely restricted. Nevertheless, 2580 were made and it was put to good use during the war, though it was scrapped very soon afterwards.

105-mm Howitzer M102

Production of the standard M2A1 continued until 1953, by which time over 10 000 had been built. For reasons not entirely clear, the nomenclature was changed to 105-mm Light Howitzer M101A1, and under this name it continues to serve the US Army and the armies of 44 other countries.

With the scrapping of the M3 howitzer, airborne and air-portable divisions needed a new lightweight weapon, and in 1966 the M102 howitzer appeared. The barrel was lengthened and given a vertical sliding breech instead of the M2A1's horizontal type, while the carriage became a splayed box trail supported in action on a firing pedestal and with a roller beneath the trail end to permit rapid traverse. The carriage is largely constructed from aluminium alloy giving a saving in weight of some 600 kg (1320 lb) yet the M102 out-ranges the M101 by about 1600 m (1750 yards).

105-mm Howitzer XM204

By 1978 an experimental howitzer, the 105-mm (4.1-in) XM204 was undergoing trials. This is an unconventional design in that the trail, instead of extending behind the gun in the accepted fashion, lies beneath the barrel, and the breech end is supported in action on a rotating platform. This design is due to the most unusual feature, the incorporation of 'soft recoil' or 'differential recoil'.

In simplest form, the idea is to pull the gun back to the fully-recoiled position before loading. Once loaded, the gun is released to run forward under the power of the recuperator. A fraction of a second before it reaches the fully run-out position, it is fired, and the recoil force therefore has first to arrest the moving mass and then reverse its direction. This reduces the amount of recoil stress transmitted to the carriage by some 70%, and promises some saving in weight. The idea is not new, having been employed on French and Austrian mountain guns before the First World War. It remains to be seen whether the US Ordnance Department can make a greater success of it today.

A 105-mm (4.1-in) M101A1 fires at North Vietnamese positions surrounding Khe Sanh during the siege of the US Marine garrison in 1968-69. The M101A1 is the postwar development of the 105-mm (4.1-in) M2A1, it fires 20 different types of ammunition including an antitank shell

US Marine Corps

An empty shell case is ejected from the breech of a 105-mm (4.1-in) Howitzer M2A1 as American troops shell German positions in Normandy. It fired 13 types of ammunition and was mounted on a number of mobile chassis including the M7, M7B1 and M7B2 and the M3 halftrack

Medium Artillery

The term Medium Artillery is not one which has often been used by the US Artillery, so that there is no official definition, but it is taken here to mean the heavier weapons available to the artillery division.

In the period before the First World War a policy was adopted of arranging the calibres of weapons so that the shell weights moved up in multiples of 6.8 kg (15 lb). The 3-in (76-mm) Field Gun M1902 used a 6.8 kg (15 lb) shell, so the next gun up the scale, firing a 13.6-kg (30-lb) shell, was the 3.8-in (96.5-mm) Gun M1907, which was accompanied by a 3.8-in howitzer M1908 firing the same weight of shell. Next came the 4.7-in (120-mm) How M1906 with a 27.2-kg (60-lb) shell and finally the 6-in (152-mm) How M1908 with a 54.4-kg (120-lb) shell.

155-mm M1918

Although this was a logical and sound system, the fact remains that the US Artillery was a small corps, and the US Army as a

671

whole was not generously endowed with equipment in those days, and the entire stock of medium guns amounted to little more than a hundred. Consequently, when America entered the war in April 1917 the simple solution, as with the field guns, was to adopt a French design, the Schneider 155-mm (6.1-in) Howitzer M1917, as the standard medium gun. Modifications were later made in the design to suit American manufacturing methods and it became the M1918, and it remained the mainstay of the mediums until 1941. It was a sound, if cumbersome design and during the 1920s it was gradually improved by the use of pneumatic tyres and electric brakes to adapt it to mechanical traction. During the Second World War the M1918s were largely used as training weapons, though numbers were supplied to the British Army in North Africa.

155-mm Howitzer M1

The principal defect of the M1918 design was its limited traverse. Because of the box trail, any change greater than 3° involved man-handling the whole equipment. In 1934 development of a new split-trail carriage began, and in 1939 it was decided to do the job properly and design a new howitzer as well, and the resulting 155-mm (6.1-in) Howitzer M1 on Carriage M1 was introduced in May 1941. The new weapon used a longer barrel to obtain greater range and the new carriage gave greater mobility and flexibility. It also

proved to be phenomenally accurate. Over 6000 were eventually built and, like the 105-mm (4.1-in), they were widely distributed to other armies after the war.

4.5-in Gun M1

The 4.7-in (120-mm) howitzer had been scrapped after the First World War but the Westervelt Board recommended a new design in the same calibre, and during the 1920s a 4.7-in (120-mm) gun to fit on the same carriage as the 155-mm (6.1-in) howitzer was designed. In 1928 it was recommended for adoption, but the decision was postponed and then work was suspended until 1940 when, once more, it was put forward for approval. By this time it was beginning to look as if the British and US Armies might be working together one day, and it was suggested that the calibre might be changed to 4.5-in (114-mm), which would allow interchangeability of ammunition between the British 4.5-in Gun M1 in April 1941, mounted on the same split-trail carriage as the 155-mm Howitzer M1. However, it was not popular principally because the British-designed 24.95-kg (55-lb) shell used low-grade steel and therefore carried less explosive than was customary in American designs: consequently it was rather less effective on the ground. A number were used in Europe, but, in the main, the 4.5-in remained a training gun and was rapidly made obsolete as soon as the war was over.

155-mm Howitzer M114A1, M123A1

In the years after the war the 155-mm (6.1-in) Howitzer M1 became the 155-mm Howitzer M114A1 without exhibiting any significant change. It was gradually replaced by self-propelled equipments, which are dealt with separately, and by 1978 the towed howitzer was no longer in US first-line service, though still employed by many other armies throughout the world.

An interesting variation developed in the early 1960s was the Auxiliary Propelled Howitzer M123A1, which was the standard M114A1 with a Continental Motors 4-cylinder gasoline engine mounted on the left trail leg. This powered a hydraulic pump which, in turn, drove hydraulic motors on each gun wheel. The trail ends were supported by a dolly wheel which was steerable, and the whole equipment could move at about 8 km/h (5 mph). It was, though, a cumbersome design and had poor cross-country ability, and only a small number were taken into use. Ballistically, of course, it was no different from the ordinary towed gun.

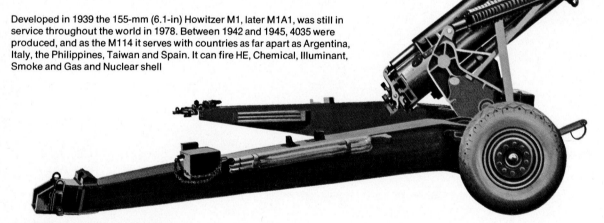

Developed in 1939 the 155-mm (6.1-in) Howitzer M1, later M1A1, was still in service throughout the world in 1978. Between 1942 and 1945, 4035 were produced, and as the M114 it serves with countries as far apart as Argentina, Italy, the Philippines, Taiwan and Spain. It can fire HE, Chemical, Illuminant, Smoke and Gas and Nuclear shell

COMPARATIVE DATA

Gun	Weight in action (kg/lb)	Length of bore (calibres)	Shell weight (kg/lb)	Muzzle velocity (m/sec/ft/sec)	Elevation limits (degrees)	Maximum range (m/yards)
3.8-in How M1908	1805/3980	13.2	13.6/30	274/900	−5 to +40	5395/5900
4.7-in. How M1907	2177/4800	12.4	27.2/60	274/900	−5 to +40	6220/6800
4.7-in Gun M1906	3984/8783	27.5	27.2/60	518/1700	−5 to +15	7270/7950
6-in How M1908	3906/8611	13.6	54.4/120	274/900	−5 to +40	6125/6700
155-mm How M1918	3712/8184	13.6	43.1/95	450/1475	0 to +42	11 340/12 400
155-mm How M1	5806/12 800	20	43.1/95	564/1850	−2 to +63	14 955/16 355
4.5-in Gun M1	5645/12 444	41	24.95/55	693/2275	0 to 65	19 315/21 125

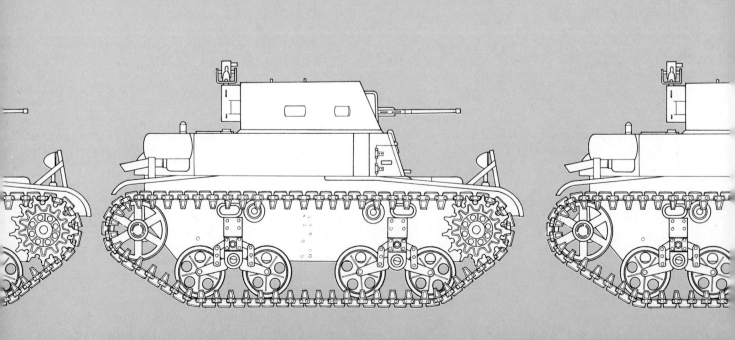